“*Mysteries of the Sacred U* … sents
an important advance in … ed in
the famed *Bhāgavata Pu* … ology
from several points of vie … that
this cosmology was intended to have multiple meanings that span the terrestrial, the astronomical, and the spiritual planes.”

—Professor Subash Kak, Louisiana State University

“Thompson takes us back in time when man regarded himself an integral part of the cosmos and shows us how, in a strange way, such a system as the *Bhāgavatam* cosmology bears an uncanny harmony with modern astronomy. More important and interesting is the way Thompson shows how the *Bhāgavatam* literature presents visual astronomy in geographical and mythological settings which, in this respect, is very reminiscent of the Pyramid Texts of ancient Egypt and many mythico-religious cosmologies of other ancient cultures of the world. . . . Gripping, scholarly and ground-breaking, *Mysteries of the Sacred Universe* deserves to be widely read and discussed.”

—Robert G. Bauval, author of *The Orion Mystery*
and coauthor of *The Message of the Sphinx*

“Dr. Thompson has a talent that may well be unique in our times: the ability to take complex, esoteric ideas that require high level mathematics, specialized technical expertise, and a familiarity with scholarship that spans the history of civilized humanity, and presenting them to the lay reader in a narrative style that is as user-friendly as a novel, but packed with sound reasoning, solid scholarship, and impressive empirical research.”

—Professor William W. Wall, Santa Fe Community College, Florida

“Mr. Thompson’s premise is that the system of the *Bhāgavatam* includes some modern understandings of the science of astronomy, not just mythology. . . . If the reader can judge what is science and what is not science, putting aside the non-science aspects of the cosmology, it seems clear that there are indeed a number of references to known scientific aspects of the sky in the *Bhāgavatam.*”

—Jeanne E. Bishop, Planetarium Director, Westlake, Ohio

“A revolution in our understanding of the cosmology of the *Purāṇas* is in the making here. This book offers a way of reading ancient Indian texts that is profoundly interesting, that overturns a long history of scholarly undervaluation of the supposedly ‘only mythological’ contents of Purāṇic literature.”

—Professor Gene R. Thursby, University of Florida

MYSTERIES OF THE
SACRED UNIVERSE
The Cosmology of the Bhāgavata Purāṇa

MYSTERIES OF THE SACRED UNIVERSE

The Cosmology of the Bhāgavata Purāṇa

Richard L. Thompson

GOVARDHAN HILL PUBLISHING
Alachua, Florida

THE COVER: A scale model of the earth-continent of Jambūdvīpa, showing the cosmic axis, Mount Meru.

Readers interested in the subject matter of this book are invited to correspond with the author at:

Richard L. Thompson
P. O. Box 1920
Alachua, FL 32616-1920
www.sacreduniverse.com

First edition.
First printing: 2000

Published by Govardhan Hill Publishing.

Printed and bound in Canada.

Cataloging-in-Publication Data

Thompson, Richard L.
Mysteries of the Sacred Universe : the cosmology of the Bhāgavata Purāṇa / by Richard L. Thompson
p. cm.
Includes bibliographical references and index.
ISBN: 0-9635309-3-3
1. Astronomy, Hindu. 2. Cosmology.
3. Purāṇas. Bhāgavatapurāṇa.
I. Title.

Library of Congress Card Number: 00-109208

Dedicated to

His Divine Grace
A. C. Bhaktivedanta Swami Prabhupāda

oṁ ajñāna-timirāndhasya
jñānāñjana-śalākayā
cakṣur unmīlitaṁ yena
tasmai śrī-gurave namaḥ

Contents

Introduction to Bhāgavata Cosmology

The way people view the universe has a profound impact on their understanding of themselves. Today we see the earth as a small, fragile globe, orbiting at just the right distance from the sun for life to flourish. It appears to be the only planet with life in the solar system, and the planets themselves are mere specks in the vacuum of space. Human life seems reduced to insignificance when set against the vast, nearly empty spaces of modern astronomy.

But before the modern era, the universe often appeared much more comfortable and accommodating. Thus medieval European cosmology placed the earth in the center of a small, spherical universe surrounded by the "*coelum empireum,*" the abode of God and the Elect. Within the sphere, the sun, the moon, and the planets out to Saturn followed regulated orbits against the backdrop of the zodiacal constellations. The earth, in the center, was at one end of a hierarchy of being, connecting human beings with the heavenly realm.

In this study we will explore a similar, earth-centered conception of the cosmos from India. This cosmological system is presented in the *Bhāgavata Purāṇa*, or *Śrīmad-Bhāgavatam*, one of India's important religious scriptures. For centuries it has provided a meaningful framework, connecting the world of observable phenomena with the transcendental world of ultimate reality.

The *Bhāgavatam* describes innumerable universes. Each one is contained in a spherical shell surrounded by layers of elemental matter that mark the boundary between the transcendental and mundane realms. The shell contains an earth disk—called Bhū-maṇḍala or "earth mandala"—that divides it into an upper, heavenly region and a subterranean domain filled with amniotic waters. The shell and its contents are characterized as the Brahmāṇḍa or "Brahmā egg."

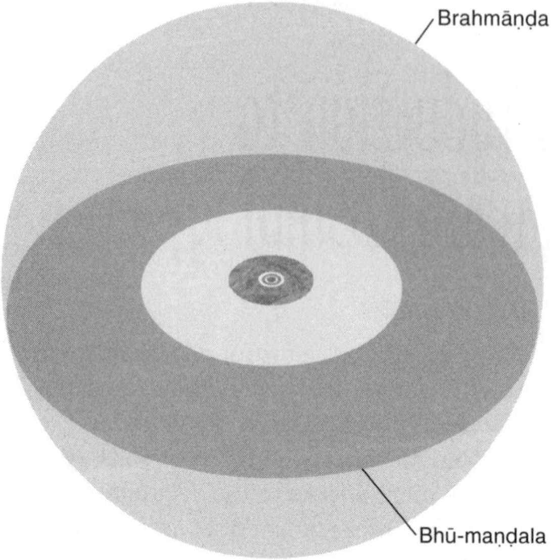

Figure 1 Model of the Brahmāṇḍa, showing the universal shell and Bhū-maṇḍala.

Although the "earth" is here conceived of as a disk, it has little in common with the familiar earth of day-to-day experience. The diameter of Bhū-maṇḍala is given in the *Bhāgavatam*, and it is about the size of the orbit of Uranus. Bhū-maṇḍala is divided into a series of geographic features, called oceans and islands (*dvīpas* in Sanskrit). But these are geometrically perfect rings of cosmic size, with no resemblance to irregular earthly continents.

In the center of Bhū-maṇḍala is the circular "island" of Jambūdvīpa, with nine subdivisions called *varṣas*. These include Bhārata-varṣa, which can be understood in one sense as India and in another as the region inhabited by ordinary human beings. Jambūdvīpa is centered on the geometrically shaped Mount Sumeru, which represents the world axis and is surmounted by the city of Brahmā, the universal creator.

At first glance, the cosmology of the *Bhāgavatam* looks like an imaginative production that has little in common with reality. However, a deeper study shows a remarkable harmony between modern astronomical findings and *Bhāgavata* cosmology. To understand this, it is necessary to realize that the *Bhāgavatam* describes reality using its own, uniquely premodern paradigm.

The *Bhāgavatam* presents astronomy in geographical and mytho-

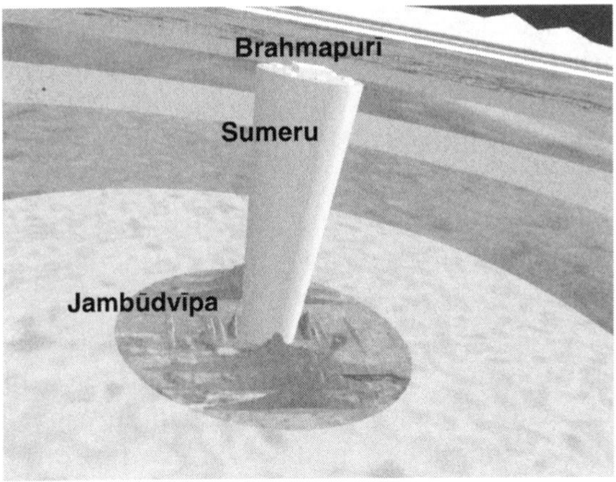

Figure 2 Close-up of Jambūdvīpa, showing Brahmapurī on top of Mount Sumeru.

logical language, and the mode of presentation is different from the familiar modern approach. Modern cosmology aims to construct an abstract model with a one-to-one correspondence between elements of the model and elements of the universe. In contrast, the *Bhāgavatam* uses concrete themes and images in multiple ways to represent different aspects of the universe. From the standpoint of the *Bhāgavatam*, the universe is a multidimensional system including transcendental elements. Since the universe therefore cannot be encompassed by a single mental model, the *Bhāgavatam* freely uses model elements in different convenient ways to represent different aspects of the universe.

Although it may look like a naive flat-earth model, careful study shows that the *Bhāgavatam* uses the earth disk of Bhū-maṇḍala to represent at least four different things. These are:

1. The earth globe, mapped onto a plane by stereographic projection.
2. A map of the geocentric orbits of the planets.
3. A local map of India, the Himalayan region, and nearby territories in south-central Asia.
4. A map of the celestial regions inhabited by demigods.

The great Bengali saint Caitanya Mahāprabhu remarked that "In each and every verse of *Śrīmad-Bhāgavatam* and in each and every syllable, there are various meanings" (*Caitanya-caritāmṛta*, *Madhya-līlā* 24.318). This appears to be true, in particular, of the cosmological section of the *Bhāgavatam*, and it is interesting to see how some of these meanings can be brought out and clarified with reference to modern astronomy.

There are bound to be contradictions when one structure is used to represent several different things in a composite map. But these do not cause a problem if we understand the underlying intent. We can draw a parallel with medieval paintings portraying several different parts of a story in one composition. These also contain contradictions (such as several instances of one character in a single painting), but a person who understands the story line will not be disturbed by them.

The *Bhāgavatam* does not describe the universe of galaxies and quasars, but it does contain a solid core of material that agrees remarkably well with the modern understanding of the earth globe and the solar system. In this work we shall use modern astronomy as a reference frame to elucidate *Bhāgavata* cosmology. Many obscure points stand out sharply in proper perspective when viewed in the light of modern astronomical knowledge. This enables us to shed new light on many topics in the *Bhāgavatam* which have long been poorly understood.

The question naturally arises as to whether modern astronomical themes seen in an old text are really there, or are simply being read into the text by hindsight. Were such themes intended by the original authors, or is their apparent presence in the text due to coincidence or loose interpretation? It is difficult to clearly answer this question in all cases. Some of the correspondences with modern astronomy are consistent with ancient Greek astronomy, and they could have been intentionally built into a medieval Sanskrit work. Others go beyond Greek astronomy, and it is hard to account for them historically.

Although some of these correspondences may be products of chance, it is possible to show that some of them are statistically significant. These might be the results of conscious scientific endeavor in ancient times. Or they might be seen as intuitive harmonies between nature and the *Bhāgavatam*, depending on divine inspiration.

This study has been organized as a book and as a CD-ROM. The book and the CD contain essentially the same text, but the book is designed to be read sequentially from beginning to end, while the CD has a hierarchical structure with hypertext links and a search engine. The main body of the CD is illustrated with some 250 color pictures, 13 interactive picture sequences, and 24 animations, including a video summarizing both this book and the CD.

1

Introduction to Texts

The source material for traditional Hindu astronomy and cosmology consists of Sanskrit texts that are being reproduced and republished today as part of a living tradition. Unlike the situation in Egypt, Mesopotamia, or Mesoamerica, there is practically no Indian cosmological material available in the form of ancient manuscripts, tablets, or inscriptions. Archeology may shed light on the material living conditions of ancient Indian people, but it conveys practically nothing about what they had to say. In India, long documents have generally been written on palm leaves, which last for at most a few centuries in the Indian climate.

Since we are dealing with a living cosmological tradition, none of the material that we examine is demonstrably older than a few hundred years. Texts preserved and reproduced by human beings are inevitably subject to alteration, revision, imperfect copying, and loss. However, a living tradition may preserve ideas and information that date back arbitrarily far into the distant past. In this study, our main emphasis is on the content of surviving cosmological ideas and not on their history. But inevitably, we will run across material that sheds light on the early development of astronomy and cosmology.

In this book, we present the cosmology of the *Bhāgavata Purāṇa* or *Śrīmad-Bhāgavatam*, one of the eighteen principal *Purāṇas*. We supplement this with references to other *Purāṇas*, to the Indian epics (the *Mahābhārata* and *Rāmāyaṇa*), and to the texts on mathematical astronomy called *Jyotiṣa Śāstras*.

The *Viṣṇu Purāṇa* is one of the eighteen principal *Purāṇas*. Its cosmology is essentially the same as that of the *Bhāgavatam*, and we draw upon it for clarification and additional information. The *Mahābhārata* is an epic of some 100,000 verses that is said to be an encyclopedia of traditional Indian lore, and it also sheds light on *Bhāgavata* cosmology.

The *Jyotiṣa Śāstras* are medieval Indian astronomy texts which contain instructions for calculating planetary motions and solar and lunar eclipses. They present astronomy in a different way than the *Purāṇas*, but they nonetheless have much in common with them. We will refer to the *Jyotiṣa Śāstra* known as *Sūrya-siddhānta* to supplement our presentation of the astronomy of the *Bhāgavatam*.

1.1 PURĀṆAS

The Sanskrit texts called *Purāṇas* are compendiums of Indian mythology, theology, and traditional lore. They are generally considered to have been compiled within the current era, but they may contain material that is much older. The *Purāṇas* present a comprehensive world view which attempts to place humanity in a meaningful position in relation to the universe. Thus they provide a window through which we can observe an ancient way of seeing the world.

The major *Purāṇas* traditionally deal with ten topics, including the creation and annihilation of the universe, the history of humans and demigods, cosmology, and the relation between the soul and God. The eighteen *Mahāpurāṇas* (Great *Purāṇas*) are said to contain 400,000 verses in total. In addition there are eighteen *Upapurāṇas* and a number of other works claiming Purāṇic status.

In India, the traditional view is that the *Purāṇas* complement the *Vedas*—the ancient texts seen as the ultimate authority in Hindu society. Some of the *Purāṇas* themselves declare that they and Sanskrit historical epics (such as *Mahābhārata*) are the fifth *Veda*. For example, the *Bhāgavatam* makes this claim in verse 1.4.20.

The *Vedas* are still dated by scholars according to the scheme shown in Table 1.1, which dates back to the pioneering nineteenth-century Indologist Max Muller (O'Flaherty, 1975, pp. 17–18).

The most important epics are the *Mahābhārata*, dated from around 300 B.C. to A.D. 300, and the *Rāmāyaṇa*, dated from 200 B.C. to A.D. 200. Scholars generally assign the *Purāṇas* to the period from about A.D. 250 up to A.D. 1500.

The Indologist Ludo Rocher proposed that the *Purāṇas* served as companions to the *Vedas,* and he used this to push back the period

TABLE 1.1
Dates of the Vedas

Text	Date
Ṛg Veda	1200 B.C.
Atharva Veda	900 B.C.
Brāhmaṇas	900–700 B.C.
Upaniṣads	700 B.C.
Nirukta of Yaska	500 B.C.

of their composition. He argued that "Another natural conclusion derived from the belief that the *Purāṇas* were necessary companions to the *Vedas,* is that this companion literature was essential and, therefore, in existence from Vedic times onward" (Rocher, 1986, p. 16). This is consistent with the *Purāṇas*' account of their own origin, which maintains that they were written down when the sage Vyāsadeva divided the *Vedas* and committed them to written form.

This would put the *Purāṇas* back to 1200 B.C., using Muller's chronology. The apparent contradiction can be resolved by observing that many *Purāṇas* have evidently been revised within the last 2,000 years. However, the *Purāṇas* as a genre may date back long before this. According to Wendy O'Flaherty, "since the Epics and *Purāṇas* represent an oral tradition that was constantly revised over a period of several thousand years, a passage actually composed in the twelfth century A.D. may represent a surprisingly accurate preservation of a myth handed down since the twelfth century B.C.—or a completely original retelling of that myth" (O'Flaherty, 1975, p. 16). Which of these alternatives holds true has to be judged for each *Purāṇa,* and each Purāṇic story, on an individual basis.

The Purāṇic tradition in India maintains that the division of the *Vedas* by Vyāsadeva dates back to just before the advent of the Kali-yuga, the age of quarrel and degradation. Since at least the fifth century A.D., traditional Hindus have dated the beginning of Kali-yuga back to about 3102 B.C. Thus the famous Indian astronomer Āryabhaṭa said that sixty times sixty years of Kali-yuga had elapsed on his twenty-third birthday, which fell in A.D. 499 (Dikshit, 1969b, p. 55). The Kali-yuga date of 3102 B.C. is connected with astronomy, and some scholars maintain that it was defined by astronomical back-calculations at some point within the current era. The story of this date involves many interesting details in the history of astronomy, and we discuss it in Chapter 8.

1.2 BHĀGAVATA PURĀṆA

The *Bhāgavata Purāṇa* (*Śrīmad-Bhāgavatam* or, briefly, *Bhāgavatam*) is one of the most popular scriptures of the Vaiṣṇavas or worshipers of Viṣṇu and Kṛṣṇa. According to the *Bhāgavatam* itself,

> After Lord Kṛṣṇa departed for His abode along with religious principles and transcendental knowledge, this *Purāṇa, Śrīmad-Bhāgavatam*, has arisen like the sun in this age of Kali to enlighten those who have no spiritual vision (*Bhāgavatam* 1.3.43).

Unlike a number of the *Purāṇas*, the *Bhāgavatam* is a unified composition, and this has led some scholars to allege that it was a forgery—perhaps perpetrated by a thirteenth-century grammarian named Vopadeva. However, even though Vopadeva wrote two works based on the *Bhāgavatam*, his authorship of the original text has been generally rejected (Rocher, 1986, p. 145).

The Indologist Ludo Rocher observed that, apart from a few voices alleging fraud, "the *Bhāgavata Purāṇa* has been acclaimed as the most popular of all purāṇas. It is also the most famous purāṇa, which has influenced Indian thought and religion more strongly than any other composition of this genre" (Rocher, 1986, p. 148).

The *Bhāgavatam* is noted for being written in difficult and archaic Sanskrit. Some have taken this as evidence of great age, while others see it as evidence of an effort to create the impression of great age. It is interesting that many archaisms in the *Bhāgavatam* cannot be readily traced back to known literary sources. Thus a study by F. J. Meier concluded that "alongside a few archaisms for which the Vedic context is either indicated or suggested, there are many more the origin of which can no longer be traced" (Rocher, 1986, p. 146).

Scholars have been unable to reach a clear consensus regarding the date of the *Bhāgavatam*. Here is a list of scholarly dates for this text compiled by Rocher (Rocher, 1986, pp. 147–48):

TABLE 1.2
Dates of the *Bhāgavatam*

Date	Authority
1200–1000 B.C.	S. D. Gyani
900–800 B.C.	Vyāsa
A.D. 200–300	Ramacandra Dikshitar
A.D. 300–400	Tagare
A.D. 400–500	Krishnamurti
A.D. 500–550	Hazra
A.D. 500–600	Majumdar
A.D. 550–600	Ray
A.D. 750	Gail
before A.D. 800–900	Kane
A.D. 800–850	Shastri
A.D. 800–900	Pargiter
A.D. 800–1000	Ingalls
A.D. 850	Hopkins
A.D. 850–1000	R. K. Mukerjee
A.D. 900	Farquhar
A.D. 900+	Sharma
A.D. 900–1000	Vaidya, Winternitz
A.D. 1000	Dasgupta
A.D. 1200–1300	Colebrooke, Wilson, Burnouf, Lassen, Macdonell, etc.

To this we may add that Hardy dates the *Bhāgavatam* to the ninth or early tenth century (Hardy, 1983, p. 488), and Hudson argues that at least part of the material in the *Bhāgavatam* was present all over India from at least the third century B.C. (Hudson, 1995, p. 172). Hudson suggests that the archaic language in the *Bhāgavatam* may reflect an authentic tradition dating back to c. 400 B.C. In this study, Chapter 8 presents astronomical evidence bearing on the date of the *Bhāgavatam*.

We will have occasion to refer to several commentaries on the *Bhāgavatam*. The most famous of these is the *Bhāvārtha-dīpikā* by Śrīdhara Swami (c. A.D. 1350–1450). We will also refer to the commentaries by Viśvanātha Cakravartī and Vaṁśīdhara, who wrote in the sixteenth century, as well as to the commentaries of Vīrarāghava and Vijayadhvaja Tīrtha.

Our original source of information on the *Bhāgavatam* was the English translation of this work written by Śrīla A. C. Bhaktivedanta Swami Prabhupāda (Bhaktivedanta, 1982). His translation used an explanatory approach incorporating the commentaries of several Vaiṣṇava commentators, including those mentioned above. In some cases, we will refer to retranslations of these verses by Dr. Howard Resnick, who presented their literal meaning by removing material from commentaries that had been included in the original translations.

1.3 VIṢṆU PURĀṆA

The *Viṣṇu Purāṇa* is one of the eighteen *Mahāpurāṇas.* It is particularly useful for the purposes of this study because it contains an extensive section on cosmology which complements the cosmological section of the *Bhāgavatam.*

The date of the *Viṣṇu Purāṇa*, like that of *Purāṇas* in general, is uncertain. Here is a list of scholarly dates for this text compiled by Ludo Rocher (Rocher, 1986, p. 249):

TABLE 1.3
Dates of the Viṣṇu Purāṇa

Date	Authority
700–500 B.C.	Ramacandra Dikshitar
700–300 B.C.	Ramacandra Dikshitar
400–300 B.C.	Smith
A.D. 100–350	Hazra
A.D. 275–325	Hazra
A.D. 300–500	Kane
before A.D. 400	Farquhar
after A.D. 400–500	Pargiter
A.D. 550	Gail
A.D. 800–900	C. V. Vaidya
after A.D. 800–900	Roy

For further information on the date of the *Viṣṇu Purāṇa*, see Chapter 8.

1.4 JYOTIṢA ŚĀSTRAS

The *Jyotiṣa Śāstras* are Sanskrit texts expounding native Indian astronomy. These texts present parameters and computational rules for predicting planetary positions and other astronomical phenomena. They may also include cosmological and geographical material, but this tends to be different in character from the cosmology and geography of the *Purāṇas*. The *Purāṇas* generally do not explicitly mention the earth as a globe, and they describe an earth-disk (Bhū-maṇḍala) that is billions of miles in diameter. In contrast, when the *Jyotiṣa Śāstras* mention the earth, they treat it explicitly as a globe of realistic dimensions.

The earliest *Jyotiṣa Śāstra* is the *Jyotiṣavedāṅga*, which gives simple calculations for the motions of the sun and moon relative to the *nakṣatras* (lunar mansions) and to each other. (See Appendix 1 for information on the *nakṣatras*.) Later Jyotiṣa texts describe the geocentric orbits of the nine *grahas*. These are the sun, the moon, the five planets (Mercury, Venus, Mars, Jupiter, and Saturn), and the pseudoplanets Rāhu and Ketu. The motions of the five planets are calculated using an epicycle system reminiscent of Ptolemy, and rules are given for calculating the timing of eclipses of the sun and the moon.

Modern scholars generally view Indian astronomy in terms of foreign influences they see as paramount in its development. The following table by David Pingree summarizes the history of Indian astronomy as it is presently understood by scholars (Pingree, 1981, p. 9). It divides this history into five periods that, except for the first, are named after sources of foreign input:

1. Vedic (ca. 1000 B.C.–400 B.C.), characterized by elementary calendaric concepts with rudimentary mathematical development.
2. Babylonian (ca. 400 B.C.–200 A.D.)
3. Greco-Babylonian (ca. 200–400)
4. Greek (ca. 400–1600)
5. Islamic (ca. 1600–1800)

As always in Indology, these dates should be regarded as tentative.

The *Jyotiṣavedāṅga* is the most important work showing purely Babylonian affinities. It exists in two recensions, that of the *Ṛg Veda* in thirty-six verses and that of the *Yajur Veda* in forty-three to forty-five verses. Pingree makes the interesting remark that the former gives the length of the year as 366 sidereal days (or 365 civil days) (Pingree, 1981, p. 9).

The distinction between a sidereal day and a civil day is that the first is the time for one revolution of the stars (from star rise to star rise) and the second is the time for one revolution of the sun (from sun rise to sun rise). It is noteworthy that this concept was understood in the period of the *Jyotiṣavedāṅga.*

Pingree sees the *Pañcasiddhāntikā* of Varāhamihira (sixth century A.D.) as the prime example of an early form of Hellenistic astronomy that also displays strong Babylonian influence. He grants, however, that "no extant Greek texts can be pointed to as sources" for some of the non-Babylonian material in this work (Pingree, 1981, p. 11).

The period of Greek influence is marked by the introduction of epicyclic models for the motion of the planets. The epicyclic models place the earth globe in the center, surrounded by the planetary orbits. These models are similar to those of the second-century Alexandrian astronomer Claudius Ptolemy, but they also have their own distinct features that cannot be derived directly from Ptolemy's work. It is hard to say how much they owe to Greek ideas and how much they derived from independent invention in India.

Epicyclic planetary orbits are presented in a class of works called *Siddhāntas*. The earliest appears to be the *Paitāmahasiddhānta*, which is found as a part of the *Viṣṇudharmottarapurāṇa*.

An important work of the Siddhānta class is the *Āryabhaṭīya* of Āryabhaṭa, who was twenty-three years old in A.D. 499. This work is famous for its statement that the earth rotates daily on its axis—a point that was severely criticized by later Indian astronomers, such as Varāhamihira and Bhāskarācārya.

Another important work in this class is the *Sūrya-siddhānta*, which became one of the most popular astronomy texts in India. It represents Indian astronomy in its mature state and is usually dated to about the tenth century A.D.

1.5 SŪRYA-SIDDHĀNTA

According to the early eleventh-century author Alberuni, the *Sūrya-siddhānta* (or some work of the same name) was composed by Lāṭa (Sachau, 1910, p. 153). According to the text itself, it was spoken by an emissary of the sun-god to the Asura (demon) named Maya at the end of Kṛta-yuga, over two million years ago.

In his translation of the *Sūrya-siddhānta*, Ebenezer Burgess notes that some manuscripts seem to connect Maya with the Roman Empire. In the manuscripts without commentary, the sun-god is presented as saying to Maya, "Go therefore to Romaka-city, thine own residence; there, undergoing incarnation as a barbarian, owing to the curse of Brahmā, I will impart to thee this science" (Burgess, 1860, p. 3). If Romaka is actually Rome (or a Roman city), this could be interpreted as evidence that the *Sūrya-siddhānta* was derived from Greco-Roman astronomy. Of course, it might also be seen as evidence of tampering with the text.

The *Sūrya-siddhānta* in its present form can be dated firmly as far back as the fifteenth century A.D. There exists a fifteenth-century palm leaf manuscript (No. XXI, N. 8 of the Adyar Library, Madras) of the text of the *Sūrya-siddhānta* along with a commentary by Parameśvara (Shukla, 1957, p. 1). We will have occasion to refer to this manuscript in Appendix 8, where we argue that remnants of advanced astronomical knowledge may survive in the *Sūrya-siddhānta*.

The astronomy of the *Sūrya-siddhānta* presents an epicyclic theory of planetary motion similar to that of Claudius Ptolemy, but it also has many features that may be of Indian origin. It begins with a detailed discussion of the Indian system of world chronology known as the *yuga* system. This system is based on a *catur-yuga* of 4,320,000 solar years and a *kalpa* of one thousand *catur-yugas*.

In the *Sūrya-siddhānta*, these immense periods of time are used as a convenient device for presenting the orbits of the planets. The orbits are described by a series of cycles and epicycles that are combined trigonometrically to reproduce observed planetary motions. Each cyclic period is defined by giving its number of revolutions in a *kalpa*. Since this is given as a whole number, it follows that all planetary motions will return exactly to their starting point in one *kalpa*. A similar idea is found in the "great year" of Hellenistic astronomy, and the idea of cyclic time is also prominent in the Indian *Purāṇas* and in the *Mahābhārata*.

The *Sūrya-siddhānta* describes the periodic motions of the sun, moon, and planets with good accuracy. It also gives the earth-moon distance to within about 11% of the modern value. However, its figures for the distances of the sun and planets are unrealistically small. They are calculated on the assumption that the sun, moon, and planets all move with the same (mean) speed in their orbits, and therefore orbital radii are proportional to orbital periods.

In contrast, Kepler's third law makes the radius proportional to the $2/3$ power of the period. For the planets, the proportionality constant in Kepler's law is also much larger than the one used in *Sūrya-siddhānta*, which is based on the orbit of the moon.

It is noteworthy that Ptolemy also made the planetary orbits much too small, but he used a different approach. Each geocentric orbit ranges from its perigee (point closest to the earth) to its apogee (furthest point). His idea was that the apogee of each orbit must equal the perigee of the next one out, so that there would be no unused space (see Appendix 4). The result is that the orbit of Saturn is smaller than the earth's orbit as we know it today.

In the *Sūrya-siddhānta*, the motion of the planets is said to be controlled by cords of air. The text explains that

> Forms of Time, of invisible shape, stationed in the zodiac (*bhagaṇa*), called the conjunction (*śīghrocca*), apsis (*mandocca*), and node (*pāta*), are the causes of the motion of the planets. The planets, attached to these beings by cords of air, are drawn away by them, with the right and left hand, forward or backward, according to nearness, toward their own place. A wind, moreover, called provector (*pravāha*) impels them toward their own apices (*ucca*); being drawn away forward and backward, they proceed by a varying motion (Burgess, 1860, p. 53).

It is interesting to compare this with the cosmology of the *Purāṇas*, where we find similar ideas. In the *Bhāgavata Purāṇa*, the rotation of the stars and planets around the polar axis is said to be caused by the *dakṣiṇāvarta* wind. This is called the *pravāha* wind in the *Viṣṇu Purāṇa*, where a more detailed account is given of the control of planetary motions by cords of air:

> I have thus described to you, Maitreya, the chariots of the nine planets, all which are fastened to Dhruva by aerial cords. The orbs of all the planets, asterisms, and stars are attached to Dhruva, and travel accordingly in their proper orbits, being kept in their places by their respective bands of air (Wilson, 1980, p. 346).

Chapters 4–6 of the *Sūrya-siddhānta* present rules for calculating the times of solar and lunar eclipses. These are based on the same theory of eclipses used in modern astronomy. However, the ascending node of the moon is identified as Rāhu, the eclipse demon of the *Purāṇas* (see Section 3.4.1). Rāhu's counterpart, Ketu, is not mentioned (Burgess, 1860, p. 56).

The *Sūrya-siddhānta* contains a chapter on cosmology and geography, in which the earth is portrayed as a self-supporting globe floating in space and surrounded by the planetary orbits. The Purāṇic Mount Meru is defined as a literal polar axis, passing through the poles, with dwellings of the gods at the northern end and dwellings of the demons at the southern end. In the four quarters, extending south from the north pole to the equator, are four continents with four equatorial cities, as follows (Burgess, 1860, p. 286).

TABLE 1.4
Jambūdvīpa in Sūrya-siddhānta

Direction	Continent	City
east	Bhadrāśva	Yamakoṭi
south	Bhārata	Laṅkā
west	Ketumāla	Romaka
north	Kuru	Siddhapura

These can be compared with the continents (*varṣas*) of the Purāṇic Jambūdvīpa (see also Section 2.4.1). The general view of scholars is that the flat Jambūdvīpa was adapted to the earth globe when Greek astronomy was introduced into India. However, we argue in this work that Jambūdvīpa of the *Purāṇas* was understood as a planisphere model of the earth when the Purāṇic texts were written. Thus the idea of an earth globe was originally there in the Purāṇic Jambūdvīpa. Whether or not this idea was imported from the Greeks is hard to say. The accepted dates for the surviving recensions of the *Purāṇas* would allow this, and Ptolemy is known to have authored a work on the planisphere projection, mapping a globe onto a plane.

2

The Islands and Oceans Of Bhū-maṇḍala

2.1 OVERVIEW OF BHŪ-MAṆḌALA

The main focus of *Bhāgavata* cosmology is on Bhū-maṇḍala—the "circle of the earth"—and we will therefore begin by giving an overview of its qualitative and quantitative features. The structure of Bhū-maṇḍala turns out to be primarily astronomical in nature, and we will discuss this in detail in later chapters. At the same time, its qualitative features refer both to earthly geography and to the world of demigods. Some of the qualitative details appear to be derived from a historical background that begins with the descriptive geography of India and adjoining parts of Asia. In this chapter we will look briefly at this history, but since it is difficult to reconstruct, our main emphasis throughout this book will be on the cosmology of the *Bhāgavatam* as it stands in its present form.

Bhū-maṇḍala is a disk that bisects the sphere of the Brahmāṇḍa, the Purāṇic universe, and it has the same diameter as this sphere. The most noteworthy feature of Bhū-maṇḍala is that it is described in the *Bhāgavatam* and other *Purāṇas* in geographical terms. The central region of Bhū-maṇḍala is divided into seven annular or ring-shaped "islands" and "oceans" which alternate, forming a bull's eye pattern. Here the Sanskrit word for island is *dvīpa*, which literally means two waters. This term is appropriate, since most of the *dvīpas* are rings with an ocean on the inside and on the outside.

The seven *dvīpas* and oceans are collectively called Sapta-dvīpa, and they are surrounded by three larger ring-shaped regions which extend out to the edge of Bhū-maṇḍala. Since they are presented as parts of the earth, many scholars have attempted to identify the seven *dvīpas* with earthly regions or countries. Thus Colonel Wilford, an

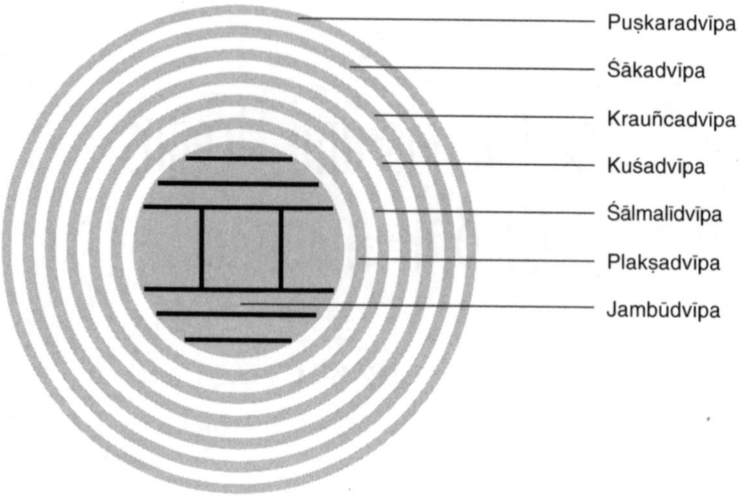

Figure 2.1 Sapta-dvīpa (with *dvīpas* labeled and shown as equal bands).

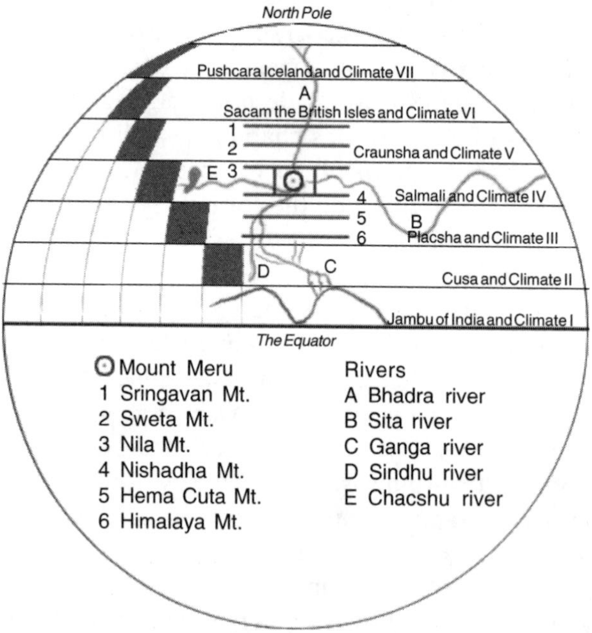

Figure 2.2 Francis Wilford's interpretation of Sapta-dvīpa as a series of "climates" in the northern hemisphere (*Asiatic Researches*, vol. 8, p. 367). Note the subdiagram of Jambūdvīpa's mountain ranges, just to the north of India.

early Indologist, interpreted the *dvīpas* as seven "climates," or zones of latitude, and he assigned specific countries to them, more or less by imagination (Wilson, 1980, p. 292).

M. P. Tripathi and D. C. Sircar identify Śākadvīpa as the land of the Sakas—the Greek Scythia—corresponding to Sakasthana (Seistan in East Iran) and areas to the north of this region. Sircar identifies Kuśadvīpa with the ancient land of Kush, which he thinks is Ethiopia (Sircar, 1960, pp. 163–64). But Tripathi disagrees and identifies Kuśadvīpa with the land of the Kushans, powerful people from Central Asia who invaded northern India in the early centuries of our era (Tripathi, 1969, p. 181).

It is possible that the *dvīpas* originally did refer to regions of this earth, but in the existing *Purāṇas* they are defined as gigantic circles that do not at all correspond to irregular earthly land masses. We will argue that these structures play an essentially astronomical role in Purāṇic cosmology, although Wilford's climate theory is not completely off the mark.

The features of Bhū-maṇḍala are all defined quantitatively using a unit, called the *yojana*, which is about eight miles in length. The innermost island of Bhū-maṇḍala is Jambūdvīpa, which has the form of a disk 100,000 *yojanas* in diameter. Jambūdvīpa is surrounded by the salt water ocean (Lavaṇoda), which is a ring 100,000 *yojanas* across from its inner to its outer edge. This ocean, in turn, is surrounded by the ring-shaped island of Plakṣadvīpa, which is 200,000 *yojanas* across. The successive islands and oceans enlarge in as indicated in Table 2.1 (with distances expressed in thousands of *yojanas*).

In this table, thickness is the distance from the inner radius of a ring-shaped feature to its outer radius. The seven islands and oceans follow the rule that the thickness of an ocean equals the thickness of the island it surrounds and the thickness of that island is twice the thickness of the ocean it surrounds. The circular Jambūdvīpa is an exception. It surrounds no ocean, and its thickness is its diameter.

The doubling of thicknesses is belied by Figure 2.1, where we show the seven oceans and islands as equal bands. We do this because the oceans and islands do not fit easily in one picture if the doubling rule is followed. For this reason, most traditional diagrams of Bhū-maṇḍala show equal bands.

TABLE 2.1
Sizes of the Circular Features of Bhū-maṇḍala

N	Radius	Thickness	Geographical Type	Sanskrit Name
1	50	100	Island (*dvīpa*)	Jambūdvīpa
2	150	100	Ocean	Lavaṇoda
3	350	200	Island	Plakṣadvīpa
4	550	200	Ocean	Ikṣurasoda
5	950	400	Island	Śālmalīdvīpa
6	1,350	400	Ocean	Suroda
7	2,150	800	Island	Kuśadvīpa
8	2,950	800	Ocean	Ghṛtoda
9	4,550	1,600	Island	Krauñcadvīpa
10	6,150	1,600	Ocean	Kṣīroda
11	9,350	3,200	Island	Śākadvīpa
12	12,550	3,200	Ocean	Dadhi-maṇḍoda
13	15,750	3,200	½ Island & mtn.	Mānasottara mtn.
14	18,950	3,200	½ Island	Puṣkaradvīpa
15	25,350	6,400	Ocean	Svādūdaka
16	41,100	15,750	Region	Loka (Inhabited)
17	125,000	83,900	Region & mtn.	Lokāloka mtn.
18	250,000	125,000	Region	Aloka-varṣa

Feature 13, called Mānasottara Mountain, is a circular mountain range, reminiscent of some of the large craters on the moon. Since it cuts Puṣkaradvīpa in half (see 5.20.30), we listed it in the table as "½ Island & mtn." Mānasottara Mountain links Bhū-maṇḍala with the orbit of the sun. The axle of the sun's chariot is said to to rest at one end on Mount Meru in the center of Bhū-maṇḍala. On the other end, it is supported by a wheel that rolls continuously on the circular track of Mānasottara Mountain. As we will see, this solar chariot plays a key role in the astronomical interpretation of Bhū-maṇḍala.

The Inhabited Region (Loka) is an exception to the rule of doubling that applies to Sapta-dvīpa. Its width is defined in the *Bhāgavatam* verse 5.20.35 to be equal to the radius of Mānasottara Mountain, and this is somewhat more than twice the thickness of Svādūdaka, the ring that it immediately surrounds. The next ring, called the Golden Land

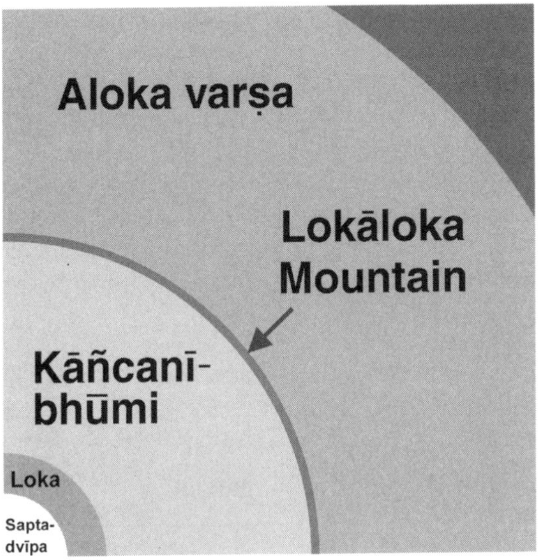

Figure 2.3 The region called Loka (inhabited), with the Golden Land (Kāñcanībhūmi), Lokāloka Mountain, and Aloka-varṣa.

(Kāñcanībhūmi), is assigned a thickness that brings its outer radius to exactly half the radius of Bhū-maṇḍala. This is a bit over twice the radius of Loka. Thus the table of distances is generated (roughly) by doubling, but this doubling is carried out in different ways in different parts of the table.

We note that "Loka" means an inhabited area. In contrast, the *Bhāgavatam* states that the Golden Land is uninhabited. The fifteenth-century commentator, Śrīdhara Swami, clarifies the dimensions of these two regions as follows. He says that the distance from Mānasottara to Meru equals the width of the inhabited earth beyond Svādūdaka, and it is 1½ *koṭi* and 7½ *lakhs* (15,750,000) of *yojanas*. Beyond this is another, golden land measuring eight *koṭi* and thirty-nine *lakhs* (83,900,000) of *yojanas*. This reading gives the figures listed in our table. (Here *koṭi* and *lakh* are commonly used terms in Sanskrit designating ten million and one hundred thousand, respectively.)

There is one other circular mountain in addition to Mānasottara. This is Lokāloka Mountain, with a radius of 125,000 thousand *yojanas* (see 5.20.38). This circle divides the illuminated region of Bhū-maṇḍala from the dark, uninhabited region, called Aloka-varṣa, which extends from Lokāloka to the shell of the Brahmāṇḍa.

2.2 THE NOMENCLATURE OF SEVEN DVĪPAS

In addition to their bare dimensions, the *dvīpas* are vividly described as populated geographical regions. With one exception, each *dvīpa* is named after a prominent plant said to grow there. The "oceans" are named after various liquids, such as salt water, sugarcane juice, and liquor. The inhabitants of the *dvīpas* are described, and they are said to worship the Supreme God in the form of various demigods. This information is summed up in the following table. In the third column, the terms fire, water, and air refer to the demigods presiding over these elements.

TABLE 2.2
The Oceans and Dvīpas of Bhū-maṇḍala

Dvīpa	Named After	Worship	Surrounding Ocean
Jambū	Rose apple tree	complex	Lavaṇoda (Salt water)
Plakṣa	Indian fig tree	sun	Ikṣura (Sugarcane juice)
Śālmalī	Silk-cotton tree	moon	Suroda (Liquor)
Kuśa	Kuśa grass	fire	Ghṛtoda (Ghee)
Krauñca	Mount Krauñca	water	Kṣīroda (Milk)
Śāka	Teak tree	air	Dadhyoda (Yogurt)
Puṣkara	Lotus flower	Brahmā	Svādūdaka (Fresh water)

The five *dvīpas* from Plakṣadvīpa to Śākadvīpa follow a simple pattern, and each is described in a few lines in the *Bhāgavatam*. Each of these *dvīpas* is divided into seven regions called *varṣas*, with seven mountains and seven rivers. Each *varṣa* is ruled by a grandson of Mahārāja Priyavrata, a famous personality who is said to have created a second sun by following 180° behind the sun on a brilliantly glowing chariot. The oceans are said to have been ruts created by his chariot wheels.

According to the table, Kuśadvīpa is named after a kind of grass. It is noteworthy that a person performing a Vedic fire sacrifice will traditionally sit on a mat made of *kuśa* grass and offer ghee into the fire. Therefore it may be no coincidence that fire is worshiped in Kuśadvīpa, which is surrounded by the Ghee Ocean.

In addition to its geography, founding kings, and peoples, each of the *dvīpas* surrounding Jambūdvīpa is described as having a particular, unusual feature. These are listed as follows:

TABLE 2.3
Unique Features of Dvīpas

Dvīpa	Unique feature
Plakṣa	Fire with 7 flames at the root of the Plakṣa tree.
Śālmalī	Garuḍa lives there in the Śālmalī tree.
Kuśa	*Kuśa* grass there is likened to a form of fire.
Krauñca	Mount Krauñca was attacked by Kārttikeya.
Śāka	The Śāka tree bathes Śākadvīpa in fragrance.
Puṣkara	Lotus seat of Brahmā with 100,000,000 petals.

These picturesque accounts of the islands and oceans of Bhū-maṇḍala have sometimes invoked ridicule, as when Lord Macaulay disparaged seas of treacle in his "Minute on Indian Education" (Macaulay, 1952, p. 723). Certainly, this is not geography in the familiar European sense of the term. However, as we will see later on, the

Figure 2.4 The Plakṣa tree (*Ficus infectoria*), with a fire of seven flames at its root.

geography of Bhū-maṇḍala encodes a combination of astronomical and geographical maps which is both rational and scientific. It appears that the elements of Bhū-maṇḍala geography have either been introduced or adapted to convey a number of meaningful messages, some of which may still remain obscure. This process may be linked to the historical development of Purāṇic cosmology, and we now turn to this topic.

2.3 HISTORICAL DEVELOPMENT OF BHŪ-MAṆḌALA FEATURES

If we survey traditional Sanskrit cosmological texts, we find a number of variations in the nomenclature and layout of the geography of Bhū-maṇḍala. Followers of the *Purāṇas* traditionally say that such variations pertain to different *kalpas*, or periods of creation, but modern scholars tend to see them in historical terms. In this section, we will carry out a comparative study of texts to see what we can learn about the historical development of cosmological ideas.[1]

Our main conclusion from the study is that the cosmology of the *Bhāgavatam* is unified and well organized, in contrast to many other *Purāṇas* (and related texts) that present cosmology in an incomplete or inconsistent way. We seem to see a historical process of imperfect preservation, rather than one of creative development. Unfortunately, the creative phase of Purāṇic cosmology largely remains hidden, at least as far this study is concerned.

The *Purāṇas* largely agree on the names applied to the features of Bhū-maṇḍala, but they may permute them, and some *Purāṇas* omit features present in others. Table 2.4 summarizes the situation found in eleven readily available *Purāṇas*, in the *Mahābhārata*, and in the *Jyotiṣa* text, *Siddhānta-śiromaṇi*. In this table, the feature numbers from Table 2.1 (p. 22) are used to indicate the sequence of Bhū-maṇḍala

---

[1]The references used in this study are: *Bhāgavata P.*, Bhaktivedanta, 1982; *Viṣṇu P.*, Wilson, 1980; *Kūrma P.*, Tagare, 1981; *Vāyu P.*, Tagare, 1987; *Śiva P.*, 1990; *Narasiṁha P.*, Jena, 1987; *Nārada P.*, Tagare, 1980; *Mārkaṇḍeya P.*, Pargiter, 1981; *Vāmana P.*, Mukhopadhyaya, 1968; *Siddhānta-śiromaṇi*, Wilkinson, 1861; *Varāha P.*, Bhattacharya, 1981; *Matsya P.*, Taluqdar, 1916; *Mahābhārata*, Ganguli, 1970; *Padma P.*, Deshpande, 1988; *Ramayana*, Shastri, 1976.

features listed in each text. The features run from Jambūdvīpa (1) in the center, out to the outermost feature mentioned. (Number 17a stands for the Golden Land, Kāñcanībhūmi, which in Table 2.1 was combined with feature 17b, the Lokāloka Mountain.)

TABLE 2.4
Different Versions of Bhū-maṇḍala

Text	Features																		
Bhāgavata	1	2	3	4	5	6	7	8	9	10	11	12	13	14	15	16	17a	17b	18
Viṣṇu	1	2	3	4	5	6	7	8	9	12	11	10	13	14	15		17a	17b	18
Kūrma	1	2	3	4	5	6	7	8	9	12	11	10	13	14	15		17a	17b	18
Vāyu	1	2	3	4	5	6	7	8	9	12	11	10	13	14	15		17a	17b	
Śiva	1	2	3	4	5	6	7	8	9	12	11	10		14	15		17a	17b	
Narasiṁha	1	2	3	4	5	6	7	8	9	12	11	10		14	15		17a	17b	
Nārada	1	2	3	4	5	6	7	8	9	12	11	10		14	15			17b	
Mārk.	1	2	3	4	5	6	7	8	9	12	11	10		14				17b?	
Vāmana	1	2	3	4	5	6	7	8	9	12	11	10		14	15				
S-śiromaṇi	1	2	11	10	5	12	7	8	9	4	3'	6		14	15				
Varāha	1	2	11	15	7	12	9	8	5	10	3'	6	13	14	15				
alternates				10						8					4				
Matsya	1	2	11	10	7	8	9	12	5	6	3'	4	13	14	15		17a	17b	
Mahābh.	1	2	11		7	8	5	12	9	6				14	15				

Several observations can be made here. First of all, the *Siddhānta-śiromaṇi*, the *Matsya* and *Varāha Purāṇas*, and the *Mahābhārata* differ as a group from the other *Purāṇas* in the table. In the first three of these texts, Plakṣadvīpa (3) is replaced by Gomedadvīpa (3') and switched with Śākadvīpa (11).

In the *Mahābhārata*, Plakṣadvīpa is missing, even though Sañjaya, the narrator, says he will describe seven islands (Ganguli, vol. V, p. 24). Only six islands are mentioned (respectively 1, 11, 7, 5, 9, 14), as well as five oceans (respectively 2, 8, 12, 6, 15). The relationship between the islands and oceans is not indicated, and we have therefore arranged them in the table (preserving order) so as to line up as much as possible with the *Matsya Purāṇa*. The good matches indicate a strong relationship between the arrangement given in the

Mahābhārata and the one given in this *Purāṇa*.

In the *Purāṇas*, the seven *dvīpas* and oceans of Bhū-maṇḍala are alternating concentric rings, and their sizes are generally given by the doubling rule of Table 2.1 (p. 22). But in the *Mahābhārata*, it is not clear that *dvīpas* are intended to be concentric rings. *Dvīpas* are said to be surrounded by oceans, but oceans are not said to be surrounded by *dvīpas*. The *dvīpas* in the *Mahābhārata* are said to double as one goes north, but no mention is made of their extent in other directions. Doubling is applied even more extensively in the *Mahābhārata* than in the *Purāṇas*, since various mountains are also said to double in size as one goes north (Ganguli, vol. V, pp. 26–27).

Since the *Mahābhārata* is generally dated before the *Purāṇas*, one might suppose that its cosmography is ancestral to Purāṇic cosmography. This is possible. But the cosmography of the *Mahābhārata* is incomplete and unsystematic, and if it does represent an ancestral system, it presents only a fragment of that system—whatever it may have been.

This naturally leads to the thought that the text of the *Mahābhārata* has become corrupt, and this idea is not new. For example, in his *Mahābhāratatātparyanirṇaya*, verses 2.3–4, the thirteenth-century philosopher and religious teacher, Madhvācārya, stated that

> In some places (of the *Mahābhārata*) verses have been interpolated and in others verses have been omitted. In some places, the verses have been transposed and in others, different readings have been given out of ignorance or otherwise.
>
> Though the works are really indestructible, they must be deemed to be mostly altered. Mostly all of them have disappeared and not even one *crore* [ten million] (out of several *crores* of *ślokas*) now exists (Resnick, 1999).

Many *Purāṇas* also present cosmography in an inconsistent fashion. For example, the *Varāha Purāṇa* mentions duplicate names for three of the oceans. (These are indicated by stacking one alternative above the other in the table.) The *Padma Purāṇa* contains a nearly verbatim copy of cosmological material from the *Mahābhārata*—with the interlocutors Sañjaya and Dhṛtarāṣṭra being replaced by the Purāṇic narrator, Sūta, and a group of sages. But in another place, it gives a different list following the pattern of the *Bhāgavatam*. Thus the

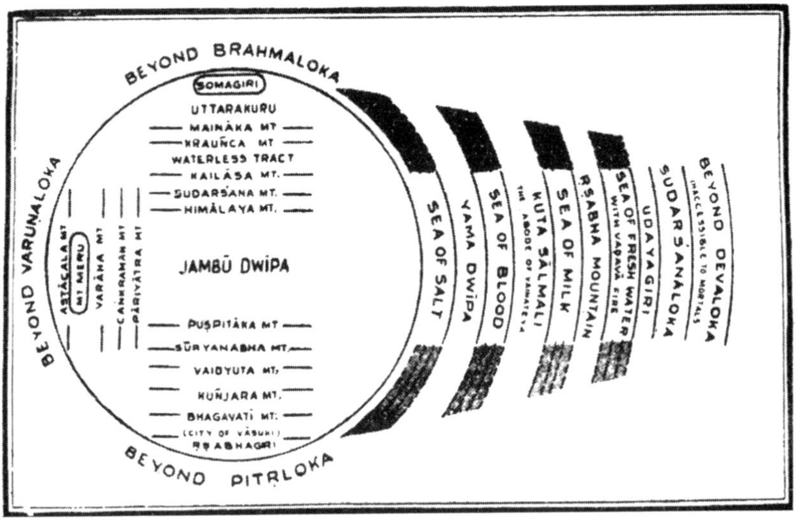

Figure 2.5 Approximate cosmographical map, based on the account in the *Rāmāyaṇa* of the travels of the Vānaras (monkeys) in search of Sītā (after Ali, 1966, p. 23).

Padma Purāṇa contains a mixture of material from different works.

The *Rāmāyaṇa* does not mention doubling, and its earth, bounded by dark, inaccessible regions, does not seem to have a succession of alternating oceans and islands. The center is India, and Mount Meru is placed to the west rather than to the north. On the east there is an island of Yava, which might be Java. There is also a Milk Ocean (Kṣīroda) and a fresh water sea (Jalada). The Śālmalī tree of Garuḍa is located in the east, and the Krauñca mountain is placed in the Himalayas to the north. Apart from this, there is little to remind us of the Purāṇic Bhū-maṇḍala.

Although the *Rāmāyaṇa* may seem to represent an earlier stage in the development of the cosmology, there are earlier references to oceans and land areas that surround one another and double in size from one to the next. For example, the *Bṛhad-āraṇyaka Upaniṣad* states that "This world is thirty-two times the space crossed by the sun's chariot in a day. The earth twice as that, surrounds it. Surrounding that earth is the ocean twice as large. Then, in between, there is the space as fine as a razor's edge, or as subtle as the wing of a fly" (Sivananda, 1985, p. 294). The *Upaniṣads* are generally thought to be much earlier than the *Rāmāyaṇa*, but this description is reminiscent of the

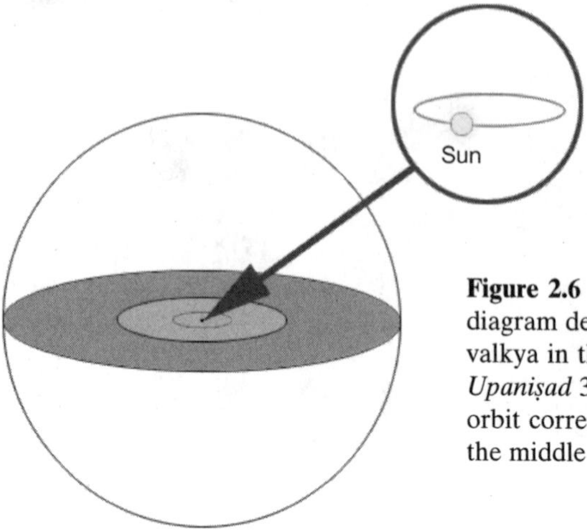

Figure 2.6 Cosmographical diagram described by Yājña-valkya in the *Bṛhad-āraṇyaka Upaniṣad* 3.3.2. Note: the sun's orbit corresponds to the dot in the middle of the globe.

Purāṇas, which are held to be later. The reference to the sun's motion suggests that the "earth" and the "ocean" must be extremely large, and this is also seen in the *Purāṇas*. The "space as fine as a razor's edge" has been described as a minute opening between the two hemispherical shells of the Brahmāṇḍa through which souls may pass.

The first nine *Purāṇas* agree on feature names and their order, but some of them list fewer features than others. These *Purāṇas* all seem to reflect a single system different from the one in the *Matsya Purāṇa*. The *Bhāgavatam*, followed by the *Viṣṇu Purāṇa*, gives the most detailed list of ring-structures in Bhū-maṇḍala. At the same time, some *Purāṇas*, such as the *Vāyu*, give much more detailed accounts of the geography of Jambūdvīpa than the *Bhāgavatam*.

We may ask whether the *Purāṇas* with longer lists added some features, or whether the ones with shorter lists dropped some. Our impression on reading the texts is that in many cases, the *Purāṇas* refer to the geography of Bhū-maṇḍala in a very cursory way, as though the reader was expected to be already familiar with it. Thus some *Purāṇas* neglect to mention all of the feature names.

Since the *Bhāgavatam* differs from all of the other *Purāṇas* in its assignment of the Milk (10) and Curd (12) Oceans (Table 2.1, p. 22), it appears that these have been switched for some reason in the *Bhāgavatam*. Likewise, feature 16 (Loka) is listed only in the *Bhāgavatam*, and we can ask whether it is unique to this text. The answer is that indirect evidence suggests that the *Bhāgavatam's* calculations for Loka and the Golden Land were used in other texts as well.

Thus the *Bhāgavatam* makes the radius of Lokāloka one fourth the diameter of the Brahmāṇḍa, and the distance from the Sweet Water Ocean to Lokāloka Mountain comes to about ten *crores* of *yojanas*, where a *crore* is ten million. (The exact figure is 99,650,000 *yojanas*.) H. H. Wilson finds similar figures in the *Śiva Tantra*. He says, "According to the Śiva Tantra, the golden land is ten crores of Yojanas, making, with the seven continents, one fourth of the whole measurement" (Wilson, 1980, p. 294). Thus the *Bhāgavatam's* calculations—which make use of feature 16—appear to be reflected in the *Śiva Tantra*, and they may have a further, unknown background.

In contrast, the *Viṣṇu* and *Kūrma Purāṇas* (which are closest to the *Bhāgavatam* in Table 2.4) both say that the Golden Land has twice the thickness of the Sweet Water Ocean (Svādūdaka). This results in a radius of 38,150,000 *yojanas* for Lokāloka Mountain. All of the *Purāṇas* agree that the Brahmāṇḍa is 250,000,000 *yojanas* in radius, and so the radius of Lokāloka Mountain comes to about 15% of the universal radius.

It is not clear whether this version came before that of the *Bhāgavatam* or after it. But if we assume the former, it is hard to say why the boundary of the Brahmāṇḍa was placed so far away from Lokāloka Mountain. The *Viṣṇu Purāṇa* cannot produce a figure as large as the universal radius by further doubling. For example, doubling thickness again by adding twice the Golden Land would bring one out to only 63,750,000 *yojanas*. In contrast, the *Bhāgavatam* does generate the universal radius by doubling, and this involves feature 16.

In summary, it does not seem possible at present to trace the geography of Bhū-maṇḍala back to its origins. The existing texts do not explain their calculations, and many of them appear to be corrupt and incomplete. At some point, descriptive geography (perhaps represented by the *Rāmāyaṇa*) must have given way to a quasi-geographical system based on circles of immense size. As we will argue later on, the motivation for this was apparently astronomical and involved an analogy between the earth and the sun's path through the heavens. It could have happened at any time in the development of the tradition leading up to the *Bhāgavatam*.

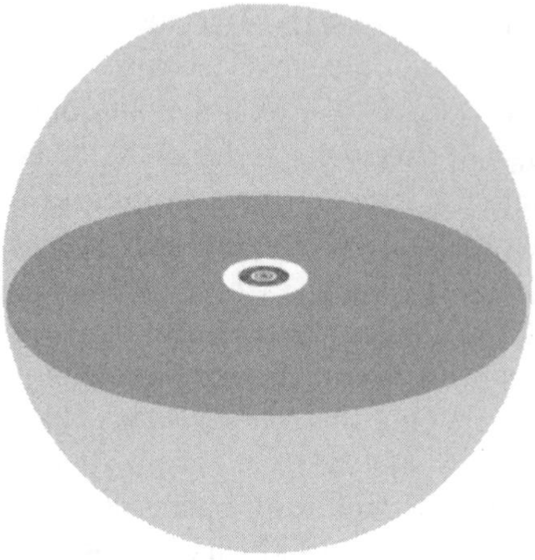

Figure 2.7 The *Viṣṇu Purāṇa* places the Golden Land directly outside of Sapta-dvīpa, with a thickness twice that of the Sweet Water Ocean. This gives the surrounding Lokāloka Mountain a radius only 15% of the radius of the Brahmāṇḍa, as shown here. (Compare with the *Bhāgavatam's* version in Figure 1 (p. 2) of the Introduction.)

2.4 THE ISLAND OF JAMBŪDVĪPA

In the *Purāṇas*, Jambūdvīpa is a disk 100,000 *yojanas* in diameter situated in the center of Bhū-maṇḍala. In the center of Jambūdvīpa is Mount Meru (or Sumeru) which, in one interpretation, corresponds astronomically to the polar axis of the earth. But even though the center point of Meru may represent the north pole, the cardinal directions east, west, north, and south are defined from it. We will argue later on that Jambūdvīpa also represents a local map centered on the Pamir mountains, and these cardinal directions are appropriate for this map (see Section 5.1).

On the top of Mount Meru, the cardinal directions and intermediate directions (northeast, southeast, southwest, and northwest) are marked by the eight cities of the Loka-pālas, surrounding the central city of Brahmā. It turns out that this arrangement of directional demigods is related to a system of Indian architecture in which a building site on the earth is identified with the ecliptic—the path of the sun through the heavens. This is discussed below, in Section 2.5. It is significant, because a key interpretation of the earth-mandala is that it represents the ecliptic and the planetary orbits.

The disk of Jambūdvīpa is divided in the *Purāṇas* into nine *varṣas*, or continents, by a series of mountain ranges, as shown in Figure 2.9. The disk is first of all divided into seven horizontal strips by six ranges that run east-west. In the *Bhāgavatam*, each range is said to be

10,000 *yojanas* high and 2,000 *yojanas* wide. The three strips to the north and the three to the south are single *varṣas*, and they are said to extend for 9,000 *yojanas* in a north-south direction. This leaves 34,000 *yojanas* for the seventh strip, which consists of three *varṣas*. These features and their north-south dimensions are listed in Table 2.5, going from north to south.

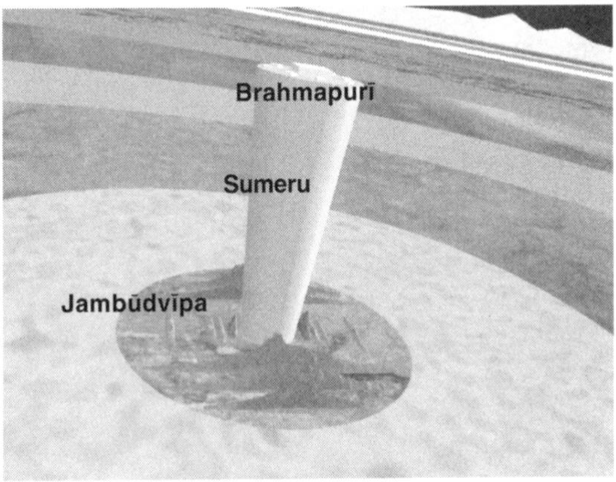

Figure 2.8 Close-up of Jambūdvīpa, showing Brahmapurī on top of Mount Sumeru.

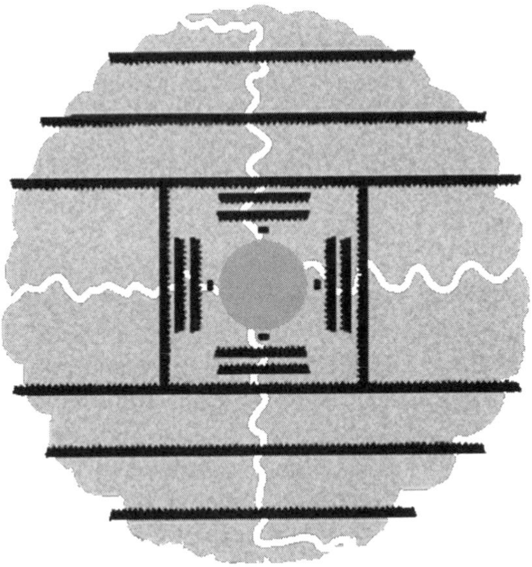

Figure 2.9 Map of Jambūdvīpa, with mountain ranges shown in black and the base of Mount Meru shown in the center.

TABLE 2.5
Geographical Features of Jambūdvīpa, from North to South

Feature Name	Width (*yojanas*)
Kuru-varṣa	9,000
Śṛṅgavān Mountain	2,000
Hiraṇmaya-varṣa	9,000
Śveta Mountain	2,000
Ramyaka-varṣa	9,000
Nīla Mountain	2,000
Central strip	34,000
Niṣadha Mountain	2,000
Hari-varṣa	9,000
Hemakūṭa Mountain	2,000
Kimpuruṣa-varṣa	9,000
Himālaya Mountain	2,000
Bhārata-varṣa	9,000
Total	100,000

According to 5.16.8, the east-west length of these mountains is supposed to be reduced by a little more than 10% as one goes from mountain to mountain from the center outward. This is roughly true if we extend each mountain range until it meets the circular boundary of Jambūdvīpa. These lengths appear in Table 2.6.

The central strip is divided into three *varṣas* (making nine in total) by two mountain chains that run north-south and extend for 2,000 *yojanas*. Their north-south length must be 34,000 *yojanas*. Taking their width in the east-west direction to be 2,000 *yojanas*, and taking Ilāvṛta-varṣa in the center to be square, the east-west dimensions of these features are in Table 2.7.

The inhabitants and topography of Jambūdvīpa are described in considerable detail. In 5.17.11, Bhārata-varṣa is singled out as the field of fruitive activities, and the other eight *varṣas* are said to be meant for elevated persons who are enjoying the remainder of their

TABLE 2.6
Lengths of Mountains in Jambūdvīpa, from North to South

Mountain	Length (*yojanas*)
Śṛṅgavān	60,000
Śveta	81,462
Nīla	93,295
Niṣadha	93,295
Hemakūṭa	81,462
Himālaya	60,000

TABLE 2.7
Features Ranging from West to East in Jambūdvīpa

Feature	Width (*yojanas*)
Ketumāla-varṣa	31,000
Gandhamādana Mountain	2,000
Ilāvṛta-varṣa	34,000
Mālyavān Mountain	2,000
Bhadrāśva-varṣa	31,000

pious credits after returning from the heavenly planets. This suggests that, in one sense, Bhārata-varṣa is the entire earth and the other eight *varṣas* represent otherworldly, heavenly regions. This is one of the major interpretations of Jambūdvīpa and Bhū-maṇḍala, and it is discussed in Chapter 6.

Within Ilāvṛta-varṣa there are a number of mountains and rivers surrounding Mount Meru. Meru is described in 5.16.7 as being 100,000 *yojanas* high, with 16,000 *yojanas* extending beneath the earth and 84,000 *yojanas* above the earth. It is said to be 32,000 *yojanas* in diameter at the top and 16,000 *yojanas* in diameter at the base.

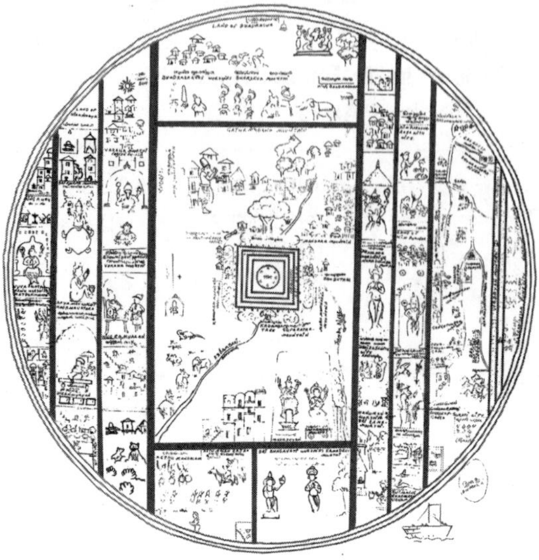

Figure 2.10. This diagram of Jambūdvīpa shows the Deities worshiped in different *varṣas*, nearly according to the *Bhāgavatam*. It is copied from a painting on the wall of the compound of the Kutalmanika temple in Kerala.

TABLE 2.8
Worship in Jambūdvīpa

Varṣa	Worshiper	*Avatāra*	Reference
Ilāvṛta-varṣa	Śiva	Saṅkarṣaṇa	5.17.16
Bhadrāśva-varṣa	Bhadrāśva	Hayaśīrṣa	5.18.1
Hari-varṣa	Prahlād	Nṛsiṁhadeva	5.18.7
Ketumāla-varṣa	Lakṣmī	Kāmadeva	5.18.15
Ramyaka-varṣa	Manu	Matsya	5.18.24
Hiraṇmaya-varṣa	Aryamā	Kūrma	5.18.29
Uttarakuru-varṣa	Bhūdevī	Varāha	5.18.34
Kimpuruṣa-varṣa	Hanumān	Rāmacandra	5.19.1
Bhārata-varṣa	Nārada Muni	Nara-Nārāyaṇa	5.19.9

Mount Meru is therefore in the form of an inverted cone, and it is compared to the pericarp or seed pod of the lotus flower of Bhū-maṇḍala. In the *Vāyu Purāṇa*, Meru is said to be four-sided, with the colors white (east), yellow (south), black (west), and red (north) (Tagare, 1987, pp. 237–38).

In each *varṣa* it is said that an *avatāra* of Viṣṇu is worshiped by a particular famous devotee. In this way, Jambūdvīpa also plays the role of a divine mandala representing the faith of the Vaiṣṇavas, for whom the *Bhāgavatam* is an important sacred text. The *avatāras* and their worshipers are listed in Table 2.8.

In Bhārata-varṣa, Nara-nārāyaṇa is said to be worshiped by Nārada Muni in Badarikāśrama, a famous site of pilgrimage for thousands of Hindus. This provides a link with a known location in the Himalayas, but we do not have earthly counterparts for the other centers of worship.

2.4.1 Jambūdvīpa in the *Mahābhārata*

The *Bhīṣma Parva* of the *Mahābhārata* describes a circular island called Sudarśana which is very similar to the Purāṇic Jambūdvīpa. The geographical layout of this island is the same as that in Tables 2.5 and 2.7, with the exception that the vertical spacing between the east-west ranges is set at 1,000 *yojanas* (Ganguli, vol. V, pp. 13–14). However, the height of Mount Meru, situated between the Mālyavān and Gandhamādana mountains, is defined to be 84,000 *yojanas*, as in the *Purāṇas*.

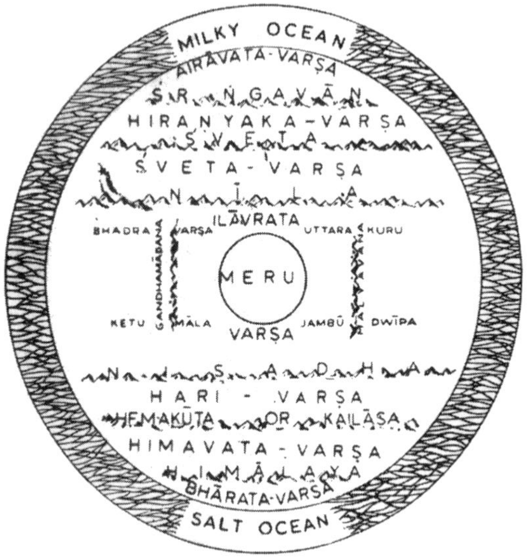

Figure 2.11 Circular continent of Sudarśana, as described in the *Mahābhārata* (after Ali, 1966, pp. 32–33). This corresponds to Jambūdvīpa in the *Purāṇas*.

While Sudarśana corresponds to the Purāṇic Jambūdvīpa, the term Jambūdvīpa is used in a different sense in the *Mahābhārata*. Thus, in the *Bhīṣma Parva* it is said that "Jamvu Mountain" extends over 18,600 *yojanas* and the Salt Ocean is twice as big. Śākadvīpa is twice as big as Jambūdvīpa, and another ocean surrounding Śākadvīpa is twice the size of that island (Ganguli, vol. V, p. 24). Except for the small size of Jambūdvīpa, this sounds like Purāṇic geography as given in the *Matsya Purāṇa*.

But in the *Śānti Parva*, it is said that King Yudhiṣṭhira once ruled Jambūdvīpa, Krauñcadvīpa on the west of Meru and equal to Jambūdvīpa, Śākadvīpa on the east of Meru and equal to Krauñcadvīpa, and Bhadrāśva, on the north of Meru and equal to Śākadvīpa (Ganguli, vol. VIII, p. 24). This gives us three *dvīpas* and one *varṣa* arranged as equal units around Meru in the cardinal directions. This geographical arrangement is clearly quite different from the one given in the *Bhīṣma Parva*.

Then again, if we look back to the *Bhīṣma Parva*, we find the statement that "Beside Meru are situated, O lord, these four islands, *viz.*, Bhadraswa, and Ketumāla, and Jamvudwipa otherwise called Bharata, and Uttar-Kuru which is the abode of persons who have achieved the merit of righteousness" (Ganguli, vol. V, p. 14). It appears that the *Mahābhārata* is reporting different geographical systems without attempting to systematically reconcile them.

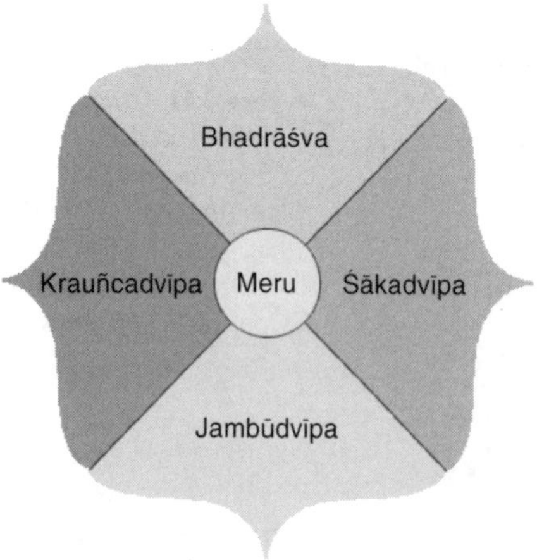

Figure 2.12 This diagram is based on a text from the *Śānti Parva* of the *Mahābhārata*. It differs from the *Purāṇas* and other parts of the *Mahābhārata* by defining Jambūdvīpa as one of four regions surrounding Mount Meru.

According to Joseph Schwartzberg, an earlier Hindu and Buddhist map of the earth placed four continents in the cardinal directions around Mount Meru, with the continent called Bhārata or Jambūdvīpa to the south (Schwartzberg, 1987, p. 336). The *Sūrya-siddhānta* follows this pattern by putting Bhadrāśva to the east, Bhārata to the south, Ketumāla to the west, and Kuru to the north (Burgess, 1860, p. 286).

In Figure 2.13, published by the early Indologist Francis Wilford, Jambūdvīpa is presented as a lotus, with four continents arranged around Meru as listed in the *Sūrya-siddhānta* (Wilford, 1805). Note that Kuru-varṣa (Curu) is identified as Siberia, so that Meru falls somewhere in the mountainous region north of India. Additional lands near India have been added as extra petals.

Schwartzberg maintains that the original system of four continents was modified over time until it took the form given in Figure 2.9. This may be true, but we may also be dealing with independent traditions making use of the same set of names for islands and continents.

We can distinguish between the two maps of Jambūdvīpa on purely functional grounds. In relation to actual earthly geography, the

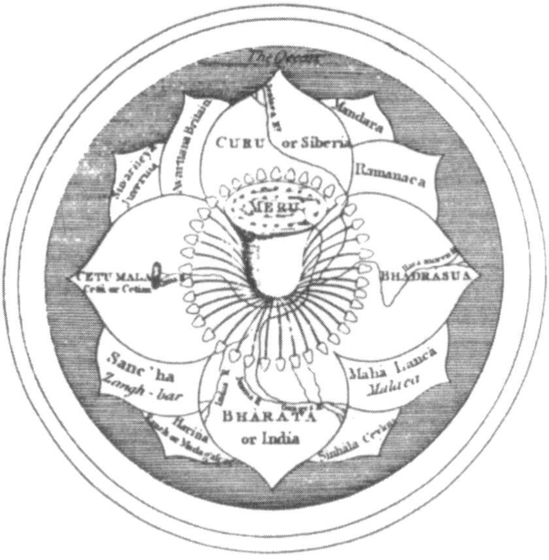

Figure 2.13
Jambūdvīpa, depicted as a lotus flower by the early Indologist Francis Wilford.

four-continent map simply assigns names to lands in the four cardinal directions around Mount Meru (which lies somewhere to the north of India). In contrast, the map in Figure 2.9 gives a more detailed picture of the mountain ranges and valleys in this part of south-central Asia (see Chapter 5). This may explain how these two systems could coexist in the same text.

A basic theme of this study is that models in the *Bhāgavatam* are sometimes used to convey more than one meaning (see the Introduction to *Bhāgavata* Cosmology). Here it appears that the *Mahābhārata* is using geographical terms (such as Śākadvīpa) with more than one meaning. One might argue that as alternative meanings accumulated over a long period of time, commentators became tolerant of apparently conflicting meanings, and they tended to resolve conflicts by looking at statements from the standpoint of local context.

2.5 LORDS OF THE DIRECTIONS

Concluding this chapter, we show how an apparently minor detail of Jambūdvīpa is connected with the astronomy of the ecliptic and with rich astronomical traditions of Indochina. This connection provides data which corroborates the close correlations between Bhū-maṇḍala and modern astronomy that we will discuss in Chapter 4.

The *Bhāgavatam* verse 5.21.7 describes four cities of the demigods situated on Mānasottara mountain in the cardinal directions:

TABLE 2.9
Directional Cities on Mānasottara Mountain

Direction	Demigod	City
East	Indra	Devadhānī
South	Yama	Saṁyamanī
West	Varuṇa	Nimlocanī
North	Soma	Vibhāvarī

It turns out that these cities are connected with a larger system of directional demigods, and these in turn are connected with the traditional Indian system of architecture known as Vāstu Śāstra.

Figure 2.14 The *aṣṭa-dik-pālaka,* the rulers of the eight directions (after Dubreuil-Jouveau, 1937, p. 107).

Verse 5.16.29 mentions cities of eight Loka-pālās, or lords of the worlds, beginning with Indra. These cities are said to be situated on top of Mount Sumeru, surrounding the city of Lord Brahmā (Brahma-purī). The Loka-pālas are also known as the Aṣṭa-dik-pālaka, or eight lords of the directions. They are situated as follows (Dubreuil-Jouveau, 1937, p. 107):

TABLE 2.10
The Cities of Brahmā and the Eight Loka-pālas

	West	Center	East
North	Vāyu	Kuvera	Īśāna
Center	Varuṇa	Brahmā	Indra
South	Niruti	Yama	Agni

Figure 2.15 The figure of the Vāstupuruṣa in the 8×8 Vāstupuruṣa-maṇḍala.

Note that with the exception of Kuvera in the north, the lords of the cardinal directions are the same as the demigods ruling the cardinal points of Mānasottara mountain.

In *Vāstu Śāstra,* the layout of a temple or residential house is based on an 8×8 or 9×9 grid of squares, known as the Vāstupuruṣamaṇḍala. This grid is associated with the figure of a person called the Vāstupuruṣa, as indicated for the 8×8 grid in the illustration. These grids are always aligned with the cardinal directions.

There are 28 squares in the outer border of the 8×8 grid, and 32 squares in the outer border of the 9×9 grid. These are associated with demigods called Padadevatās. The central 3×3 squares of the 9×9 grid are dedicated to Brahmā, and thus the entire grid resembles the top of Mount Sumeru, with Brahmapurī in the center. This is enhanced by the close similarity between the eight Loka-pālas and the eight Padadevatās situated at the cardinal and intermediate directions.

For the 9×9 grid, the Padadevatās are listed in the table below. Different sources give small variants in the list of Padadevatās, and in the first three columns we give three lists from (1) (Kramrisch, 1946, p. 32), (2) (Tarkhedkar, 1995, p. 31), and (3) (Sthapati, 1997, p. 205).

TABLE 2.11
The 32 Padadevatās and the Loka-pālas

Direction	Padadevatās (1)	(2)	(3)	Loka-pālas
NE:	Agni	Ish Shiki	Esa	Īśāna
	Parjanya	Parjanya	Parjanya	
	Jayanta	Jayant	Jayanta	
	Indra	Indra	Indra	
E:	Sūrya	Surya	Surya	Indra
	Satyā	Satya	Satya	
	Bhṛśa	Bhrush	Bhrisa	
	Antarikṣa	Aakash	Antariksha	
SE:	Anila	Agni	Agni	Agni
SE:	Anila	Agni	Agni	Agni
	Pūṣan	Pusha	Poosha	
	Vitatha	Vitatha	Vitata	
	Bṛhatkṣata	Brihakshat	Gruhakshata	
S:	Yama	Yama	Yama	Yama
	Gandharva	Gundharv	Gandharva	
	Bhṛṅgarāja	Bhrig Raj	Brunga Raja	
	Mṛga	Mriga	Mruga	
SW:	Pitaraḥ	Pitav	Niruti	Niruti
SW:	Pitaraḥ	Pitav	Niruti	Niruti
	Dauvārika	Dwarpal	Douvarika	
	Sugrīva	Sugriv	Sugriva	
	Kusumadanta	Pushpa Devata	Pushpadanta	
W:	Varuṇa	Varun	Varuna	Varuṇa
	Asura	Asur	Asura	
	Śoṣa	Shesh	Sosha	
	Pāpayakṣman	Pap	Papayakshma	
NW:	Roga	Rog	Vayu	Vāyu
NW:	Roga	Rog	Vayu	Vāyu
	Ahi	Nag	Naga	
	Mukhya	Mukhya	Mukhya	
	Bhallāṭa	Bhallat	Bhallata	
N:	Soma	Som	Soma	Kuvera
	Bhujaga	Rishi	Bhujaga	
	Aditi	Aditi	Aditi	
	Diti	Diti	Diti	
NE:	Agni	Ish Shiki	Esa	Īśāna

The eight Loka-pālas are listed for comparison in the fourth column of the table. The demigods are listed in groups of nine for each side of the 9×9 square, and each corner demigod therefore comes at the end of one list and the beginning of the next one. The corner demigods should be compared with the Loka-pālas for the intermediate directions, and the demigods in the center squares of the sides should be compared with the Loka-pālas for the cardinal directions. The similarity is close enough to indicate a strong connection between the *Vāstu Śāstras* and the Purāṇic lords of the directions. Note that the Padadevatā for the center of the northern side is listed as Soma. This disagrees with the Loka-pāla list, which has Kuvera, but it agrees with 5.21.7.

There is a connection between the Vāstupuruṣamaṇḍala and the ecliptic. The ecliptic is the path of the sun against the background of stars, and in Indian astronomy it is marked by 27 or 28 constellations called *nakṣatras*. The Vāstupuruṣamaṇḍala, which is situated on the earth, is linked with the ecliptic in the heavens by identifying the four cardinal directions with the solstices and equinoxes and by identifying 28 intermediate directions with the *nakṣatras*.

The Indian art historian Stella Kramrisch described this connection as follows for the 9×9 Vāstupuruṣamaṇḍala with 32 squares in its border:

> The 27 and 28 divisions of the Ecliptic become fixed in position like a great, fixed, square dial with the numbers ranging not along the equator, but along the Ecliptic itself. The square, cycle of the Ecliptic, would thus have to be sub-divided into 27 or 28 compartments. Instead of this, the number of Nakṣatras is augmented to 32, so that each field of the border represents a lunar mansion or Nakṣatra. In the Vāstumaṇḍala their number is thus adjusted to the helio-planetary cosmogram of the Pṛthivīmaṇḍala. There, the four cardinal points, with reference to the Ecliptic are the equinoxial and solstitial points in the annual cycle. The solar cycles of the days and years are shown in the Vāstumaṇḍala together with the lunations, the monthly revolutions of the moon around the earth. The solar-spatial symbolism is primary and the lunar symbolism is accommodated within the Vāstu-diagram (Kramrisch, 1946, p. 31).

According to Kramrisch, the Vāstumaṇḍala represents a composite of different traditions, and she also mentions a different scheme in which *nakṣatras* and their presiding demigods are linked to the cardinal directions (Kramrisch, 1946, p. 34). These demigods are said to rule over positions of entrances to the planned building, and they differ from the 32 Padadevatās.

The ecliptic/Vāstumaṇḍala link represents a scheme in which part of the earth (where a building is to be erected) is identified with the ecliptic in the sky. There is a similar identification in the *Bhāgavatam*, where the earth-disk, Bhū-maṇḍala, represents the ecliptic plane. It may therefore be significant that the Purāṇic Loka-pālas on Mount Meru are connected with the Vāstupuruṣamaṇḍala of *Vāstu Śāstra.*

Adrian Snodgrass describes the symbolism of the Vāstupuruṣa-maṇḍala, and he also relates it to a cosmological account in which the Trāyaśtriṁsa Heaven of Indra is situated on Mount Meru, along with 32 directional demigods representing the equinoxes and solstices and the 28 *nakṣatra* divisions of the ecliptic. He points out that this symbolism was reflected in the medieval Burmese kingdom of Pegu, in which 32 provinces surrounding the capital city represented the ecliptic and the Loka-pālas (Snodgrass, 1990, pp. 210–11).

Snodgrass also points out that elaborate astronomical symbolism was built into the temple of Angkor Wat in Cambodia. Thus Angkor Wat "incorporates at least twenty-two significant alignments to equinoctial and solstitial solar risings" (Snodgrass, 1990, p. 216). This implies that Hindu temple builders in Indochina must have been interested in making quantitative astronomical observations, and it may indicate some of the practical astronomy lying behind the Vāstumaṇḍala concept.

Snodgrass also listed over thirteen different astronomical quantities that were built into the temple of Angkor Wat in multiples of a unit of length called the *hat* (Sanskrit *hasta*). For example, "the interior axial lengths of the nine chambers in the central tower are 27 on the east-west axis and 28 on the north-south axis, referring to the 27 or 28 lunar mansions (*nakṣatra*) and to the 28 days on which the moon is visible each month" (Snodgrass, 1990, p. 217).

An interesting feature is the latitude of Angkor Wat, which equals the local elevation of the polar axis. This is expressed in the building by several lengths of 13.43 *hat*, where one *hat* represents one degree of latitude. This is accurate to 60–90 seconds of arc (Snodgrass, 1990,

p. 221). Also, several lengths of 432, 864, 1,296, and 1,728 *hat* in different parts of the building express the four *yugas*—time periods which endure for corresponding numbers of millenia (Snodgrass, 1990, p. 223). (The *yuga* system is discussed in Section 8.4.)

The *hat* itself is 0.43454 meters, which is very close to the 0.432 meter *hasta* discussed in Section 4.5 on the length of the *yojana* (Snodgrass, 1990, p. 217). This unit, in turn, emerges independently in the study of the correlation between planetary orbits and Bhū-maṇḍala reported in Section 4.4.

3

The Solar System in Projection

3.1 THE FLAT EARTH AS A PLANISPHERE

In this chapter and Chapters 4 through 6, we present the four major interpretations of Bhū-maṇḍala listed in the Introduction (p. 3). We first interpret Bhū-maṇḍala as a polar projection map of the earth. Like the others, this interpretation requires us to focus on certain features of Bhū-maṇḍala while neglecting others.

The features to be neglected in this case are the large dimensions assigned to the *dvīpas* of Bhū-maṇḍala in the *Bhāgavatam*. These begin with 100,000 *yojanas* for both the diameter of Jambūdvīpa and the width of the surrounding, annular Salt Ocean. They proceed by a

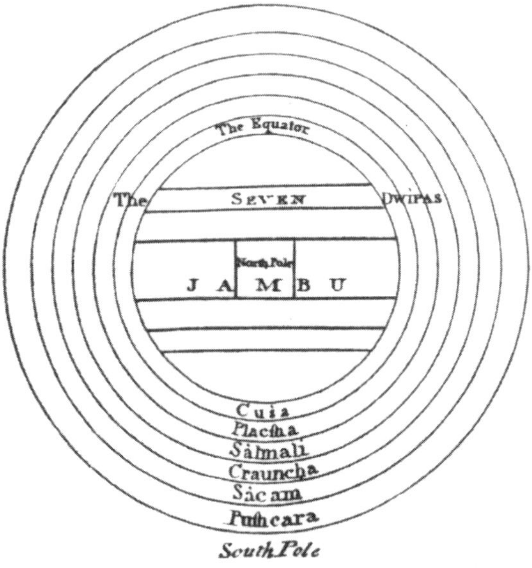

Figure 3.1 Diagram of Bhū-maṇḍala published by Francis Wilford in 1805.

process of doubling, in which the width of each annular ring is twice (or more) the width of the one inside it, resulting quickly in rings the size of planetary orbits.

This is not appropriate for a representation of the earth globe. But we see that cosmological drawings from India typically neglect this doubling, and compress all of Bhū-maṇḍala into a compact picture with equal rings. Figure 3.1 is an example published by the early British Indologist, Francis Wilford (1805).

The map with equalized rings can be interpreted as a stereographic projection of the earth-globe onto a flat plane (Figure 3.2). Stereographic projection maps the surface of a globe onto a plane tangent to the globe's north pole. This is done by drawing a line from the south pole through any given point on the globe and extending it until it reaches the tangent plane.

The resulting map of the earth is called a planisphere (Figure 3.3). This method is one of many ways of creating a polar projection of the earth globe. It has the advantage that it is simple and it maps any great circle on the globe onto a circle in the plane. It was known by Greek astronomers in the time of Ptolemy.

If Bhū-maṇḍala is a planisphere, or stereographic projection of the globe, then the original globe must be as shown in Figure 3.4. Here, we simply map Bhū-maṇḍala with equalized rings onto a sphere, using

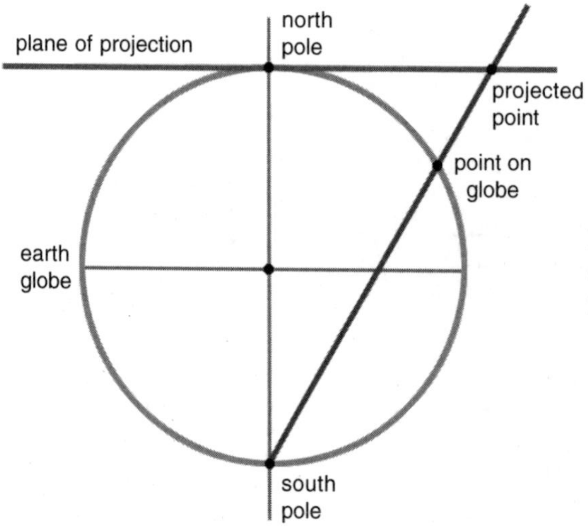

Figure 3.2 Diagram defining stereographic projection.

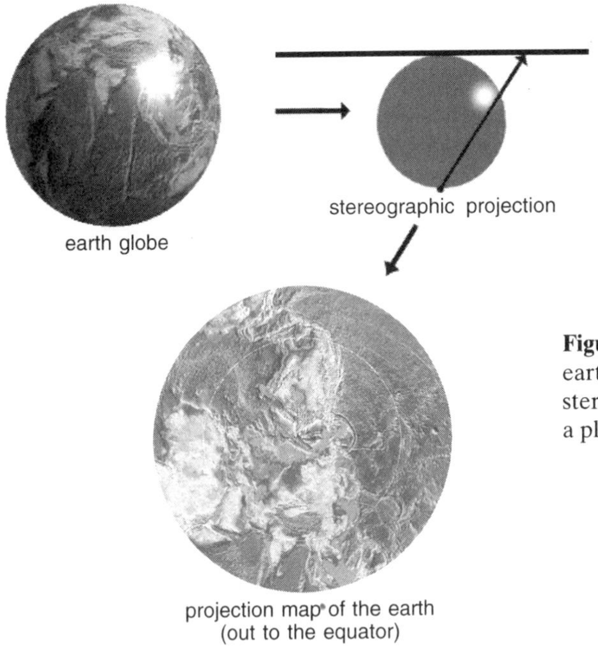

Figure 3.3 The earth globe projected stereographically onto a plane.

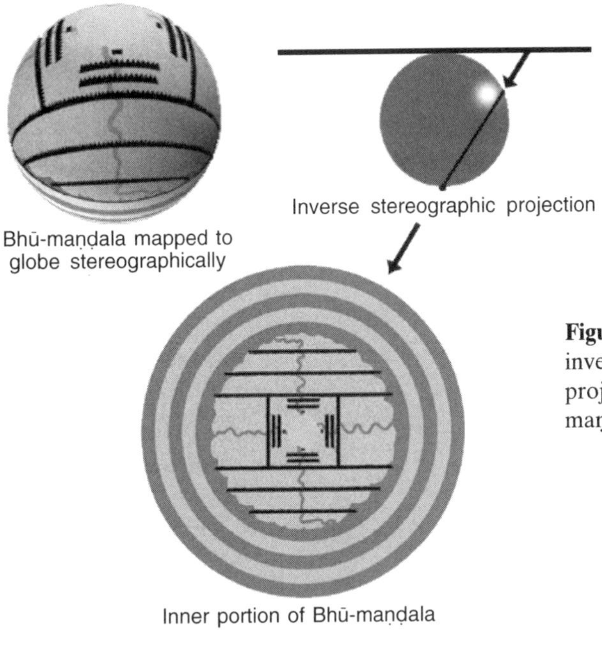

Figure 3.4 The inverse-stereographic projection of Bhū-maṇḍala onto a globe.

Figure 3.5 Globe commissioned by King Jai Singh of Jaipur, showing Jambūdvīpa in the northern hemisphere and the other six *dvīpas* in the southern hemisphere (after Gole, 1989, pp. 72–73).

inverse stereographic projection. This was done in such a way as to map the circular boundary of Jambūdvīpa onto the equator.

In fact, such globes exist in India. The one in Figure 3.5 was probably commissioned by Sawai Jai Singh, Raja of Jaipur, in the early eighteenth century. Indian astronomical texts (*Jyotiṣa Śāstras*), such as *Siddhānta-śiromaṇi* also describe the layout of the globe in this way.

In the picture of this globe on the left, the land area between the equator and the mountain arc is Bhārata-varṣa. Some thirty-six place names for locations in India have been transliterated by Joseph Schwartzberg in this region (Schwartzberg, 1987, pp. 396–97). The Ganges and Yamunā rivers are shown, flowing past Kashmir, Delhi and Agra, to Prayāga and Kāśī (Benares), where they join. This is one of several small inaccuracies, since these rivers actually join at Prayāga. The Ganges is shown reaching the sea at Calcutta, and a large temple of Jagannātha is depicted nearby. Lanka is centered on the prime meridian along with Ujjain, as is stated in *Jyotiṣa Śāstras*. Outside of Bhārata-varṣa there are relatively few recognizable names. These include Mecca (Makkah) in the west, Mānasaghati (the ghats on lake Manasarowar in Tibet?) in the north, and Mahachin and Chin (Greater China and China) in the east.

If we interpret Bhū-maṇḍala as a planisphere, the north pole must be the center of Mount Meru and the footprint of Meru roughly matches the Arctic region. Bhārata-varṣa corresponds to India, which is known as Bhārata even today by the Indian people. The ring-shaped *dvīpas* surrounding Jambūdvīpa represent parallel bands of equal latitude falling in the southern hemisphere. However, none of the eight *varṣas* of Jambūdvīpa other than Bhārata-varṣa corresponds to a recognizable region of the earth globe.

This map is therefore clearly intended for astronomical, rather than geographical, purposes. Indeed, it can be argued that the geographical features of Jambūdvīpa actually do not relate to the earth globe as a whole, but to a localized region of south-central Asia centered on the Pamir mountains (see Section 5.1). This is another important interpretation of Jambūdvīpa.

Nonetheless, Jambūdvīpa has evidently been interpreted as a polar projection map for a long time. There is even evidence that this interpretation somehow made its way into Europe. In 1569, Gerhard Mercator published a polar projection map of the Arctic region. This map shows an imaginary circular continent centered on the north pole, with a mountain at the pole, and what appear to be four rivers emanating from the pole at right angles. This corresponds to Jambūdvīpa, with the four branches of the Ganges extending at right angles from Mount Meru.

One may ask whether Jambūdvīpa, as described in the *Bhāgavatam* and other *Purāṇas*, was originally seen as a planisphere, or whether the planisphere interpretation was made later on in the *Jyotiṣa Śāstras* when the idea of the earth as a globe was introduced by the Greeks. The answer is that there are several points in the text of the *Bhāgavatam* that make sense in light of the planisphere interpretation, but that do not make sense if Jambūdvīpa and Bhū-maṇḍala are thought of as lying literally in one plane. This lends support to the hypothesis that the planisphere interpretation was originally built into the *Purāṇas*.

In the remainder of this chapter, we discuss these points step by step, along with several related topics that arise in connection with the planisphere model. These include the length of the day, the zodiac, the distance of the moon, eclipses, and constellations.

3.1.1 Day and Night Reverse at the Antipodes

There are statements in the *Bhāgavatam* that indirectly treat the earth as a globe. In texts 5.21.8–9, the *Bhāgavatam* says:

> The sun sets at the diametrically opposite point from where it rises. The sun puts people to sleep [as at midnight] at the diametrically opposite point from where it heats with perspiration [as at midday]. Those who go [to the opposite point] do not see [the sun] as the same.

This clearly works on the earth globe, since a point where the sun is rising is diametrically opposite to a point where it is setting and a point in daylight is diametrically opposite to a point in darkness. But it does not work on a plane.

According to the *Bhāgavatam*, the sun orbits just above Bhū-maṇḍala on its chariot. Its rays should spread out smoothly over a literal plane, leaving no points of sunrise or sunset and no area in total darkness. This contradicts the *Bhāgavatam's* statement in 5.21.8–9, but there is no contradiction if we adopt the planisphere interpretation. Since the planisphere model is a map of a globe, it does have a sharp boundary between day and night, as well as a meaningful definition of "diametrically opposite."

The *Aitareya Brāhmaṇa* contains a statement similar to 5.21.8–9 in the *Bhāgavatam*. It says that

> He (i.e. the sun) neither sets nor rises. What is believed to be his set is his turning himself around at the end of the day. He makes night on this side and day on the other. Similarly, what is taken to be his rise in the morning is his turning himself around at the end of the night, when he makes day on this side and night on the other side. In fact, he never sets (Dikshit, 1969a, p. 9).

This suggests that the idea of the earth as a globe may date back to Vedic times, well before the period of the known *Jyotiṣa Śāstras*.

The equator, the tropic of Cancer, the tropic of Capricorn, and the ecliptic are shown in Figure 3.6, projected onto the surface of a globe. These circles can be projected stereographically, as shown in Figure 3.7. The sun is always positioned somewhere on the great circle of the ecliptic, which is tilted on the globe at an angle of 23½° to the equator. The sun's position on the globe and its corresponding position on the planisphere map both represent the point on the earth where the sun is at the zenith.

The terminator, or boundary between day and night, is a great circle on the globe that is perpendicular to the sun's zenith position. It

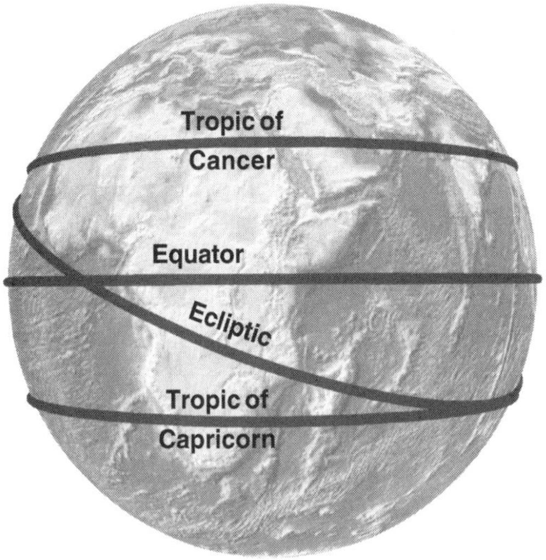

Figure 3.6 The earth globe, showing the ecliptic, the equator, and the tropics of Cancer and Capricorn.

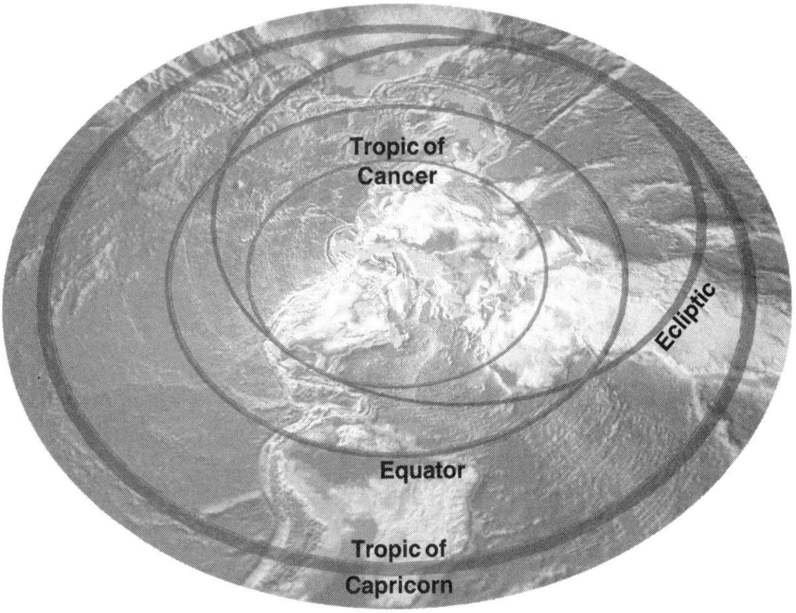

Figure 3.7 Stereographic projection of the earth globe on a plane, showing the ecliptic, the equator, and the tropics.

projects stereographically onto a circular arc on the planisphere that rotates once every 24 hours. At the equinoxes, this arc becomes a straight line. At the solstices it bends so that the north polar region is in light (northern summer) or in darkness (northern winter). This is shown in Figures 3.9–11.

According to the *Bhāgavatam* 5.21.7, the passage of day and night is caused by the rotation of the sun around the circle of Mānasottara mountain in Bhū-maṇḍala. At the cardinal points along this circle are four cities of the demigods, listed in Table 2.9 (p. 40).

As the sun moves past these cities, the half circle within plus or minus 90° of the sun is in light and the opposite half circle is in darkness. This motion is clarified by a passage in the *Viṣṇu Purāṇa*: "When the sun (at midday) passes over [one] of the cities of the gods on Mānasottara mountain (at the cardinal points), his light extends to three cities and two intermediate points; when situated in an intermediate point, he illuminates two of the cities and three intermediate points (in either case one hemisphere)" (Wilson, 1980, p. 316). As before, the four cities of the gods are situated at the cardinal points, with an angle of 90° from one to another. When the sun is over a city, the three illuminated cities are at -90°, 0°, and 90° from the sun. The two intermediate points are at -45° and 45°.

This description of day and night makes no sense on a literal plane, but it corresponds exactly to the planisphere model at a time near the equinoxes, when the day/night terminator is a straight line. This gives support to the hypothesis that the *Bhāgavatam* makes deliberate use of the planisphere model.

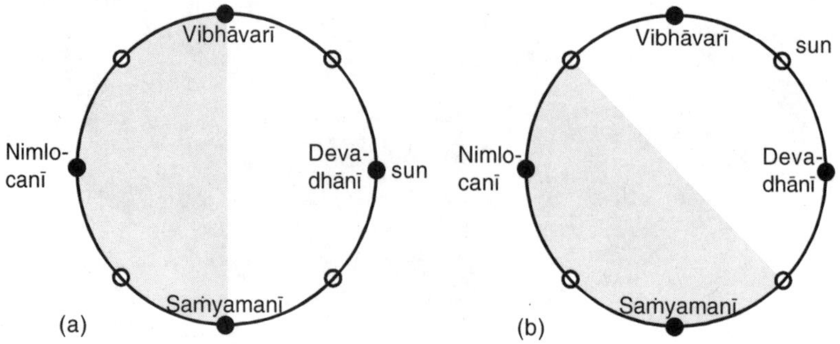

Figure 3.8 The sun at a demigod city (a) or at an intermediate point (b), according to the *Viṣṇu Purāṇa*.

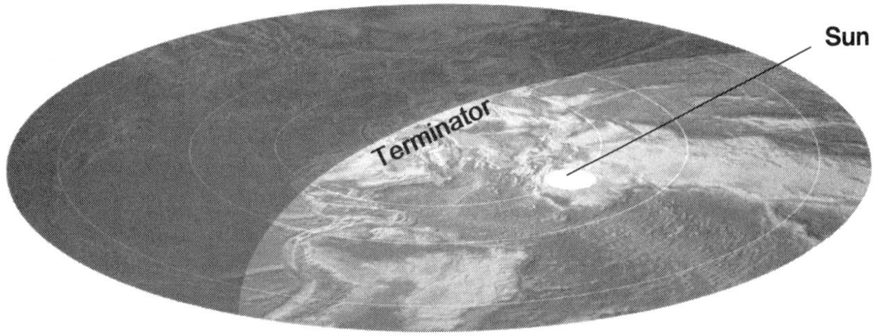

Figure 3.9 The terminator during the summer solstice.

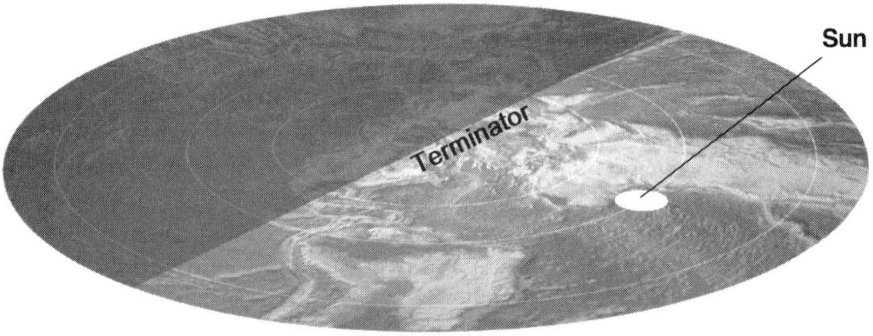

Figure 3.10 The terminator during an equinox.

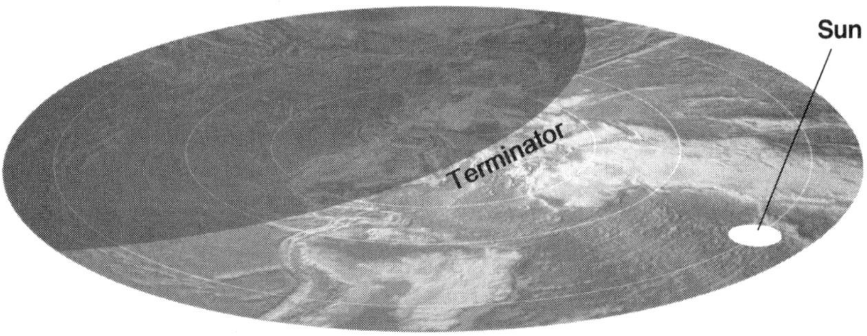

Figure 3.11 The terminator during the winter solstice.

3.1.2 The Speeds of the Sun

In a planisphere, the zodiac projects onto the earth map as we see in Figure 3.12. The sun moves around the zodiac once per year, and it spends half the year going from north to south and half going from south to north. While going north, the sun approaches the center of the planisphere, and while going south it moves towards the periphery. This is due to the off-centered projection of the ecliptic caused by stereographic projection.

In the course of a day, the zodiac and ecliptic circles sweep around the planisphere relative to the fixed earth map. This daily motion is clockwise, whereas the yearly motion of the sun around the ecliptic is counterclockwise. Since the projected ecliptic circle is off-center, the sun moves faster in the northern winter, when its distance from the center of the planisphere is greater, and it moves slower in the northern summer, when it is closer to the center.

The same is true of the sun's yearly motion. In the simplest model, the sun moves around the ecliptic at a constant speed. (Due to its elliptical orbit, the sun's speed around the ecliptic actually varies slightly.) But due to the distortion caused by stereographic projection, the sun's yearly motion is faster on the planisphere when it is to the south (away from the center) and slower when it is to the north (close to the center).

The days in the northern hemisphere become shorter when the sun is beneath the equator and longer when the sun is above it, and thus longer days are associated with slower speed of the sun on the

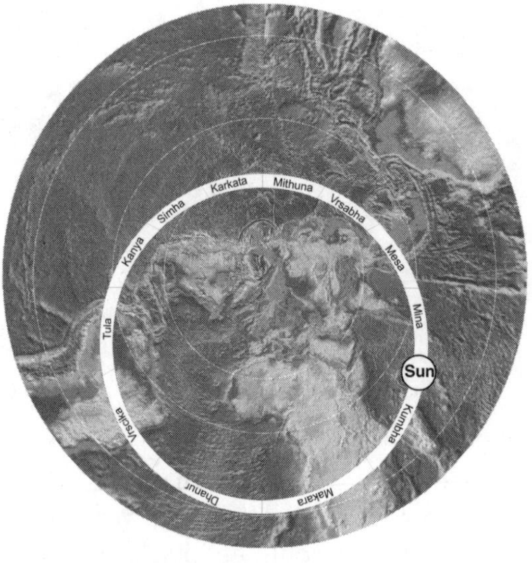

Figure 3.12 Stereographic projection of the ecliptic and the zodiac onto a planisphere map of the earth. The sun is shown, orbiting along the ecliptic, marked by the signs of the zodiac.

planisphere, and shorter days are associated with faster speed.

The *Bhāgavatam* 5.21.3 sums up all of these points as follows:

> The sun makes days and nights short, long, and medium, while advancing according to the time with low, high, and moderate speeds, called north-going, south-going, and middle-going. It does this in the sign Makara, etc., which are places of ascent, descent, and staying midway.

Note that all of the points in this statement make sense on a plane if and only if it is interpreted as a planisphere.

In this text, "north-going" (*udagayana*) and "south-going" (*dakṣiṇāyana*) are used in a nonstandard sense. In *Jyotiṣa Śāstras*, these terms refer to the periods when the sun is moving north or south, respectively. But here they refer to the times when the sun is situated to the north or to the south (i.e. north or south of the equator). Grammatically, in *udagayana, udag* can be interpreted as being in the accusative or in the locative. In the former case, the meaning is "toward the north," and in the latter, it is "within the north" (Howard Resnick, personal communication). The same point can be made regarding *dakṣiṇāyana* and the south.

The reason for the sun's three speeds is not explicitly mentioned in the *Bhāgavatam*, but the *Viṣṇu Purāṇa* does refer to it:

> As the circumference of a potter's wheel revolves most rapidly, so the sun travels rapidly on his southern journey. . . . As the center of the potter's wheel revolves more slowly than the circumference, so the sun in his northern path again revolves with less rapidity, and moves over a less space of the earth in a longer time . . . (Wilson, 1980, p. 319).

This implies that the sun moves near the center when it moves north and near the circumference when it moves south, in agreement with the planisphere model. One consequence of this is that the sun should cross the *dvīpas* of Bhū-maṇḍala as it moves to the north and to the south.

The movement of the sun across the *dvīpas* and oceans is indirectly discussed by Vaṁśīdhara in an extensive commentary on the *Bhāgavatam* verse 5.1.30 (see Appendix 2). This verse describes how Priyavrata created a second sun by orbiting opposite the sun in a brilliant chariot created by mystic power:

> While Bhagavān Āditya [the sun] illumines the gods' mountain [Meru], continuously going around, he heats only half of the land up to Lokāloka Mountain, and he covers half [with darkness]. Not approving of this, Priyavrata, having accumulated superhuman power by the worship of the Lord, [thought] 'I shall make night into day.' With a chariot built of light of the same speed, he went seven times around, following the movement of the sun like a second sun.

Vaṁśīdhara gives an interpretation in which Priyavrata's counter-sun crosses the seven oceans and *dvīpas* in half a year while moving out from the center, and again crosses them in half a year while moving back towards the center. The real sun moves opposite Priyavrata's sun and does the same thing in reverse order. Vaṁśīdhara's interpretation is backed up by statements in the *Matsya Purāṇa* (Taluqdar, 1916, pp. 339–41) and the *Vāyu Purāṇa* (Tagare, 1987, pp. 338–39). These statements seem to refer to the path of the sun covering different *dvīpas* at different times of the year, but unfortunately the numbers cited in these texts are corrupt (at least in the English translations). They support the planisphere interpretation of Bhū-maṇḍala, without explicitly recognizing it.

We finally note that Caitanya Mahāprabhu referred to the motion of the sun across the *dvīpas* and oceans in his teachings to Sanātana Goswami. He said, "The sun moves across the zodiac (*jyotiś-cakra*) day and night and crosses the oceans between the seven islands one after the other" (*Caitanya-caritāmṛta*, *Madhya-līlā* 20.387).

3.1.3 Mapping Canopus

The *Vāyu Purāṇa* gives an interesting example of a point that can be interpreted easily in terms of the planisphere model. This text says that "Agastya (the star Canopus) traverses quickly over the guardians of the worlds stationed in the four quarters over the mountain Lokāloka" (Tagare, 1987, p. 340). The ring-shaped Lokāloka Mountain is defined in the *Bhāgavatam* 5.20.34 as the outer boundary of the illuminated region of Bhū-maṇḍala, and Canopus is a southern-hemisphere star with a declination of 52° 41.7' south. It is named after the sage Agastya, who is famous for having traveled to the south without ever returning.

It appears that the *Vāyu Purāṇa* is mapping the latitude of Canopus to Lokāloka Mountain in the planisphere map. The rapid motion of Agastya is due to the fact that Canopus maps to a planisphere radius nearly three times the radius of the planisphere equator. Thus Agastya's rate of daily rotation is three times as great as that of an equatorial star. It makes sense for Agastya to circle quickly over Lokāloka mountain in the planisphere interpretation, but without this interpretation its motion is difficult to understand.

3.1.4 Bhū-maṇḍala and the Astrolabe

In 1985, W. Randolph Kloetzli published an article giving a planisphere interpretation to the cosmology of the *Viṣṇu Purāṇa*, and he compared Bhū-maṇḍala and the sun's chariot with an astrolabe—a medieval instrument that performs spherical astronomy in a plane through stereographic projection (Kloetzli, 1985). His reasoning suggests that Bhū-maṇḍala and its accompanying planetary orbits may have been deliberately laid out as a kind of astrolabe model.

It is not clear whether or not there is any historical connection between the astrolabe and Purāṇic cosmology, but there are strong

Figure 3.13 Mercator's astrolabe (1545), in the Moravska Gallery, Brno.

conceptual parallels between the two. The structure of an astrolabe involves a stack of plates marked with stereographic projections representing, among other things, the earth, the orbit of the sun (ecliptic), and selected stars. This arrangement can be compared with Purāṇic cosmology, in which the sun, moon, stars, and planets are assigned to a series of levels above the earth plane. We discuss this below in Section 3.4, in connection with the orbits of the sun and moon.

Otto Neugebauer traced the theory of stereographic projection back to the Greek astronomer Hipparchus, who lived around 150 B.C., and possibly to Eudoxus, who lived two centuries previously (Neugebauer, 1975, p. 858). However, Neugebauer admitted that the evidence in this regard is scanty. In the second century A.D., Ptolemy wrote a treatise on stereographic projection, known as *Planisphaerium*. The first evidence of an actual astrolabe comes from Theon of Alexandria, who lived in the fourth century (Neugebauer, 1975, p. 877). If the Purāṇic idea of a planisphere was borrowed from the Greeks, this could conceivably have happened as far back as Eudoxus. Of course, this idea could have been invented independently in India.

3.2 DAY, NIGHT, AND THE SEASONS

As we have seen, the *Bhāgavatam* gives a simple rule for the passage of day and night which, from the point of view of the planisphere model, is realistic at the time of the equinoxes. For times on either side of the equinoxes, the *Bhāgavatam* gives a linear correction term that works well in northern India. Let us examine this correction to see how accurate it is.

The *Bhāgavatam* verses 5.21.4 and 5.21.5 state that the vernal equinox occurs in the beginning of Meṣa (Aries), as we would expect in a tropical zodiac. The day increases at the expense of the night by one *ghaṭikā* (24 minutes) per month in the morning and evening until the beginning of Cancer. The day then decreases at the same rate until the equinox in Libra, and continues decreasing until the winter solstice in Capricorn. Then it again increases at the same rate until the beginning of Aries.

A *ghaṭikā* is half of a *muhūrta*, and a *muhūrta* is 1/30 of a full day and night. The rule assumes that one *ghaṭikā* per month is added in both the morning and the evening. Therefore, it says that when the sun is going north, the length of the day in *muhūrtas* is 15 + t, where t is the number of months before or after the vernal equinox (and t ranges from -3 to +3). When the sun is going south, this becomes 15 - t, with t centered on the autumnal equinox.

In the Vedic astronomical text called *Jyotiṣavedāṅga*, the rule is that six *muhūrtas* are added to the daytime in a northern progress of the sun from the winter to the summer solstice. The same (in reverse) takes place in a southern progress. This is the same as the *Bhāgavatam* rule.

The *Jyotiṣavedāṅga* places the winter solstice in the beginning of the *nakṣatra*, Dhaniṣṭhā, and this enables us to use precession of the equinoxes to estimate its date (Dikshit, 1969a, p. 87). This calculation is done by determining the time when the beginning of the Dhaniṣṭhā interval of the ecliptic falls on the winter solstice. If we assume that the principal star of the Dhaniṣṭhā constellation (Beta Delphini) marks the beginning of the interval, then the date comes to about 1400 B.C. But if we use the intervals given in medieval *Jyotiṣa Śāstras*, the date falls about 300 years later. Unfortunately, neither calculation is reliable because we do not know how *nakṣatra* intervals were defined when the *Jyotiṣavedāṅga* was written.

The Indologist David Pingree rejected precessional dating and reduced the date of the *Jyotiṣavedāṅga* to the fourth or fifth century B.C. He argued that its day-length rule was imported from Babylon, where it was in use since about 700 B.C. (Pingree, 1973, pp. 3–4).

We note that Pingree's date doesn't work precessionally, since the principal star of the Śravaṇa *nakṣatra* (Altair) was nearly on the winter solstice in 300–500 B.C., thus ruling out Dhaniṣṭhā. However, one could argue that the text referred back to an earlier period, when the winter solstice was in Dhaniṣṭhā.

The modern rule for the length of the day is given by a smooth trigonometric curve that depends on latitude. One way to compare the modern rule with the ancient one is to take the average of the absolute values of the difference between the two rules over an entire year. This is given for a number of ancient cities in the following table:

TABLE 3.1
The Day-Length Rule at Different Latitudes

City	Latitude (degrees N)	average day-length difference (in minutes)
Babylon	32.54	9.07
Jerusalem	31.78	7.85
Lahore	31.49	7.46
Ur	31.03	6.97
Eridu	30.89	6.84
Delhi	28.70	6.56
Mathurā	27.50	7.98
Vārāṇasī	25.43	13.16

The behavior of the *Jyotiṣavedāṅga* rule at the solstices is sometimes used to argue that it came from the Near East. Thus Pingree points out that the rule's ratio of longest to shortest day is 3:2, "a ratio inappropriate to all parts of India save the extreme north-west, but one that is well-attested in cuneiform texts" (Pingree, 1973, p. 4). This argument assumes that people would consider only the longest and shortest days when formulating a day-length rule.

However, people might also be interested in overall accuracy. From this standpoint, the rule works as well in much of northern India as it does in the Near East, and thus it may have been devised in India. For example, at the latitude of Delhi, the rule works quite well over a broad range of dates centered on the equinoxes, but it tends to become inaccurate near the solstices (see Figure 3.14). At the latitude of Babylon, it is better near the solstices, but worse overall. On the whole, the rule creates smaller errors for Delhi than for Babylon.

Since the *Bhāgavatam* focuses attention on the equinoxes, it is worth our while to see how the day-length rule works when time is measured relative to the vernal equinox. An order zero approximation to day length is simply 15 *muhūrtas*, corresponding to equal day and night. A first order approximation is a straight line with a slope of 1 *muhūrta* per month. In fact, this is close to the slope of the true day-length curve at the vernal equinox at the latitude of Delhi. (For the autumnal equinox, the slope is -1.)

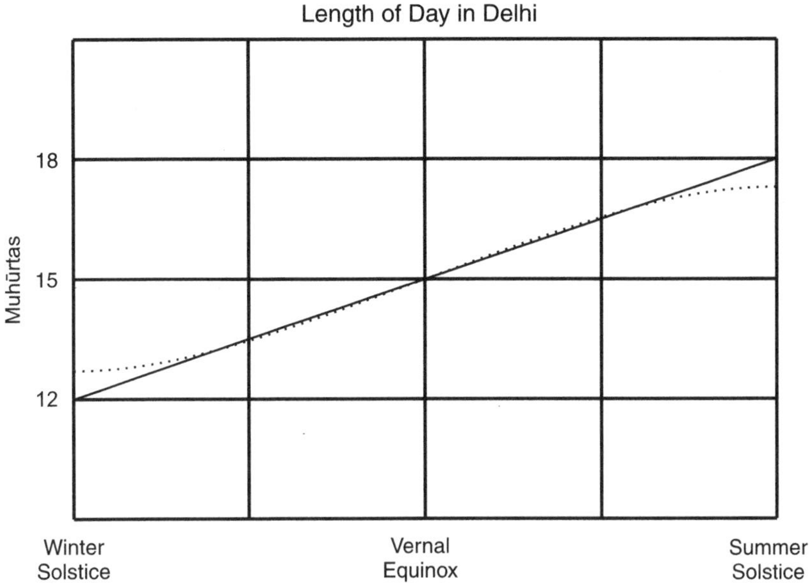

Figure 3.14 Day length at different times of the year at Delhi (solid line: *Bhāgavatam* rule; dotted line: actual day-length graph at the latitude of Delhi).

The *Jyotiṣavedāṅga* makes use of a five-year cycle based on a year of 365 civil days or 366 sidereal days (see Section 1.4). In this regard, Pingree remarks that "the acceptance of this cycle by Indians for a period of six or seven centuries or even more demonstrates among other things that they were not interested in performing the simplest acts of observational astronomy" (Pingree, 1973, p. 9). Although this is a rather extreme statement, we do see a tendency for Indian sacred texts to preserve astronomical information for long periods of time without observational checking. Thus the *Ṛg* version of the *Jyotiṣa-vedāṅga* continues to be recited today as a limb of the *Vedas,* even though the winter solstice is by now far removed from Dhaniṣṭhā. Likewise, the day-length rule works well in northern India, but it is also recited in southern India where it is quite inaccurate.

S. B. Dikshit remarked that in the *Ṛg* version of the *Jyotiṣavedāṅga*, "a number of verses contain words giving erroneous meaning. The words are incorrect; still it is interesting to see that these are recited throughout India in this form" (Dikshit, 1969a, p. 67). Dikshit concluded from this that the text was once nearly lost. It was imperfectly restored, perhaps from a single faulty copy, and was then recited by rote down to the present day.

People devoted to faithfully copying or reciting religious texts are not likely to be interested in observational verification, but they do play a useful role in preserving ancient knowledge. The existence of processes of rigid preservation does not imply that scientific investigations of nature were not carried out in India in the distant past. Rather, such processes provide a way of preserving some of the findings of such investigations from the ravages of time.

3.3 THE ZODIAC IN INDIA

Since we have run across several references in the *Bhāgavatam* to the signs of the zodiac, we should examine this topic in greater detail. In India, these signs, called *rāśis*, represent 30° intervals of the ecliptic, and their Sanskrit names are close in meaning to the traditional names used for the tropical zodiac in the West:

TABLE 3.2
Signs of the Zodiac

Sanskrit Name	Western Name
Meṣa (ram)	Aries
Vṛṣabha (bull)	Taurus
Mithuna (couple)	Gemini
Karkaṭa (crab)	Cancer
Siṁha (lion)	Leo
Kanyā (daughter)	Virgo
Tulā (scales)	Libra
Vṛścika (scorpion)	Scorpio
Dhanur (bow)	Sagittarius
Makara (shark/crocodile)	Capricorn
Kumbha (pot or waterpot)	Aquarius
Mīna (fish)	Pisces

The similarities are close enough that these two lists of names surely derive from a common source. The names of the signs went through a series of historical stages in Babylon, and they originally referred to a series of constellations distributed roughly along the ecliptic. For example, a Babylonian tablet of 700 B.C. lists eighteen "constellations in the path of the moon." These can be identified as follows (van der Waerden, 1953, p. 219):

TABLE 3.3
Early Babylonian Constellations of the Zodiac

Meaning of Babylonian Name	Western Name
The hair bush	Pleiades
The bull of Anu	Taurus
Anu's true shepherd	Orion
The old man	Perseus
Sword	Auriga
The great twins	Gemini
AL.LUL	Prokyon or Cancer
Lion or lioness	Leo
Furrow	Spica
The scales	Libra
Scorpion	Scorpio
Archer?	Sagittarius
Goatfish	Capricornus
Great star or giant?	Aquarius
The tails	Pisces
The great swallow	Pisces SW and Epsilon Pegasi
The goddess Anunitum	Pisces NE and middle of Andromeda
The hireling	Aries

This list underwent various changes, until the well-known twelve zodiacal constellations were established in late-Babylonian times.

In India, the *rāśis* appear only in the form of twelve 30° divisions of the ecliptic (Dikshit, 1969b, p. 397), a stage reached in Babylon in about 419 B.C. (van der Waerden, 1953, p. 217). The zodiacal constellations are not described in Indian literature.

S. B. Dikshit reports that the twelve *rāśi* names do not appear in the *Mahābhārata*, even though this work contains many references to the twenty-eight *nakṣatras*, which are themselves divisions of the ecliptic named after constellations (Dikshit, 1969a, p. 108). The *rāśis* do not appear in the *Jyotiṣavedāṅga* texts (Dikshit, 1969a, p. 96) or in the *Vedas*. This suggests that they were not current in India when these works were written. The common source for the zodiac is therefore likely to be located in the Near East.

It is possible, however, that the signs of the zodiac were simply inserted into an already existing system in India, based on solar months. Verse 5.22.5 states that the sun "passes through the twelve months, the parts of the year that are named after the *rāśis*." The names of the sun and the month names are listed as follows in the *Bhāgavatam* (12.11.33–44), but contrary to 5.22.5, they are not related to the names of the zodiacal signs:

TABLE 3.4
Seasonal Month Names in the Bhāgavatam

Name of Sun	Month Name
Dhātā	Madhu
Aryamā	Mādhava
Mitra	Śukra
Varuṇa	Śuci
Indra	Nabhas
Vivasvān	Nabhasya
Pūṣā	Tapas
Parjanya	Tapasya
Aṁśu	Sahas
Bhaga	Puṣya
Tvaṣṭā	Iṣa
Viṣṇu	Ūrja

The names of the sun are ancient Indian names for demigods. The month names are also ancient in India and are based on the seasons (with Madhu and Mādhava being the sweet months of spring). The signs of the tropical zodiac could easily have been inserted into this system, once they were introduced into India. Here the point is that a twelvefold division of the sun's path that is based on seasons is tropical by definition. It differs from the tropical zodiac only in the names of the divisions. (The tropical zodiac and its implications for the dating of the *Bhāgavatam* are discussed in greater detail in Section 8.2.)

3.4 THE SUN AND THE MOON

The *Viṣṇu Purāṇa* states that the sun orbits 100,000 *yojanas* above the earth (Wilson, 1980, p. 307), and the *Bhāgavatam* is consistent with this figure. The *yojana* is roughly eight miles long (see Section 4.5), and so this comes to about 800,000 miles. However, this distance refers to height above Bhū-maṇḍala, and it does not say how far the sun is from the earth globe.

In the planisphere model, the height of the sun is not physical. In this model, different planes are used to accommodate different orbiting bodies. The position of an orbiting body over the earth plane simply tells us the point on the earth globe where that body is directly overhead. The height of the body above the earth plane is irrelevant.

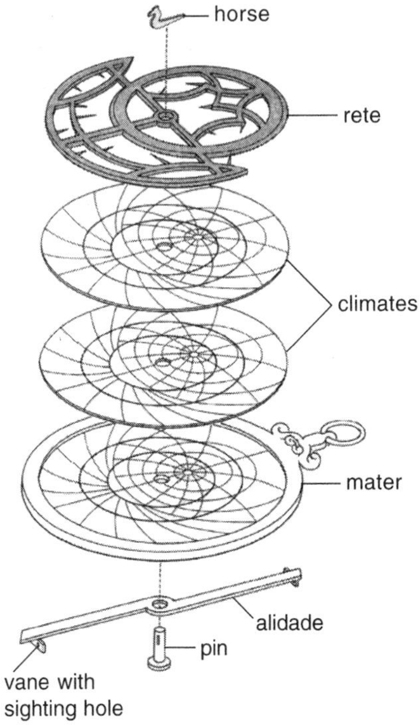

Figure 3.15 Exploded picture of an astrolabe, showing plates representing the earth (*mater*) and the ecliptic and star positions (*rete*) (Kloetzli, 1985).

In Section 3.1.4 above, we compared Bhū-maṇḍala, interpreted as a planisphere, with a medieval astrolabe. In an astrolabe, there is a ring representing the orbit of the sun (the ecliptic) and a series of points representing the locations of stars. These elements are part of the "rete," which is positioned over the "mater" plate representing the earth. For comparison, above Bhū-maṇḍala there is a plane for the solar orbit and another plane for the *nakṣatra* constellations.

There is also a separate plane for the orbit of the moon. The *Bhāgavatam* verse 5.22.8 says that the moon is 100,000 *yojanas* above the sun, and this is often taken as a highly unscientific statement. However, it makes perfect sense from the viewpoint of the planisphere interpretation. The sun and the moon both require planes above the earth plane, but this has nothing to do with their distances from the earth globe. If the earth is represented as a planisphere in the *Bhāgavatam*, then it stands to reason that the sun and the moon could also be part of the planisphere model.

According to the *Bhāgavatam*, the planets have the following heights in *yojanas* above Bhū-maṇḍala:

TABLE 3.5
Heights of Celestial Bodies Above Bhū-maṇḍala in Yojanas

Body	Interval	Height
Dhruvaloka	1,300,000	3,800,000
Sapta-ṛṣi	1,100,000	2,500,000
Saturn	200,000	1,400,000
Jupiter	200,000	1,200,000
Mars	200,000	1,000,000
Mercury	200,000	800,000
Venus	200,000	600,000
28 nakṣatras	200,000	400,000
Moon	100,000	200,000
Sun	10,000	100,000
Rāhu [and Ketu]	90,000	90,000
Bhū-maṇḍala	0	0

Note: A textual variant in the *Bhāgavatam* assigns 300,000 *yojanas* to the distance from the moon to the 28 *nakṣatras*.

The mechanical model shown in Figure 3.16 was designed to illustrate how the sun and the moon fit into the planisphere interpretation. In the model, levels are included for the sun, the moon, the twenty-eight *nakṣatras* or lunar mansions, and Rāhu and Ketu. All of the celestial bodies in the table of heights could be included on different levels of such a planisphere model.

The sun orbits on the ecliptic circle, which moves in accordance with the earth's daily rotation. The moon's orbit is also projected stereographically onto a plane, and it is very similar to the sun's orbit.

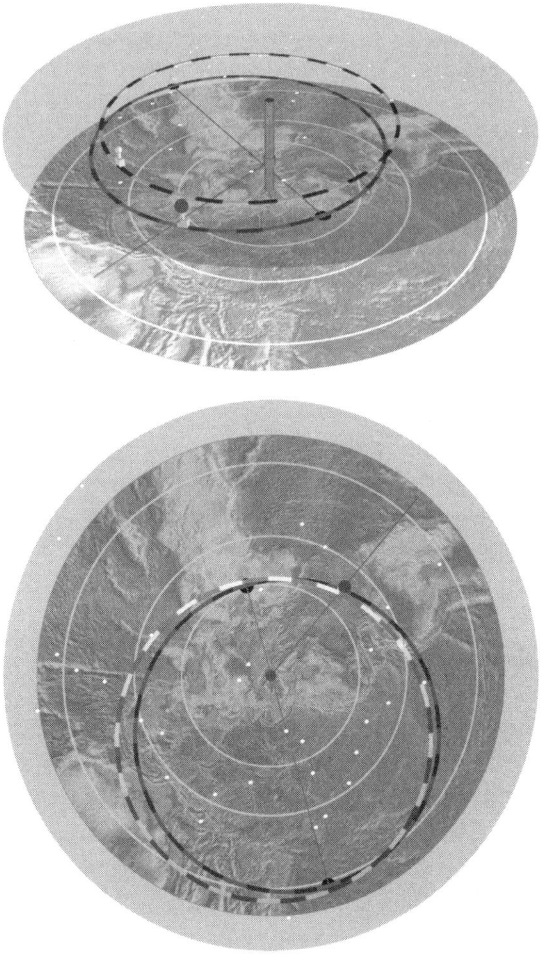

Figure 3.16 Model of the sun, moon, and the twenty-eight *nakṣatras*, over a planisphere map of the earth. The sun's orbit is depicted as a dark, dashed circle, and it lies beneath the moon's orbit, shown as a light, dashed circle. The twenty-eight *nakṣatras* are placed on the gray disk above the moon's orbit.

Seen from above, the orbits of the sun and moon intersect at two points, corresponding to the ascending and descending nodes of the moon. In the model, black disks representing Rāhu and Ketu are placed at these points in a lower plane. In Indian astronomy, these points are treated as dark planets connected with eclipses of the sun and moon (see Section 3.4.1, below).

One may ask what view was held regarding the relative positions of the sun and moon in the Vedic period. Dikshit cites the following verse from the *Taittirīya Saṁhitā*, indicating that the moon was believed to be higher than the sun:

> Agni had to stand in a lower position before wind and space on account of the earth. The wind stooped low before the sun and sky on account of space. Similarly, the sun had to stand low in position on account of the moon and the stars; and the moon had to bend low before Varuṇa on account of stars (Dikshit, 1969a, p. 5).

Here the sequence, "earth, sun, moon, stars," agrees with the table of heights. It is quite possible that this statement dates back to a period before the planisphere model was introduced, when the moon was regarded as literally further away than the sun. In that case, one could argue that traditional ideas about the relative heights of the sun, moon, and stars were preserved in the planisphere model, since that model works equally well for any assignment of heights.

Then again, the idea that the moon is literally further away than the sun may have came about through a misunderstanding of more sophisticated astronomical concepts. Such misunderstanding has certainly prevailed in recent centuries, since it appears that the planispherelike structure of *Bhāgavata* cosmology has generally gone unrecognized in medieval and recent times.

Cosmological models centered on Mount Meru were brought to Eastern Asian countries by Buddhism. In Figure 3.17, we see a cosmological model representing Mount Meru, a series of square *dvīpas* and oceans, and a series of orbits at different levels. Constellations of stars are placed at one level on several small stands. Since the orbits are not off-center relative to Meru, it would seem that the person who made this picture was not explicitly aware of the planisphere model. Since Buddhism is thought to have split off from Hinduism before the Purāṇic period, it would be interesting to know how this apparently Purāṇic imagery entered East Asian tradition.

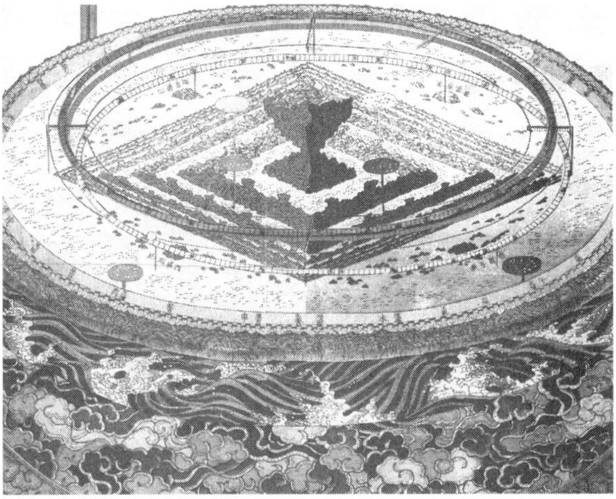

Figure 3.17 East Asian planetary model, showing planetary orbits, star positions, and a square version of Mount Meru and the seven oceans and *dvīpas*.

Although the planetary heights are arbitrary and nonphysical in the planisphere interpretation, they do have physical meaning in the interpretation of Bhū-maṇḍala as the ecliptic plane. This interpretation is discussed in Chapter 4, and the topic of planetary heights is addressed in the Section 4.7.

3.4.1 Eclipses

The *Bhāgavatam* says relatively little about eclipses, and what it does say is connected with a being named Rāhu. Verse 5.24.2 gives the diameters of the sun, moon, and Rāhu as multiples of ten thousand *yojanas*, and it says that Rāhu tries to attack them out of enmity. Rāhu is commonly described as a dark planet, but in the *Bhāgavatam* verses 8.9.24–25, it is explained that Rāhu is the decapitated head of a demon who tried to steal the nectar of immortality after the churning of the Milk Ocean. Since the sun-god and moon-god foiled Rāhu's attempted theft and brought about his decapitation by Viṣṇu, his head has been inimical to the sun and moon ever since and is responsible for solar and lunar eclipses.

In their comments on 5.24.3, Śrīdhara Swami and Viśvanātha Cakravartī point out that although it is commonly said that Rāhu swallows the sun or the moon, this actually does not happen because of the intervening distance between Rāhu and these heavenly bodies. This distance is mentioned in 5.24.1, where it is stated that, according

Figure 3.18 In Indian iconography, the nine planets (*navagraha*) are sometimes depicted as eight figures representing the sun and moon, the five planets Mercury through Saturn, and a single body representing Rāhu and Ketu (Hartner, 1938, figure 7).

to some authorities, Rāhu is situated 10,000 *yojanas* beneath the sun. Vīrarāghava also says that there is no actual swallowing because of this distance. Thus the commentators accept the quantitative statement about Rāhu's distance from the sun, and they thereby reject the story that Rāhu eclipses the sun and moon by literally swallowing them.

Rāhu has a counterpart called Ketu, which is also held responsible for eclipses and is sometimes described as Rāhu's headless body. In Indian iconography, the nine planets (*navagraha*) are sometimes depicted as eight figures representing the sun and moon, the five planets Mercury through Saturn, and a single body representing Rāhu and Ketu. This is the figure on the right in the illustration. Ketu is not discussed in the *Bhāgavatam*, but one hundred Ketus are briefly mentioned in 6.6.37. These may represent comets and meteoric phenomena, which are generally called Ketus in Indian astronomical literature.

In the *Jyotiṣa Śāstras*, Rāhu and Ketu are identified with the ascending and descending lunar nodes, the points of intersection of the orbits of the sun and moon. Since eclipses can occur only when the sun and moon are near one of these nodes, this gives Rāhu and Ketu a role to play in eclipses. However, the *Jyotiṣa Śāstras* explain solar and lunar eclipses in the same way as modern astronomers, and they give calculations on this basis, predicting when eclipses will occur.

It is possible to reconcile this account of Rāhu and Ketu with the *Bhāgavatam* by making use of the planisphere interpretation of Bhū-maṇḍala. As we have seen, in this interpretation, the sun, moon, *nakṣatras*, and planets are assigned planes parallel to Bhū-maṇḍala. Rāhu and Ketu can also be assigned positions in a plane beneath that of the sun. In Figure 3.16, above, they are shown as black disks situated beneath the intersection points of the solar and lunar orbits. This agrees with the *Bhāgavatam*, and it yields the *Jyotiṣa Śāstra* interpretation when the planisphere model is viewed from above in projection.

However, another perspective on Rāhu is introduced in the cosmological section of the *Vāyu Purāṇa*. In a verse very similar to 5.24.2 of the *Bhāgavatam*, the *Vāyu Purāṇa* says, "The planets are brilliantly illuminated due to their contact with the rays of the Sun. The diameter of the sun is 9,000 *yojanas*. . . . The width of the Moon is twice that of the Sun. Equal to them, Svarbhānu (Rāhu) goes beneath. The planet Rāhu is created in globular form out of the shadow of the earth" (Tagare, 1987, p. 367). A nearly identical statement is found in the *Matsya Purāṇa*.

Here the diameters given to the sun and moon are unrealistic, but if we disregard them, we are left with a reasonable astronomical interpretation of Rāhu. If we regard Rāhu as the conical shadow (umbra) of the earth planet, then it can be truly said that Rāhu covers or even swallows the moon during a lunar eclipse. Of course, to give this explanation, the Purāṇic writer must have thought of the earth as a globe. A similar theory regarding the moon's shadow is needed to account for eclipses of the sun.

In Western astrology, the lunar nodes are associated with the "head and tail of the dragon," and this "dragon" seems closely related to Rāhu and Ketu. In Figure 3.19, we see an Islamic picture, drawn in A.D. 1272, showing the angel Shamhurash beheading the eclipse dragon (Hartner, 1938). This directly parallels the story of Rāhu's decapitation by Viṣṇu.

The painting in Figure 3.20 of Saint George slaying the Dragon was made by Raphael in 1504, during the Renaissance. This should be compared with the picture of Shamhurash slaying the eclipse dragon. Unless its similarity to that picture is a complete coincidence, it would

Figure 3.19 An Islamic picture, drawn in A.D. 1272, showing the angel Shamhurash fighting the eclipse-dragon. This dragon is the Western version of the Purāṇic Rāhu and Ketu (Hartner, 1938).

seem that the story of the eclipse dragon was somehow woven into the iconography of early Christianity without the preservation of any indication of its original significance. (Saint George is said to have been born in Asia Minor in about A.D. 300, but we have run across no information indicating how he came to be connected with a dragon (Chambers, 1967, p. 539).)

Evidently, the myth of Rāhu has deep historical roots. One possibility is that this story was elaborated first, and scientific information about lunar nodes or the shadow of the earth was incorporated much later. If so, this scientific refurbishing must have occurred in both India and the West, since the Rāhu story appears to be ancient in both

Figure 3.20 A picture of St. George and the Dragon, painted by Raphael in 1504.

areas. It is also possible that mythological stories and quantitative models may have grown up together over a very long period of time. Or it may even be that mythology has sometimes been added to quantitative knowledge after the quantitative knowledge was already developed.

The latter possibility is illustrated by the elaboration of astrological interpretations of the zodiacal signs. Thus B. L. van der Waerden raises the question, "How came these signs, originally a mathematical construction, afterwards to be worshiped like Gods and thought to influence our lives like Gods?" (van der Waerden, 1953, p. 216). For some further thoughts on this topic, see Section 6.4.

3.4.2 The Lunar Orbit in Sūrya-siddhānta

The *Sūrya-siddhānta* expresses distances in *yojanas*. If we take five miles/*yojana*, we can bring the *Sūrya-siddhānta's* diameter for the earth globe into agreement with modern data. Using the same ratio of miles/*yojana*, the *Sūrya-siddhānta's* diameter for the moon and its earth-moon distance also agree reasonably well with modern astronomy. This is shown in the following table, with distances listed in miles:

TABLE 3.6
Earth-Moon Distances in Sūrya-siddhānta in Miles

Length	Modern	*Sūrya-siddhānta*
diameter of earth globe	7,928	8,000
diameter of moon	2,160	2,400
earth-moon distance	238,000	258,000

Here the *Sūrya-siddhānta* value of 258,000 miles for the earth-moon distance is computed from its figure of 324,000 *yojanas* for the circumference of the moon's orbit. Since this comes to fifteen *yojanas* per minute of arc, it is clearly a very round figure.

The *Jyotiṣa Śāstras* clearly present a realistic picture of the lunar orbit and the size of the moon. The *Purāṇas* are generally considered to be more or less contemporary with the *Jyotiṣa Śāstras*, but they present what seems, at first glance, to be the highly unscientific conclusion that the moon is higher than the sun. However, this statement does not mean that the moon is further from the earth than the sun, and it can be reconciled with modern astronomy by adopting the planisphere interpretation of Bhū-maṇḍala.

Curiously, the *Sūrya-siddhānta* also encodes accurate values for the diameters of the planets. This is discussed in Appendix 10.

3.5 THE LORE OF CONSTELLATIONS

Like many cultural traditions, the Purāṇic tradition of India maintains stories about particular star patterns, or constellations. Since the

Bhāgavatam places stars in planes parallel to Bhū-maṇḍala, its treatment of stars can be best understood in terms of the planisphere interpretation, which wraps these planes around the earth globe. Therefore, we will relate a few of these stories at the end of this chapter.

Star stories typically connect demigods with stars and planets, and they may explain astronomical phenomena in terms of social interactions between celestial personalities. Such stories coexist with purely astronomical material that describes the regular behavior of heavenly bodies. The personal stories are not allowed to contradict ongoing regular phenomena, but they are sometimes used to explain the origin of such phenomena.

For example, the constellation Rohiṇī is the center of several Purāṇic star stories. According to *Bhāgavatam* 6.6.2, the twenty-seven *nakṣatra* constellations are considered to be daughters of Prajāpati Dakṣa who were given as wives to Candra, the demigod of the moon. This story refers to the role of the *nakṣatra* constellations as "lunar mansions" or markers indicating the progress of the moon in its orbit (see Appendix 1).

The *Bhāgavatam* mentions that Candra was cursed by Dakṣa in connection with these wives. Other *Purāṇas* explain that this happened because Candra's excessive fondness for Rohiṇī caused dissatisfaction among his other *nakṣatra*-wives. Their father Dakṣa therefore cursed the moon to suffer from a wasting disease, and this curse was later reduced by allowing the moon to wax and wane periodically (Śiva, 1990, pp. 1308–11).

This is one explanation of the moon's phases. Another explanation is given in the *Viṣṇu Purāṇa*, where it is said that the waxing phase of the moon is caused by the sun, who supplies the moon with ambrosia through one of his rays. The waning phase is caused by the demigods and *pitṛs*, who take turns drinking the lunar ambrosia and thereby obtain immortality (Wilson, 1980, p. 343).

The *nakṣatra* Rohiṇī consists of the five principal stars of the constellation Taurus, and its *yoga-tāra* or "junction star" is Aldebaran. (Significantly, Rohiṇī means reddish, and Aldebaran is a reddish star.) These stars are said to form a cart or wagon (*śakaṭa*). The *Sūrya-siddhānta* states that "In Taurus, the 17th degree, a planet of which the latitude is more than two degrees, south, will split the wain of Rohiṇī" (Burgess, 1860, p. 248). In Sanskrit this is called "*rohiṇī śakaṭa bheda*."

The splitting of the wain of Rohiṇī is considered to be inauspicious in astrological texts. The sixth-century astrologer Varāhamihira says that "When Saturn splits the wain of Rohiṇī here in this world, then Mādhava rains not upon the earth for twelve years. When the wain of Prajāpati's asterism is split, the earth, having as it were committed a sin, performs, in a manner, her surface being strewn with ashes and bones, the *kāpālika* penance" (Burgess, 1860, p. 249). The antiquity of these ideas is shown by their use in literary allusions—for example, in the *Mahābhārata*, Rāvana in the company of Sītā is said to be like Saturn in conjunction with Rohiṇī (van Buitenen, 1975, p. 741).

An interesting allusion to *rohiṇī śakaṭa bheda* is given in the *Bhāgavatam* 10.7.4, where it is said that Kṛṣṇa's mother Yaśodā performed a Vedic ceremony for Him on a day when the moon was in conjunction with the constellation Rohiṇī. On this occasion, Yaśodā placed the infant Kṛṣṇa beneath a handcart (*śakaṭa*) and, since she was busy receiving guests, she did not hear Him crying for milk. Kṛṣṇa became angry at His mother's neglect, and He threw His legs upward with the following result:

> Lord Śrī Kṛṣṇa was lying down underneath the handcart in one corner of the courtyard, and although His little legs were as soft as leaves, when He struck the cart with His legs, it turned over violently and collapsed. The wheels separated from the axle, the hubs and spokes fell apart, and the pole of the handcart broke . . . (*Bhāgavatam* 10.7.7).

Thus Kṛṣṇa broke a cart at the time of "*rohiṇī śakaṭa bheda*," or the breaking of the cart of Rohiṇī by the moon.

In the *Bhāgavatam* 10.3.1–5, Rohiṇī is referred to as Kṛṣṇa's birth star, and this is confirmed in the *Brahma-vaivarta Purāṇa*, where it is said that Kṛṣṇa's birth was "characterized by the predominance of Rohiṇī" (Sen, 1920, p. 129). It may, therefore, be significant that Rohiṇī was at the vernal equinox at the traditional date of Kṛṣṇa's birth.

This is shown by the accompanying illustration from the astronomy program, SkyGlobe, which indicates that Rohiṇī (Aldebaran) was situated on the vernal equinox in 3162 B.C. This figure will vary by fifty years or so (an error of about 1%), depending on the ephemeris program used to compute the date.

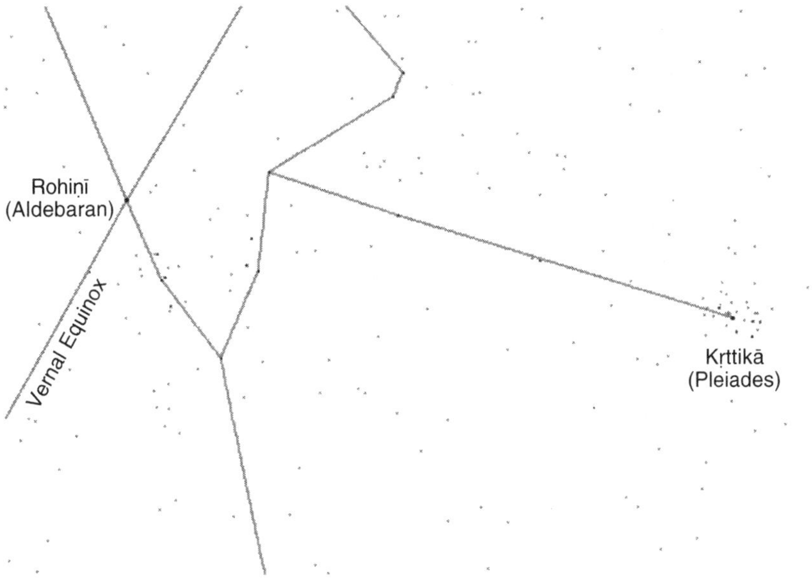

Figure 3.21 Position of Rohiṇī (Aldebaran) in 3162 B.C., in relationship to the vernal equinox.

According to traditional reckoning, Kṛṣṇa took birth 125 years before the advent of Kali-yuga in 3102 B.C. This would place the moment when Rohiṇī was exactly at the vernal equinox about midway through Kṛṣṇa's life on the earth. Since modern scholarship rejects the Kali-yuga date of 3102 B.C., this can be seen as one of the many curious coincidences connected with this date. (For others, see Section 8.3.)

The *Mahābhārata* presents some puzzling information about Rohiṇī and other asterisms that shows the complex background of Indian sky lore. It seems that six wives of the Seven Sages (the Big Dipper or Ursa Major) had been divorced by their husbands because they had become implicated in the birth of the demigod Skanda. These wives appealed to Skanda, who in turn asked Śakra (Indra) what should be done. Śakra said:

> 'The Goddess Abhijit, the younger sister of Rohiṇī and her rival, has gone to the forest to mortify herself. I am bewildered over it—hail to

> thee—for now a constellation has dropped from heaven. Ponder with Brahmā the important time that constellation measured. Brahmā measured out time from Dhaniṣṭhā onward. Rohiṇī was the first, so the number used to be full.'
>
> At Śakra's words the Kṛttikās went to heaven and now twinkle as a constellation, in the form of a cart, with Fire as their regent (van Buitenen, 1975, p. 657).

Kṛttikā is the constellation of the Pleiades, which is known to have six prominent stars. These are considered to be the divorced wives of the Seven Sages and mothers of the war-god Skanda, who is therefore also known as Kārttikeya. One of the wives of the sages remained faithful and did not become involved in Skanda's birth. She is known as Arundhatī, the wife of Vasiṣṭha, and she is identified with the star Alcor, situated next to Vasiṣṭha's star, Mizar.

Curiously, the Scholia to Aratus tells the opposite story. In this text, Electra, mother of Dardanus, left her station among the Pleiades as a consequence of Troy's fall and retired "above the second star of the beam . . . others call this star 'fox'" (de Santillana, 1969, p. 385). The second star of the beam is Vasiṣṭha in Sanskrit, and the "fox" star is Arundhatī.

Another possible cross-cultural link is given by the Vedic text called the *Śatapatha Brāhmaṇa*, which says that the Seven Sages (*sapta ṛṣayaḥ*) were formerly called "bears" (*ṛkṣāḥ*) (Eggeling, 1900, text 2.1.2.4). Of course, Ursa Major means "The Great Bear."

Abhijit is the twenty-eighth *nakṣatra* and is missing from the standard system of twenty-seven *nakṣatras*. Why she "went to the forest" is not clear, but this may refer to the historical event of her removal. The junction star of Abhijit is Vega, and it is notable for being much further from the ecliptic than the other *nakṣatras*.

The statement about Brahmā measuring time might be taken as a reference to Brahmā, the Creator. However, there is a link between this statement and the sixth-century Jyotiṣa text called the *Pañcasiddhāntikā* of Varāhamihira. In this text there is a chapter on the *Paitāmaha Siddhānta*. This is a system of astronomical computation named after Paitāmaha, a name for Brahmā (literally meaning grandfather). This system defines its epoch as 2 Saka or A.D. 80, but it also gives a rule placing the beginning of the year in Dhaniṣṭhā (Thibaut, 1968, p. 67).

Thus the reference to Brahmā could apply to the *Paitāmaha Siddhānta*, rather than to the Creator.

Varāhamihira says that "When the return of the sun towards the south (i.e. the summer solstice) took place from the middle of Aśleṣā, then the *ayana* was right; at the present time the *ayana* begins from Punarvasu" (Thibaut, 1968, p. 18). When the *nakṣatra* Aśleṣā is at the summer solstice, Dhaniṣṭhā is close to the winter solstice. This was about 1000 B.C. It is also true that the summer solstice began near Punarvasu in Varāhamihira's time (sixth century A.D.). Of course, if the *Mahābhārata* is referring to the *Paitāmaha Siddhānta*, this may be an early version of a text later rewritten by Varāhamihira.

Finally, consider the statement that the Kṛttikās ascended to heaven. In the *Sūrya-siddhānta*, the *nakṣatras* are listed beginning with Aśvinī. This *nakṣatra* interval begins with the star Revatī (identified as Zeta Piscium), which marked the vernal equinox in about A.D. 560. (The star Revatī falls 10' short of the end of its own interval, and thus Revatī + 10' defines the beginning of the next interval, Aśvinī (Burgess, 1860, p. 205).) Since many other texts (including the *Bhāgavatam*) list the *nakṣatras* as beginning with Kṛttikā, some scholars have concluded that these other texts refer back to a time when Kṛttikā was on the vernal equinox (in roughly the second millennium B.C.). If this is correct, then the statement that "the Kṛttikās went to heaven" may refer to this time period, and the statement that "Rohiṇī was the first" may refer to the earlier period (around 3200 B.C.) when Rohiṇī was on the vernal equinox.

4

The Solar System in Three Dimensions

4.1 THE FLAT EARTH AS THE ECLIPTIC PLANE

There is a considerable body of textual evidence in the *Bhāgavatam* supporting the idea that Bhū-maṇḍala corresponds to the ecliptic plane, situated in three-dimensional space. This can be contrasted with the planisphere interpretation, in which Bhū-maṇḍala plays a two-dimensional role. In the previous chapter, we followed up on the idea that Bhū-maṇḍala is a planisphere model of the earth, and we found that many points in *Bhāgavata* cosmology can be consistently understood in light of this hypothesis.

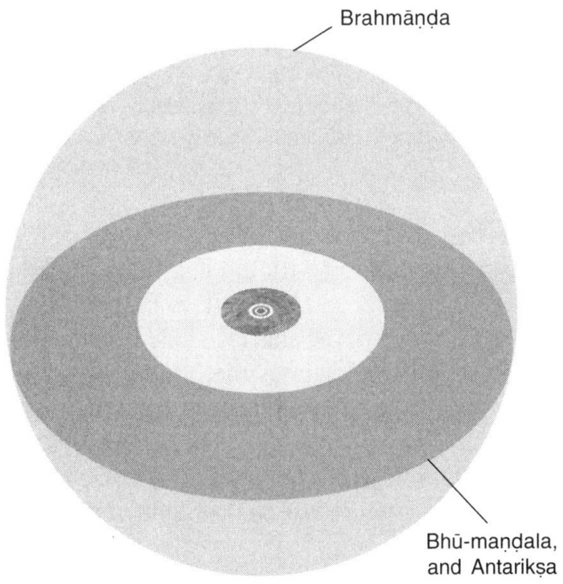

Figure 4.1 Model of the Brahmāṇḍa, showing the universal shell, Bhū-maṇḍala, and Antarikṣa.

In this chapter, we will do the same thing with the idea that Bhū-maṇḍala represents an actual disk situated in three-dimensional space. It turns out that this interpretation is also supported by many points. This makes sense according to the general hypothesis that the *Bhāgavatam* presents a multiple-aspect model of the universe, in which one structure (e.g. Bhū-maṇḍala) represents several different things.

The *Bhāgavatam* describes the universe literally as a flat disk (Bhū-maṇḍala) situated in the middle of a sphere. The sun is described as orbiting in a circular path situated parallel to this disk and very close to it. In modern astronomy, the ecliptic is the plane of the sun's apparent orbit around the earth, as seen by an earthly observer. By examining the *Bhāgavatam's* description of the sun's orbit, we can see that Bhū-maṇḍala must closely correspond to the ecliptic if we take it as a literal disk.

In the *Bhāgavatam*, the sun's orbit is described in terms of a metaphorical solar chariot. The *Bhāgavatam* verse 5.21.13 gives a description of this chariot, where it is said that the chariot wheel is composed of the parts of the year (Saṁvatsara in Sanskrit):

> The chariot of the sun-god has only one wheel, which is known as Saṁvatsara. The twelve months are calculated to be its twelve spokes, the six seasons are the sections of its rim, and the three *cāturmāsya* periods are its three-sectioned hub. One side of the axle carrying the wheel rests upon the summit of Mount Sumeru, and the other rests upon Mānasottara Mountain. Affixed to the outer end of the axle, the wheel continuously rotates on Mānasottara Mountain like the wheel of an oil-pressing machine.

When the chariot is drawn to scale (in Figure 4.2, right), we see that the chariot wheel is very small compared with the length of the axle, which extends from Meru in the center to Mānasottara in the periphery. Calculation shows that the length of the chariot's axle from Mount Meru to Mānasottara Mountain is 157.5 times the height of the sun above Bhū-maṇḍala. The latter distance equals the radius of the wheel plus the height of circular track on which it rides. Thus the sun skims along just above Bhū-maṇḍala in its orbit. Relative to the size of the Mānasottara track, Bhū-maṇḍala is very close to the plane of the sun's orbit (and is parallel to it).

The most obvious interpretation of an earth disk sandwiched

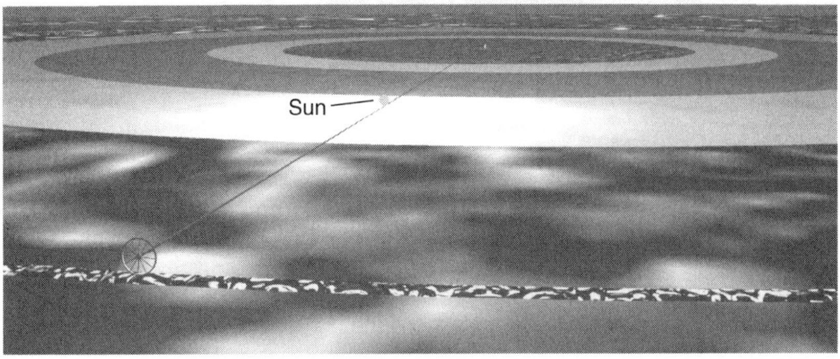

Figure 4.2 Model of the Sun's Chariot (to scale), showing the closeness of the sun's orbit to the plane of Bhū-maṇḍala.

between two hemispheres is that the disk represents the flat earth, the upper hemisphere represents the sky, and the lower hemisphere represents the underworld. According to this understanding, the sun should rise on the eastern edge of the disk, arc overhead, and set on the western edge. However, the *Bhāgavatam* has the sun moving in a circle just above the flat earth. It should therefore skim along the horizon, neither rising nor setting—a phenomenon seen in the polar regions during certain times of the year, but not observable in India.

Since the wheel of the sun's chariot is called the year (Saṁvatsara), it is reasonable to suppose that the motion of the sun around Sumeru in its orbit can be taken as the sun's yearly motion around the ecliptic. This means that Bhū-maṇḍala represents a plane parallel to the ecliptic and very close to it. Roughly speaking, Bhū-maṇḍala can be identified as the ecliptic plane. It therefore does not represent a naive flat earth. Rather, it represents a plane extending through the sky at a steep angle to the plane of an observer's local horizon.

Figure 4.3 shows the position of Bhū-maṇḍala in relation to an observer at a latitude corresponding to northern India. The square tangent to the earth globe represents the observer's local horizon—his "flat earth." The surrounding wire frame represents the celestial sphere with the celestial equator. The plane of the ecliptic tilts at 23.5° to the celestial equator, and there we have placed an annular shape representing the disk of Bhū-maṇḍala. Thus we see that Bhū-maṇḍala

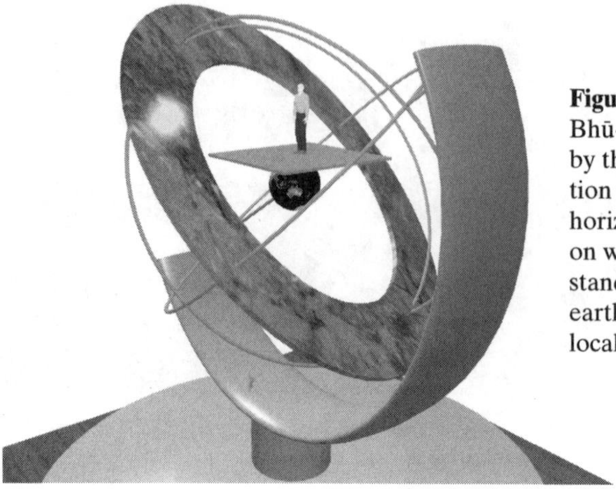

Figure 4.3 Model showing Bhū-maṇḍala, represented by the tilted ring, in relation to an observer's local horizon. The small square on which the observer is standing is tangent to the earth, and it represents his local horizon.

extends over the head of the observer and also beneath his feet.

It is noteworthy that in a cross-cultural study of myths from around the world, Giorgio de Santillana and Hertha von Dechend concluded that an archaic world culture existed in which the earth was seen as the celestial plane of the ecliptic—the realm of the gods and the planets (see Appendix 3). It may be that the concept of the naive flat earth arose when people began to take this cosmic earth-disk literally and identify it with the ground on which they stood.

In many verses, the timing of the sun's orbit around Bhū-maṇḍala clearly identifies it as the ecliptic plane. Thus the *Bhāgavatam* verse 5.20.30 says that

> In the middle of that island [Puṣkaradvīpa] there is, indeed, one mountain named Mānasottara, which forms a boundary between the inner and outer *varṣas*. . . . The sun's chariot is going around Meru on top of the mountain, and that chariot has an orbit consisting of the Saṁvatsara, which is turning around by the day and night of the demigods.

The *Purāṇas* say that the day and night of the demigods is one year (Saṁvatsara), with the day corresponding to the northern course of the sun and the night corresponding to its southern course. So this text says that the orbit of the sun around Meru on his chariot takes one year to complete, as it should if Bhū-maṇḍala represents the ecliptic.

Verse 5.22.7 of the *Bhāgavatam* says:

> The sun-god has three speeds—slow, fast and moderate. The time he takes to travel entirely around the circles of heaven, earth and space at these three speeds is referred to, by learned scholars, by the five names Saṁvatsara, Parivatsara, Iḍāvatsara, Anuvatsara and Vatsara.

The circles of heaven, earth, and space refer to Bhū-maṇḍala and the adjacent region called Antarikṣa, which we will discuss in a moment. The five names ending in *vatsara* all refer to the year. They define a five-year cycle, or *yuga*, that is well known in Vedic and Purāṇic literature. So we have the sun moving around the circle of Bhū-maṇḍala in a year, and therefore the Bhū-maṇḍala disk and its associated region of space correspond to the ecliptic.

Again, in 5.22.5 we read that

> The sun-god, the soul of all the worlds, being situated in the circle of space between heaven and earth on the wheel of time, passes through the twelve months, the parts of the year that are named after the *rāśis*.

The wheel of time is the starry heaven, which rotates once per day relative to the earth. Here the twelve solar months are identified with the 30° signs of the zodiac (*rāśis*), which extend around the ecliptic. As we mention in Section 3.3, this concept of the solar months may have been native to India, and the Western signs of the zodiac may have been grafted onto it later. Be that as it may, the "circle of space between heaven and earth" is here associated with the zodiacal signs and hence with the ecliptic plane.

This circle of space is also mentioned in verse 5.20.43:

> The sun is situated in the middle of the Brahmāṇḍa, in the area between heaven [*dyāv*] and earth. The distance between the sun and the circumference of the universe should be twenty-five *koṭi yojanas*.

The Brahmāṇḍa, or Brahmā-egg, is the sphere of the universe in *Bhāgavata* cosmology. We need to know the meaning of "the area between heaven and earth," which is situated in the middle of this sphere. Viśvanātha Cakravartī Ṭhākura says that it means the region from Bhuvarloka to Bhūrloka. Bhūrloka is another name for Bhū-maṇḍala, and Bhuvarloka is a region of space "above" Bhū-maṇḍala. Vijayadhvaja identifies it as Antarikṣa, which literally means "inner space":

> The area between heaven and earth (*dyāv-ābhūmyoḥ*) is Antarikṣa, wherein the sun, which is found in the middle of the egg, is situated. The Antarikṣa is the region in which the sun moves (into new signs), and that is the middle region of the egg.

Śrīdhara Swami and Vīrarāghava both refer to this middle region as being the space between the two shells of the egg. These two shells are the upper and lower hemispheres of the Brahmāṇḍa. Ideally, these two hemispheres are separated by the plane of Bhū-maṇḍala. But if we draw them slightly apart from one another, we create a thin cylinder of space between the two hemispheres. This is Antarikṣa.

Putting these points together, it follows that the Bhū-maṇḍala disk is the base of a thin cylinder of Antarikṣa, in which the sun orbits and passes from one sign of the zodiac to another. The ecliptic lies within Antarikṣa, and Bhū-maṇḍala is close to and parallel to it. Figure 4.1 shows the cylinder of Antarikṣa, with Bhū-maṇḍala as its base. If we turn to the distance figures given in the *Bhāgavatam*, we find that the thickness of this cylinder can be computed to be 3,800,000 *yojanas*, the height of Dhruvaloka above Bhū-maṇḍala (see Table 3.5, p. 68). This is very small, compared with its radius of 25 *koṭi* or 250,000,000 *yojanas*. Thus in the figure, Antarikṣa is barely discernible.

We would expect that if the thin disk of space between earth and heaven is the region of the ecliptic, then the *Bhāgavatam* should place the orbits of the planets in or near this region. This turns out to be true, and we discuss it below in Section 4.3. Once it is realized that the planets orbit near Bhū-maṇḍala, further study shows that the circular features of Bhū-maṇḍala serve as a map of the planetary orbits. This is discussed in Section 4.4.

In summary, we see that if we interpret Bhū-maṇḍala as the ecliptic plane, then many obscure points made in the *Bhāgavatam* and its commentaries fall into place consistently. Further points consistent with this interpretation are mentioned in later sections.

4.2 RELATIVE MOTION IN THE BHĀGAVATAM

We have cited evidence indicating that the sun orbits around Bhū-maṇḍala once per year. Yet there appears to be a contradiction, for the sun is also said to complete one orbit per day. As we will see, this apparent contradiction arises because of the way that the *Bhāgavatam* treats relative motion.

The concept of relativity of motion plays an important role in modern physics. It also arises in elementary astronomy, where we see that the sun has two motions, a daily clockwise motion from east to west and a yearly counterclockwise motion from west to east. The first motion is relative to the earth as a fixed reference frame, and the second motion is relative to the constellations.

The *Bhāgavatam* recognizes both motions, but it treats them in a paradoxical way by referring them to a single reference frame—Bhū-maṇḍala. This gives rise to the two major interpretations of Bhū-maṇḍala discussed in this chapter and in Chapter 3. These are the plan-isphere interpretation, in which the daily clockwise motion of the sun is assumed, and the three-dimensional interpretation, in which the sun's yearly counterclockwise motion around the ecliptic is assumed.

In *Bhāgavatam* 5.21.8–9, the narrator, Śukadeva Gosvāmī, says that "For the people living there [on Meru], when the sun is specifically at midday, it always heats, keeping the mountain to the left and keeping it to the right."

This appears contradictory, and it was so understood in the *Bhāgavatam* itself. Thus in 5.22.1, King Parīkṣit responds to Śukadeva Gosvāmī by asking

> Your Lordship has mentioned that the sun-god goes around Meru and Dhruva, keeping them to the right, and also facing toward the *rāśis* and moving so as to keep them to the left. So, how can we understand this reasonably?

The answer is given in 5.22.2:

> He (Śukadeva Gosvāmī) then clarified: Just as ants etc., which are spinning because they are resting on a spinning potter's wheel, actually have another movement because they are found in different places (on the wheel), similarly, the planets, the sun etc., which are going around because they are resting on the *kāla-cakra*, which is seen to be going around with *nakṣatras* and *rāśis*, keeping Dhruva and Meru to the right, actually have a different movement.

Thus the constellations correspond to the potter's wheel, and the sun and planets correspond to the ants. If we consider the earth as fixed, then the sun and all the stars and planets orbit around Mount Meru (the north polar axis) once per day, with Mount Meru to their right. In contrast, if we consider the stars as fixed, then the sun orbits around Mount Meru once per year, with Mount Meru to its left. The daily motion of the sun, stars, and planets is attributed to the *dakṣiṇā-varta* wind, which is conceived of as blowing all of these bodies around the polar axis defined by Mount Meru and Dhruvaloka. This motion is called the *kāla-cakra*, or wheel of time. In constrast, the sun's yearly motion is attributed to its chariot, which is a metaphor for the year.

This is clarified by Śrīdhara Swami in his commentary on 5.21.8–9:

> Although leftward movement, facing the *nakṣatras*, is his own motion [*svagatya*], the sun moves around Meru to the right daily, being blown by the *pravāha* wind, under the control of the *jyotiś-cakra*.

4.3 THE PLANETARY ORBITS IN 3-D

The ecliptic defines the plane of the sun's orbit around the earth, and this is the same as the plane of the earth's orbit around the sun. With the exception of Pluto, the other planets in the solar system move in planes nearly parallel to the ecliptic plane, and thus the whole solar system lies roughly in one plane. If we surround the solar system by an imaginary celestial sphere, the hemispheres above and below the

Figure 4.4 *Śrīmad Bhāgavatam* (5.21.2) compares the upper and lower hemispheres of Brahmāṇḍa with the two parts of "*nispava*," a type of pulse or bean, classed as a dicotyledon with two halves. The space between the two halves corresponds to Antarikṣa. (Compare with Figure 4.1, p. 83.)

plane of the solar system are therefore nearly empty.

The *Bhāgavatam* 5.21.2 makes a similar statement. It compares the universe (called Brahmāṇḍa or Brahmā's egg) with a spherical bean seed that divides in two halves, like the mung bean seed in the illustration. In such a seed, the embryo lies in the narrow space between the two hemispherical halves, and in the Brahmāṇḍa, Bhū-maṇḍala and the planetary orbits are similarly located in a narrow space between two hemispheres.

As we pointed out above, the sphere of the Brahmāṇḍa contains Bhū-maṇḍala and a thin cylinder of adjoining space, called Antarikṣa, which in this analogy corresponds to the space between the two halves of the bean. The orbits of the planets are assigned to a series of levels in Antarikṣa, as shown in Table 3.5 (p. 68). These levels lie between Bhū-maṇḍala and Dhruvaloka, which marks the upper limit of Antarikṣa.

The 3-D interpretation of Bhū-maṇḍala should be compared with the planisphere interpretation, given in Chapter 3. The heights listed in Table 3.5 have features that fit both the planisphere interpretation and the 3-D interpretation.

For example, the fact that planetary heights extend on only one side of Bhū-maṇḍala is a feature we might expect to see in the planisphere interpretation or in an astrolabe. The actual planetary orbits are not parallel, but are intersecting planes slightly tilted with respect to one another.

Then again, the numerical values of the planetary heights are irrelevant to the planisphere interpretation, but they can be understood in terms of the 3-D interpretation. They agree roughly with the maximum distances that the planets move from the ecliptic plane in the course of their orbits. This is explained in Section 4.7.

The heights of the planets also play a role in the system of fourteen worlds (*lokas* in Sanskrit) that include Bhū-maṇḍala and lie above and below it in the Brahmāṇḍa. This hierarchical system of worlds is connected with the demigods, and it is discussed in Section 6.2.

In brief, the planets in the solar system orbit nearly in one plane, and the planets in the Brahmāṇḍa orbit nearly in one plane within Antarikṣa. Thus the Brahmāṇḍa, bisected by Bhū-maṇḍala and Antarikṣa, is strikingly similar to the solar system placed within a celestial sphere.

4.4 THE ORBITAL MAP

The *Bhāgavatam* equates the outer diameter of Bhū-maṇḍala with the diameter of the universe, or Brahmāṇḍa. But what conception of the "universe" is intended? One way of answering this is to study the sizes assigned to Bhū-maṇḍala and its subdivisions in the *Bhāgavatam*. The most striking feature of these sizes is that they agree nicely with the size of the solar system, as given by modern astronomy.

We can see this by comparing the sizes of some key features of Bhū-maṇḍala with a variety of distances within the universe of modern astronomy. Table 2.1 (p. 22) gives the radii of all of the circular features of Bhū-maṇḍala, and Figure 4.5, below, shows their relative sizes.

To make a comparison with modern data, we must know the length of the *yojana*, the unit used to express distances in the *Bhāgavatam*. Over the centuries, there has been a great deal of variation in the length of the *yojana*, but eight miles/*yojana* is a commonly cited value and it is used in the translation of the *Bhāgavatam* that we consulted in this study (Bhaktivedanta, 1982). We will therefore begin by using this value.

We see from the list in Table 4.1 that the features of Bhū-maṇḍala are much too large for the earth globe and much too small for inter-

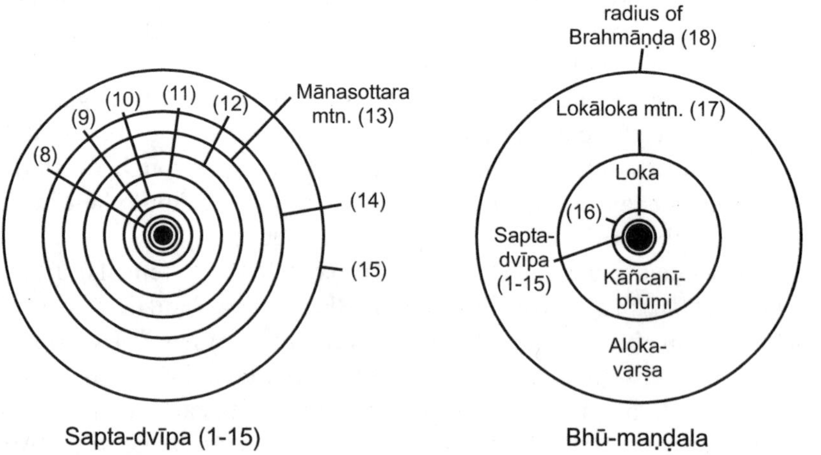

Figure 4.5 The circular features of Bhū-maṇḍala, drawn to scale. The rings on the left are collectively called Sapta-dvīpa, and they are a subset of Bhū-maṇḍala, which is shown on the right.

stellar distances within the Milky Way. But they line up nicely with distances in the solar system. Thus the pairs of numbers marked "compare" in the table are of the same order of magnitude, but the smallest of these numbers is four orders of magnitude higher than the earth's diameter. Likewise, the largest is four orders of magnitude smaller than the smallest stellar distance.

Bhū-maṇḍala agrees with the solar system in scale. We can see this in Figure 4.6, in which the Brahmāṇḍa is compared with the solar

TABLE 4.1
List of Astronomical Sizes

	7,928 miles	earth's diameter
	238,000 miles	radius of moon's orbit
	400,000 miles	radius of Jambūdvīpa
compare	142,000,000 miles	radius of Mars's orbit
	202,800,000 miles	radius of Sapta-dvīpa
compare	890,000,000 miles	radius of Saturn's orbit
	1,000,000,000 miles	radius of Lokāloka mountain
compare	1,790,000,000 miles	radius of orbit of Uranus
	2,000,000,000 miles	outer radius of Bhū-maṇḍala
	25,500,000,000,000 miles	distance to Alpha Centauri
	182,000,000,000,000,000 miles	distance to the center of the Milky Way galaxy

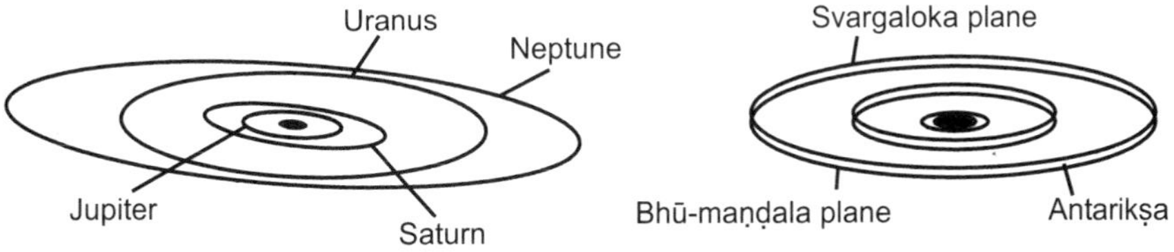

Figure 4.6 The solar system out to Neptune, compared with the region of planetary orbits, as described in the *Bhāgavatam*. (Pluto is omitted due to its highly eccentric orbit.) The planets are said to orbit between the two disks of Bhū-maṇḍala and Svargaloka. The scale assumes eight miles per *yojana*, and the angle of view is 75° from the vertical. Vertical relief (perpendicular to the ecliptic) is multiplied by three so that it can be easily seen in the figure.

system, using eight miles per *yojana*. The angle of view here is 75° from the vertical (perpendicular to the plane of the ecliptic), and vertical distances have been multiplied by three for better visibility. We see that the solar system out to Uranus corresponds closely to the thin cylinder of space called Antarikṣa, in which the *Bhāgavatam* places the planetary orbits. Thus the thickness of Antarikṣa roughly matches the vertical displacements of the tilted planetary orbits, and the radius of Antarikṣa matches the radius of the orbit of Uranus.

The match with Uranus could, perhaps, be put down to coincidence. Of greater interest is the fact that the inner ring structure of Bhū-maṇḍala also matches the planetary orbits of the five traditional visible planets, Mercury, Venus, Mars, Jupiter, and Saturn.

Consider a typical diagram of the solar system, projected on the ecliptic plane (Figure 4.7). We see a rough correspondence between the dense cluster of the orbits of the inner planets (Mercury through Mars) and the inner system of Sapta-dvīpa in Bhū-maṇḍala. (This corresponds with the first order of magnitude comparison in Table 4.1.) There is also a rough agreement between the orbits of Saturn and

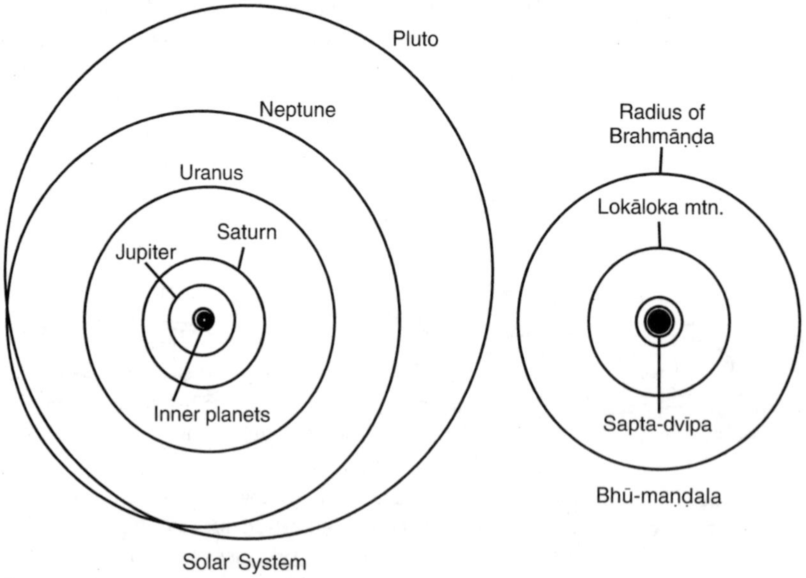

Figure 4.7 The solar system, compared with Bhū-maṇḍala. The scale assumes eight miles per *yojana*.

Jupiter and the two Bhū-maṇḍala circles lying outside of Sapta-dvīpa —the outer boundary of the "inhabited region" (Loka) and the circular Lokāloka mountain. (This corresponds to the second comparison.)

It is noteworthy that Saturn's orbit lines up with the Lokāloka mountain. This circular feature is stated in the *Bhāgavatam* 5.20.37 to be the outer limit of the luminaries, and Saturn is the outermost planet visible to the naked eye. Thus we may tentatively recognize a correlation between the orbits of the known planets of antiquity, Mercury through Saturn, and the illuminated region of Bhū-maṇḍala.

Of course, Bhū-maṇḍala is earth-centered. In contrast, the orbits of the planets are centered on the sun. How, then, can they be compared with earth-centered features of Bhū-maṇḍala?

The solution is to express the orbits of the planets in geocentric (earth-centered) form. Although modern astronomy treats these orbits as heliocentric (sun-centered), they can be expressed in relation to any desired center of observation, including the earth (see Appendix 4). When this is done, the sun and moon directly orbit the earth, and

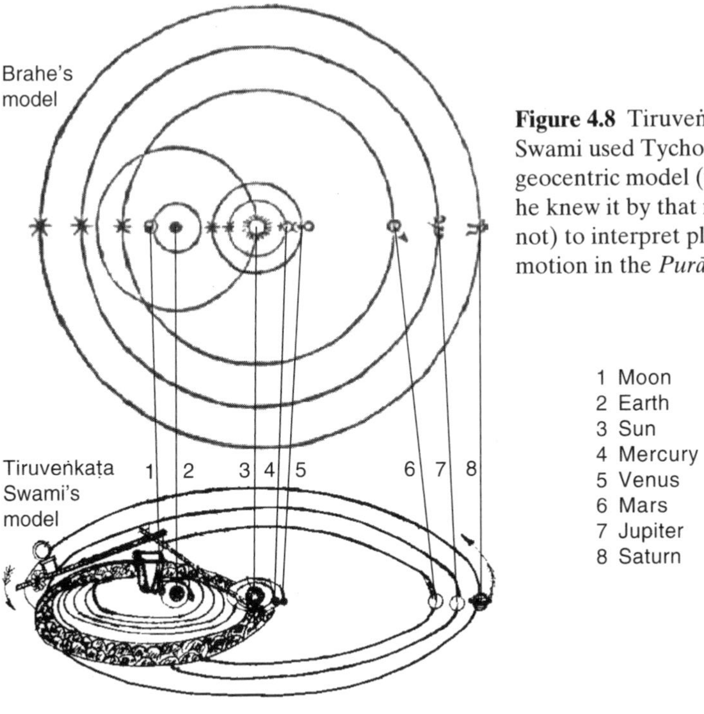

Figure 4.8 Tiruveṅkaṭa Swami used Tycho Brahe's geocentric model (whether he knew it by that name or not) to interpret planetary motion in the *Purāṇas*.

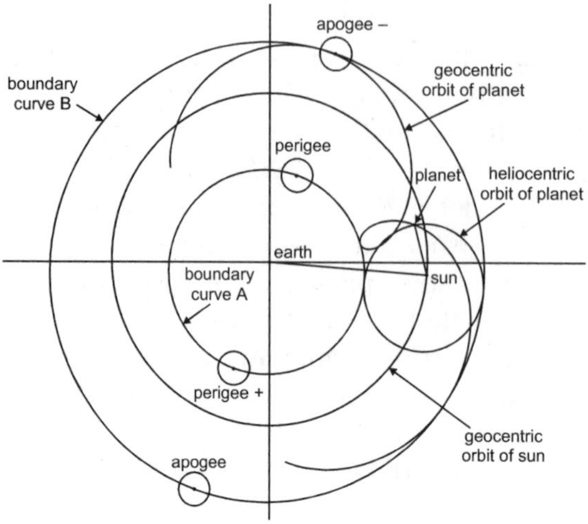

Figure 4.9 The structure of a geocentric orbit (of Mercury, in this case). The geocentric orbit of a planet is bounded by boundary curves A and B, each of which has two extreme points relative to the center. These are marked as perigee, perigee+, apogee-, and apogee.

the other planets orbit the sun. Historically, this form of earth-centered model was proposed by the famous sixteenth-century Danish astronomer, Tycho Brahe, who regarded it as a matter of absolute motion. Here, of course, we introduce the geocentric model as an expression of relative point of view.

In nineteenth-century India, Śrī Tiruveṅkaṭa Rāmānuja Jīyar Swami aligned a Tychonic, earth-centered solar system with Bhū-maṇḍala in the same way that we are doing here (see Figure 4.8). Although he may well have done this under Western influence, it is noteworthy that this interpretation of Bhū-maṇḍala was considered appropriate by an Indian traditionalist.

The general form of a geocentric orbit is shown in Figure 4.9, using Mercury as an example. The looping curve of the planet's geocentric orbit lies between two boundary curves, marked A and B in the figure. If we continue plotting the orbit for a long enough time, it completely fills in the donut-shaped area between these two curves. The boundary curves each have two turning points: the point of closest approach to the earth and the point of greatest distance from the earth. These points can be used to quantitatively compare the planetary orbits with the circular features of Bhū-maṇḍala.

We used the ephemeris programs of Duffett-Smith (1985) to compute the geocentric orbits of the five planets, Mercury through Saturn, projected onto the ecliptic plane. To compare these orbits with the features of Bhū-maṇḍala, we first converted them from miles to *yojanas*. Since the *yojana* is not exactly defined, we allowed it to vary in value. We used 1 *yojana* = y miles, where we allowed y to vary from 1 to 16, an interval covering the known historical range of possible *yojana* lengths. Then we superimposed the orbits on a map of Bhū-maṇḍala and observed the results.

For the commonly cited value of y = 8 miles, we saw that the pattern of Bhū-maṇḍala tended to match the geocentric solar system out to Saturn even more closely than it matched the heliocentric solar system. If we examine the orbits of Mercury, Venus, and Mars, we see that each orbit seems to go from a perigee near one circular feature of Sapta-dvīpa, to an apogee near another circular feature. The apogee of Saturn and the perigee of Jupiter also line up with the boundary circles of Kāñcanībhūmi. The agreement is rough for 8 miles/*yojana*, but it becomes quite striking if we shift to about 8.5 miles/*yojana*.

To properly evaluate these orbital alignments, we must consider whether or not a unique *yojana* length y gives good alignments and, if so, how y is to be determined. If many different *yojana* lengths did just

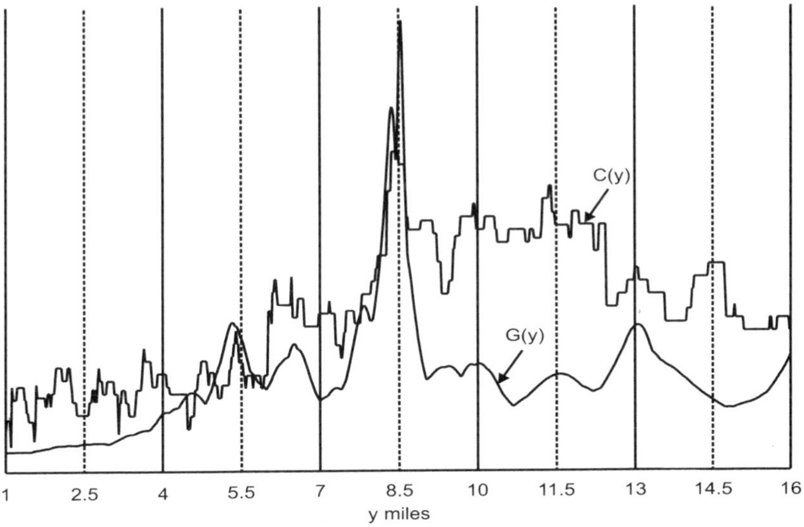

Figure 4.10 Plot of the two functions, G(y) and C(y), measuring how well Bhū-maṇḍala lines up with planetary orbits at y miles/*yojana*. The *yojana* length y ranges over one to sixteen miles, an interval that encompasses nearly all known variants of the *yojana*.

as well, that would be an indication that these alignments are simply coincidences that naturally arise when sets of circles are compared.

To find out whether or not there is a unique, optimal y, we need to define a measure of goodness of fit, G(y). This is done in Appendix 5. In Figure 4.10, G(y) is plotted as a function of y, which is allowed to range from one to sixteen miles. We can see that the curve has a pro-

TABLE 4.2
Orbit Table (Distances in Thousands of Yojanas)

N	Planet	Turning point	Turning point radius	Inner feature radius	Outer feature radius	% error
10	Mercury	perigee	6019.37	4550	6150	8.16
10		perigee+	7410.30	6150	9350	39.38
13		apogee-	14486.08	12550	15750	39.50
13		apogee	15882.92	15750	18950	4.15
8	Venus	perigee	2902.88	2150	2950	5.89
8		perigee+	3173.21	2950	4550	13.95
14		apogee-	18740.67	15750	18950	6.54
14		apogee	19014.22	18950	25350	1.00
11	Sun	perigee	10760.79	9350	12550	44.09
11		mean	10950.49	9350	12550	49.98
12		apogee	11139.72	9350	12550	44.07
9	Mars	perigee	4075.18	2950	4550	29.68
10		perigee+	7382.63	6150	9350	38.52
15		apogee-	25972.60	25350	41100	3.95
15		apogee	29282.39	25350	41100	24.97
16	Jupiter	perigee	43315.33	41100	125000	2.64
16		perigee+	48709.66	41100	125000	9.07
16		apogee-	65203.62	41100	125000	28.73
16		apogee	70599.14	41100	125000	35.16
17	Saturn	perigee	87237.21	41100	125000	45.01
17		perigee+	99819.00	41100	125000	30.01
17		apogee-	109080.82	41100	125000	18.97
17		apogee	121738.82	41100	125000	3.89

nounced peak at 8.534 miles. This length of the *yojana* is singled out as optimal, and there are no notable peaks for any other *yojana* lengths.

To check this result, we also defined another goodness of fit function, C(y), which is discussed in Appendix 6. This has a pronounced peak at 8.489 miles, and this differs by 0.53% from the *yojana* length obtained from G(y). C(y) is also plotted in the above illustration. Although it is based on a completely different approach to orbital correlations than G(y), it corroborates what we see with G(y).

Table 4.2 shows how the geocentric orbits of the five planets and the sun compare with Bhū-maṇḍala features (N), using an optimal *yojana* length of 8.489 miles. The error percentages in the table are defined as follows: A turning point falling inside Bhū-maṇḍala and outside Jambūdvīpa must lie in the annular region between two Bhū-maṇḍala circles. Its distance from the closest circle, divided by the distance between the two circles and multiplied by one hundred, is the error percentage. This measures how close the turning point is to a Bhū-maṇḍala circle. (A modified definition is used for points falling within Jambūdvīpa or outside Bhū-maṇḍala.)

The orbital turning points are calculated using a modern ephemeris program for the epoch of A.D. 500, using 8.489 miles/*yojana*. All

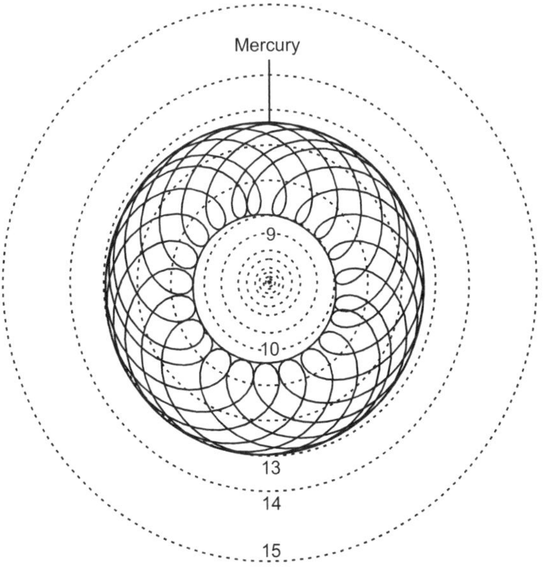

Figure 4.11 The geocentric orbit of Mercury, compared with Bhū-maṇḍala using 8.489 miles/*yojana*. The inner boundary of the orbit of Mercury swings in and nearly grazes feature 10 (inner edge of Śākadvīpa), and its outer boundary swings out and nearly grazes feature 13 (Mānasottara Mountain). We can sum this up by saying that Mercury's boundary curves are tangent to features 10 and 13.

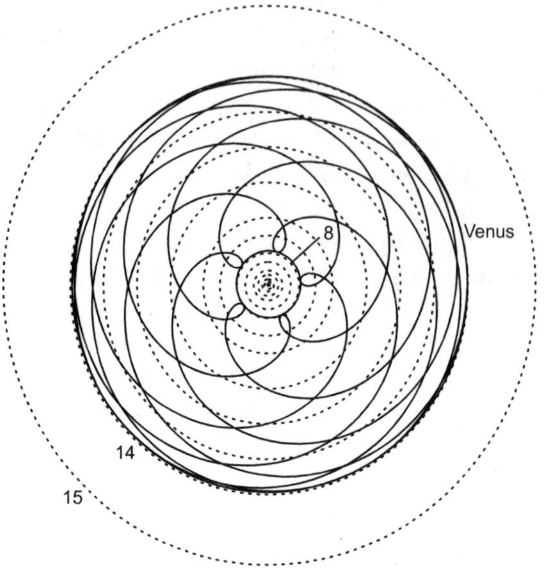

Figure 4.12 The geocentric orbit of Venus, compared with Bhū-maṇḍala using 8.489 miles/*yojana*. The inner boundary of the orbit of Venus swings in and nearly grazes feature 8 (inner edge of Krauñcadvīpa), and its outer boundary swings out and nearly grazes feature 14 (the outer edge of Puṣkaradvīpa). We can sum this up by saying that Venus's boundary curves are tangent to features 8 and 14.

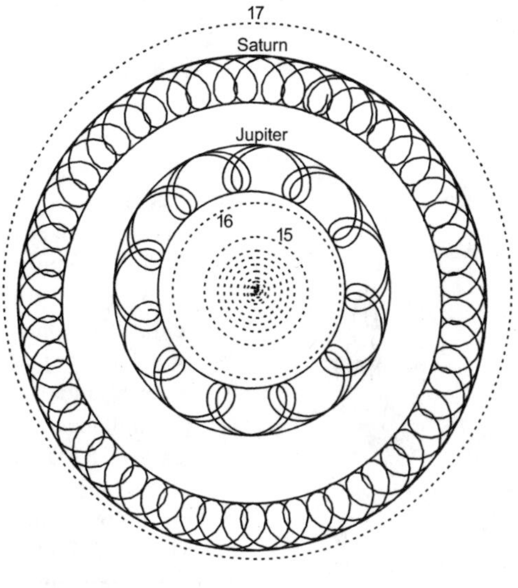

Figure 4.13 The geocentric orbits of Jupiter and Saturn, compared with Bhū-maṇḍala using 8.489 miles/*yojana*. The inner boundary of Jupiter's orbit is tangent to feature 16 (the outer edge of Loka). The outer boundary of Saturn's orbit is tangent to feature 17 (the outer edge of Kāñcanī-bhūmi). Saturn is the outermost of the known planets of antiquity. It is perhaps significant that feature 17 is also the Lokāloka Mountain, which forms the outer boundary of the luminaries. It can be argued that Saturn was understood as the outermost luminary.

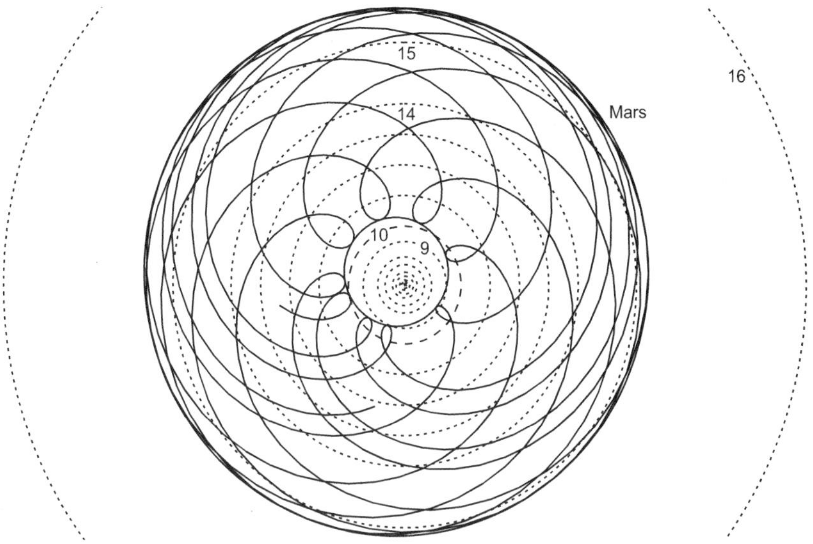

Figure 4.14 The geocentric orbit of Mars, compared with Bhū-maṇḍala using 8.489 miles/*yojana*. The inner boundary of the orbit of Mars swings in and nearly grazes feature 9 (outer edge of Krauñcadvīpa), and its outer boundary is tangent to 15 (the outer edge of Svādūdaka, the Fresh Water Ocean). Feature 15 is the outer boundary of the system of seven *dvīpas* and oceans. A curious feature of the orbit of Mars is that it partially crosses over the outer boundary of Krauñcadvīpa. The *Bhāgavatam* may refer to this indirectly, since it states in verse 5.20.19 that Mount Krauñca in Krauñcadvīpa was attacked by Kārttikeya, the regent of Mars.

distance figures are in thousands of *yojanas*, and the feature radii are as given in the *Bhāgavatam* (see Table 2.1 on p. 22).

In Table 4.2, we see a tendency for the perigees and apogees of planets to align closely with Bhū-maṇḍala circles, although this correlation is not perfect.

In the case of Mercury, the error percentages for the perigee and apogee are about 8% and 4%, respectively. Thus the inner boundary of Mercury's orbit swings in and nearly grazes feature 10 in Table 2.1, and its outer boundary swings out and nearly grazes feature 13.

For Venus, the perigee and apogee are, respectively, within about 6% of feature 8 and 1% of feature 14.

Mars does not do as well. Its perigee and apogee come within 30% and 25% of features 9 and 15, although its third turning point (apogee- in the Table 4.2) comes within 4% of feature 15.

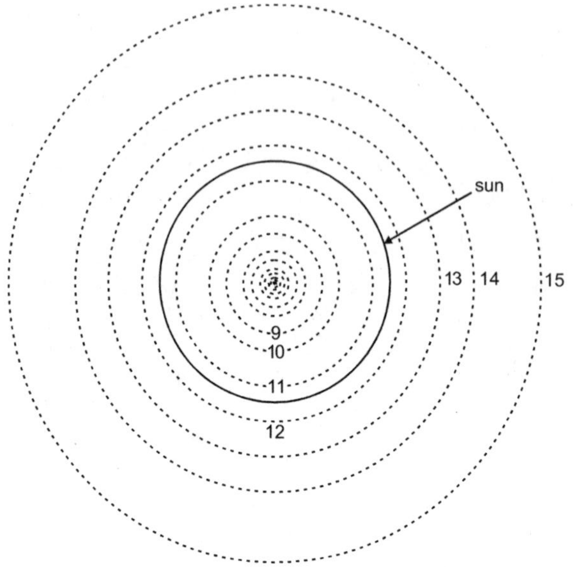

Figure 4.15 Position of the sun's geocentric orbit in relation to the oceans and *dvīpas* of Bhū-maṇḍala.

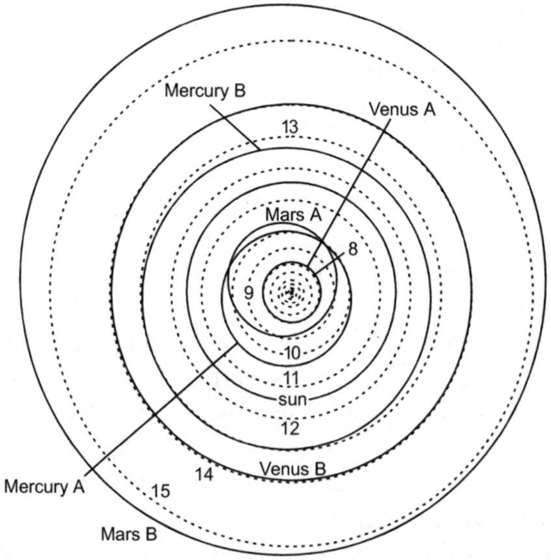

Figure 4.16 The boundary curves of the sun and Mercury through Mars, compared with Bhū-maṇḍala using 8.489 miles/*yojana*.

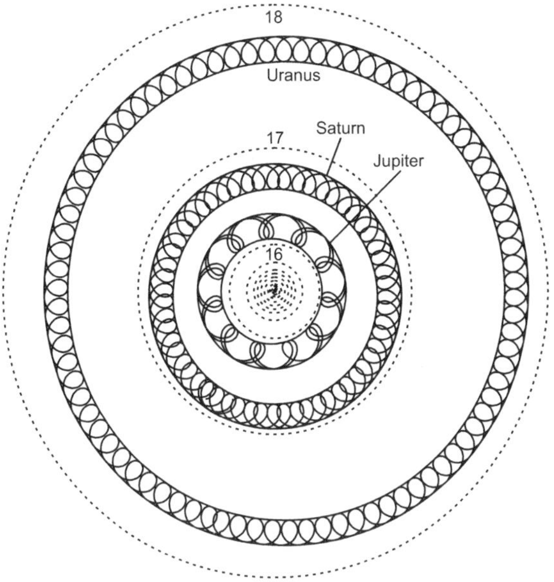

Figure 4.17 The outer boundary of the orbit of Uranus roughly lines up with feature 18, the outer boundary of Aloka-varṣa. Note that Uranus is invisible to the naked eye and, in that sense, it is not a luminary. It also lies outside the Lokāloka Mountain, which marks the outer boundary of the luminaries.

The perigee of Jupiter falls within 3% of feature 16, and its apogee falls within 35% of the same feature. Likewise, the apogee of Saturn falls within 4% of feature 17, the Lokāloka Mountain, and its perigee falls within 45% of the same feature.

Let use pause for a moment and see whether or not these results could be simply products of chance. We have just listed ten apogees and perigees as percentages. These numbers add up to 161, and each number must fall in the interval from 0 to 50%. If ten numbers were picked at random in this interval, the probability that they sum to 161 or less comes to about 3.3%. This crude analysis is not sufficient to show that Table 4.2 contains a statistically significant pattern, but it does suggest that this possibility is worth investigating. A detailed statistical analysis is carried out in Appendix 7 and reported below under Conclusions.

We include the sun in Table 4.2 as a special case. The sun's geocentric orbit is different from that of the planets, in that it is produced by a single heliocentric motion, rather than two. It therefore has only two turning points, the sun's perigee and apogee, which are nearly equal to one another. The perigee falls 44% higher than feature 11, and

Figure 4.18 The geocentric orbit of Ceres superimposed on Bhū-maṇḍala.

the apogee falls 44% lower than feature 12. Thus the mean of the sun's apogee and perigee lies almost exactly halfway across the ocean spanning features 11 and 12. (This is 10,950 = (9,350+12,550)/2 thousand *yojanas.*)

In Figure 4.16, the boundary curves of the sun and Mercury through Mars are plotted together, without the overlapping curves of the orbits themselves. This gives an overview of the orbit correlations for these planets.

Finally, for the sake of completeness we include the orbit of Uranus (Figure 4.17) and the orbit of Ceres (Figure 4.18), the largest asteroid. The orbits of Neptune and Pluto lie outside the limits of Bhū-maṇḍala and are not considered. To see if Ceres was unique, we examined the orbits of 141 main-belt asteriods. These showed some statistical scatter, but like Ceres, their orbits tended to fill out region 16 (Loka, or "inhabited land"), while overlapping region 15 (Svādūdaka).

4.4.1 Conclusions

In Appendix 7 we propose the null hypothesis that the author of the *Bhāgavatam* had no access to correct planetary distances, and therefore all apparent correlations between Bhū-maṇḍala features and planetary distances are simply coincidental. However, analysis shows that the observed correlations are, in fact, highly improbable, and this suggests that advanced knowledge of planetary astronomy may lie behind the *Bhāgavatam*.

If this is so, when did this knowledge originate and how did it come to be incorporated into the text? Unfortunately, it is difficult to give a definite answer to this question, since we know very little about the origin of the *Bhāgavatam*. Hardy (1983) attributes the *Bhāgavatam* to ninth-century South India on linguistic and literary grounds, but it is hard to say where or when specific information in the text may have originated. Thus O'Flaherty remarks that, "since the Epics and *Purāṇas* represent an oral tradition that was constantly revised over a period of several thousand years, a passage actually composed in the twelfth century A.D. may represent a surprisingly accurate preservation of a myth handed down since the twelfth century B.C.—or a completely original retelling of that myth" (O'Flaherty, 1975, p. 16).

References in the text to the zodiac, with the vernal equinox in the beginning of Aries (Meṣa), suggest input from the *Jyotiṣa Śāstras*, Indian astronomical texts that are generally traced to Hellenistic Greek sources (Pingree, 1976). However, the *Bhāgavatam* presents astronomical information in a way that is quite different from the *Jyotiṣa Śāstras*, and thus it appears to be connected with a different astronomical tradition. Of course, the *Jyotiṣa Śāstras*, in line with Greek astronomy, make the distances to the planets much smaller than they really are.

Cosmological presentations similar to that of the *Bhāgavatam* are found in other *Purāṇas*, in the *Mahābhārata*, and in Jain and Buddhist texts. The Jain and Buddhist cosmologies are particularly complex, and they seem to be imaginative elaborations of themes originating in earlier Hindu cosmology.

Purāṇic cosmology is generally similar to that of the *Bhāgavatam*, with some variations in nomenclature and in quantitative dimensions. From a survey of *Purāṇas*, we concluded that many Purāṇic presentations of Bhū-maṇḍala appear to be garbled and incomplete (see Section 2.3). Of the texts we examined, only the *Bhāgavatam* gives a complete and consistent account of the dimensions of the different features.

If the dimensions given in the *Bhāgavatam* do, in fact, represent realistic planetary distances based on human observation, then we must postulate that *Bhāgavata* astronomy preserves material from an earlier, and presently unknown, period of scientific development. Other texts would then represent elaborations of material from this earlier period, with varying degrees of divergence from the original.

Thus, if the orbital alignments are not purely coincidental, some people in the past must have had accurate values for the dimensions of the planetary orbits. In modern history, this information has become available only since the development of high-quality telescopes in the last two hundred years. Accurate values of planetary distances were not known by Hellenistic astronomers such as Claudius Ptolemy, nor are they to be found in the medieval *Jyotiṣa Śāstras* of India. If this information was known, it must have been acquired by some unknown civilization that flourished in the distant past.

The relative proportions of the planetary orbits can be obtained from Kepler's laws using naked eye observations, and Kepler formulated these laws without the aid of the telescope. Indeed, Kepler's laws arose from the work of only two astronomers, Kepler himself and Tycho Brahe, who provided Kepler's observational data. Thus it is possible that the proportions of the solar system may have been worked out in ancient times without the use of the telescope. Even this, however, implies the existence of a society inclined to support and nurture such investigations.

Although the hypothesis of an unknown, scientifically advanced civilization is radical, it is supported by additional evidence. Section 4.5 shows that the *yojana* length obtained by optimizing the two fitness measures is confirmed by an independent analysis which relates the *yojana* to the dimensions of the earth and to units of length used in the ancient Mediterranean world. This analysis yielded 8.59 miles as one of a pair of ancient *yojana* lengths, and this agrees well with the figures of 8.49 and 8.53 miles obtained by optimizing the orbit correlations.

It is therefore noteworthy that the scholar Livio Stecchini has shown that ancient Egyptian units were part of a scientific system of measures based on accurate measurements of latitude in ancient times. His findings are corroborated by the work of scholars such as A. E. Berriman and Schwaller de Lubicz (see Appendix 8).

Whatever the source of the *Bhāgavatam's* astronomical knowledge may be, it appears to have become lost or obscured by the medieval period, when the current text was supposedly written. The commentaries on the *Bhāgavatam* do not explicitly acknowledge the role of Bhū-maṇḍala as a map of the solar system or its role as a planisphere map of the earth. If the latter were an import from Ptolemaic astronomy in the early Middle Ages, then one would expect to find it explicitly recognized by medieval commentators, but this is not the case.

Medieval Indian astronomers of the Jyotiṣa school do not seem to have been aware that Purāṇic cosmology refers to the earth as a globe. Since they lacked realistic values for planetary distances, they could not know that the large sizes of features in Bhū-maṇḍala correlate well with distances in the solar system. Thus Bhāskarācārya, the eleventh-century author of the Jyotiṣa text *Siddhānta-śiromaṇi* (Wilkinson, 1861), said that he could not reconcile the relatively small diameter of the earth, which he deduced from simple measurements, with the immense magnitude attributed to the earth by the Paurāṇikas (the followers of the *Purāṇas*). Although the extant *Purāṇas* are generally attributed to the Middle Ages by scholars, this comment adds to the impression that their cosmological content was not understood during that time period, and it must date back to an earlier time.

Although the *Jyotiṣa Śāstras* do not have good values for orbital distances, the *Sūrya-siddhānta* does contain accurate values for the diameters of the planets (see Appendix 10). This information is lodged incongruously in the text of the *Sūrya-siddhānta* as though it were a fossil remnant of a previous stage of advanced scientific knowledge.

The hypothesis of lost scientific knowledge should be pursued by seeking other evidence of an earlier astronomical school. However, we should also mention another hypothesis based on the traditions surrounding the *Bhāgavatam* itself. This is that the text is a product of divine inspiration, and therefore it may encode levels of meaning not understood even by the author himself. According to this hypothesis, the *Bhāgavatam* may contain information that was unknown to human society in the period of its composition, but which can be discerned in the text now on the basis of our more advanced scientific knowledge. In this case, a simple model of the ecliptic, which could have been based on Greek astronomy, is supplemented by information reflecting advanced knowledge of planetary distances.

4.5 THE LENGTH OF THE YOJANA

In this section we examine how the Purāṇic distance unit called the *yojana* relates to ancient systems of measures, and in the course of this, we find evidence that the *yojana* length computed in Section 4.4 was actually used historically. Two appendices give supporting evidence. In Appendix 8, we investigate the empirical basis for the claims of some scholars that ancient Egyptian and Near Eastern societies had scientific definitions of weights and measures based on latitude. In Appendix 9, we cite scholarly studies of ancient mathematics to show that the mathematical tools for scientific metrology were available in ancient times.

We begin with a common misconception regarding systems of weights and measures. An encyclopedia article states that in early times distance was defined by the breadth of the palm or hand, and the length from the elbow to the tip of the middle finger (the cubit). The article goes on to say, "Such standards were both changeable and perishable, and only within modern times have definite unchanging standards of measurement been adopted" (*Microsoft Encarta*).

The Middle Ages certainly saw many conflicting and poorly defined standards of weights and measures. But exact standards of measurement are not solely a modern invention.

Consider this example. In tenth-century England, King Athelstan decreed that the king's girth, in which the king's peace is in force, should extend from the royal residence for a distance of three miles, three furlongs, nine acres, nine feet, nine palms, and nine barleycorns (Stecchini, 1971, p. 344). This sounds quaint. But it defines a circle with a diameter of 36,500 feet—almost exactly $^1/_{10}$ of a degree of latitude in southern England. (Here an acre of 66×660 square feet is used as a linear unit of 66 feet.)

4.5.1 Measuring with Latitude

To define a unit of length exactly, it is natural to use latitude as a standard, because latitude derives from the size of the earth, which is constant and can be measured astronomically. So if a fire or invasion destroys the standard measuring rod stored in some government building, astronomical readings can be used to restore the lost standard.

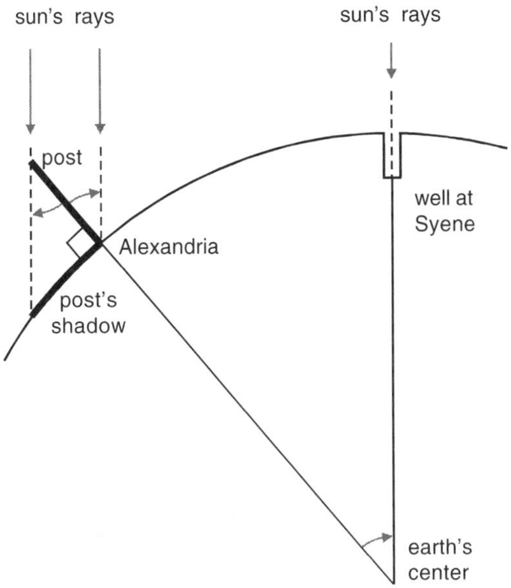

Figure 4.19 The Greek astronomer Eratosthenes noted that when the sun was directly overhead at Syene, its shadow marks an angle of 7.2° (exaggerated for clarity) at Alexandria. Knowing this and the distance between Syene and Alexandria, he calculated the circumference of the earth.

Of course, it seems unlikely that accurate astronomical measurements were being made in England in the days of King Athelstan. But if we look into the history of weights and measures, we find that distances were gauged in terms of latitude in ancient times, and medieval societies inherited many exact standards of measurement. These included standard volumes defined as length cubed and standard weights defined by filling such a volume with water.

The Greek astronomer Eratosthenes is usually credited with being the first to measure the size of the earth by observing latitudes. He is said to have noted that the sun, when directly overhead at Syene at the Tropic of Cancer, casts a shadow of 7.2° at Alexandria. Knowing the distance between Syene and Alexandria, he could compute the length of a degree of latitude and estimate the circumference of the earth.

But there is reason to believe that the size of the earth was known long before Eratosthenes. Back in the nineteenth century, Pierre-Simon de Laplace observed that Eratosthenes had obtained a result much better than his measurements, due to an apparently fortuitous cancellation of errors. He concluded that "this astronomer had only reproduced an ancient measure of the earth that had been executed with great skill and whose origin had been lost" (Laplace, 1884).

The Italian scholar Livio Stecchini has given extensive evidence that the ancient Egyptians laid out their country using latitude and longitude (Stecchini, 1971). He argues that they had accurate knowledge of the dimensions of the earth and that such knowledge was inherent in the design of the great pyramid at Giza. Since the great pyramid dates to about 2500 B.C., this implies that the earth was measured scientifically at least that long ago.

4.5.2 Defining the Yojana

Turning to India, we find a unit of distance—called the *yojana*—that at first glance seems as ill defined as the medieval English furlong or foot. The *yojana* is stated to be four *krośas* of 2,000 or 1,000 *dhanus* (bow-lengths) of four *hastas*, where a *hasta* of 24 *aṅgulas* (fingers) corresponds to a Western cubit (Burgess, 1860, p. 43). This comes to 32,000 or 16,000 *hastas*. If there are 1.5 feet in a cubit, then a finger comes to ¾ of an inch and the *yojana* comes to nine miles or 4.5 miles.

That there were at least two sizes for the *yojana* is upheld by the writings of classical Indian astronomers. The fifth-century astronomer Āryabhaṭa used a *yojana* of about eight miles, and the astronomical

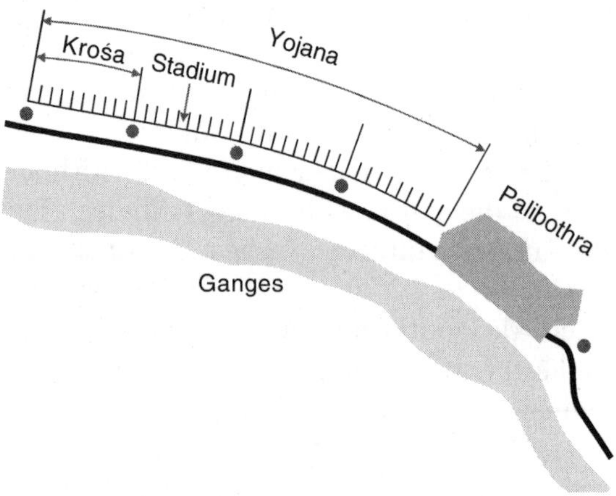

Figure 4.20 Megasthenes stated that pillars were placed every ten *stadia* along the royal road from Palibothra, and Cunningham argued that the distance from pillar to pillar was one *krośa*. This makes ten *stadia* per *krośa* and forty *stadia* per *yojana* of four *krośas*.

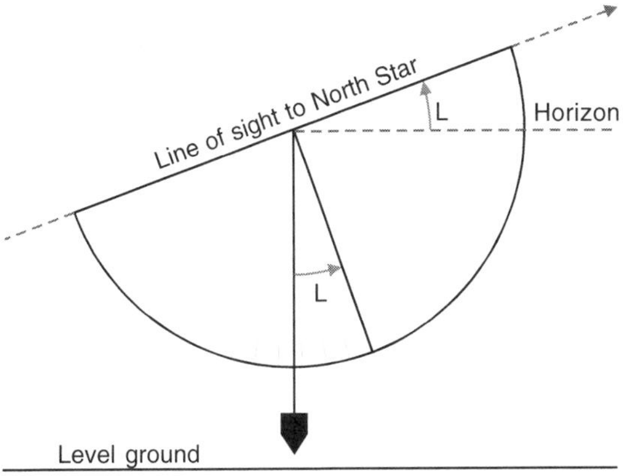

Figure 4.21 To measure latitude in the northern hemisphere, imagine that you are standing on level ground, facing north. Sight along the protractor to the North Star, as shown. The angle L from the horizon to the North Star is your latitude.

text *Sūrya-siddhānta* used a *yojana* of roughly five miles (Sarma, 1956, p. 83).

The first hint of the ancient history of the *yojana* comes from Strabo, who describes the experiences of Megasthenes, a Greek ambassador to India in the period following Alexander the Great. Strabo cites Megasthenes as saying that along the royal road to the Indian capital of Palibothra (thought to be near modern Pātnā), pillars were set up every ten stadia (Cunningham, 1871, p. 484). The British scholar Alexander Cunningham argues that the pillars marked an interval of one *krośa*. Since there are traditionally four *krośas* per *yojana*, this implies forty stadia per *yojana*. Stecchini gives 400 cubits per stadium, and this implies 16,000 cubits per *yojana*.

Since the smaller of the two definitions for the *yojana* assigns it 16,000 *hastas*, we can tentatively identify the *hasta*, or Indian cubit, with the Greek cubit. This unit is well known, and it enables us to compute the length of the *yojana*. The Greek cubit is 462.42 millimeters. This gives us a small *yojana* of about 4.6 miles, in rough agreement with texts such as the *Sūrya-siddhānta* and Purāṇic definitions.

Stecchini points out that the stadium was defined as $^1/_{600}$ of a degree of latitude (Stecchini, 1971, p. 314). This would mean that there are fifteen small *yojanas* per degree. Likewise, there are sixty *krośas* per degree, or one *krośa* per minute.

The above illustration shows what is involved conceptually in measuring latitude in the northern hemisphere (leaving out the technical details required for highly accurate measurements). Imagine that

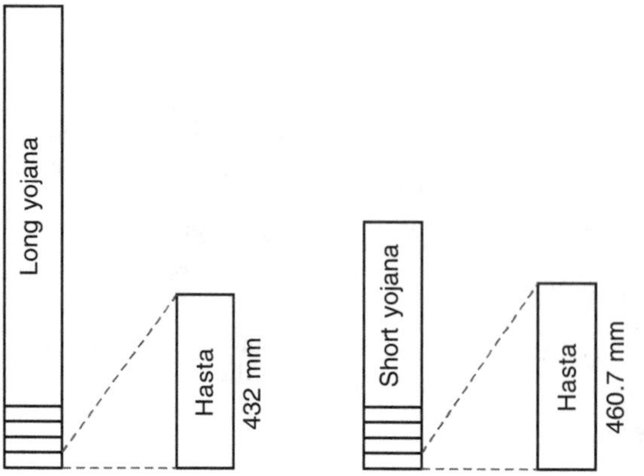

Figure 4.22 There are at least two *yojana* standards: A long *yojana* of 32,000 *hastas* and a short *hasta* of 16,000 *hastas*. The *hasta* of the short *yojana* is slightly longer than that of the long *yojana*.

you are standing on level ground, facing north. Sight along the protractor to the celestial north pole, as shown. (In some historical periods, this point in the sky is conveniently marked by a polestar—Polaris at present.) The angle L from the horizon to the celestial north pole is your latitude. This angle is 0° at the equator and grows to 90° at the geographical north pole.

The length of a degree of latitude is the distance a person would have to travel northward for his latitude to increase by 1°. On a perfect sphere, this distance would be the same at all latitudes. But the earth is slightly flattened at the poles, and it bulges at the equator. This makes for a degree of latitude slightly smaller at the equator than further north.

Stecchini noted that the Greek stadium is 1/600 of a degree of latitude at Mycenae in Greece, and he argued that it was deliberately defined this way in ancient times. It can be argued that to define the *yojana* in India, the degree of latitude at the equator was used. This means that the *hasta* should be 460.7 millimeters instead of 462.4 millimeters (and the *yojana* would still be about 4.6 miles). We will see below why this fine distinction is important.

At first glance, the *yojana* of 32,000 *hastas* should be twice as long as this, or about 9.2 miles. But there is reason to think that these two *yojanas* use different standards for the *hasta*.

Hiuen Thsang, a Buddhist pilgrim who visited India in the seventh century, wrote of *yojanas* in terms of a Chinese unit of measure called the *li*. He reported that a *yojana* consisted of forty *li* according to

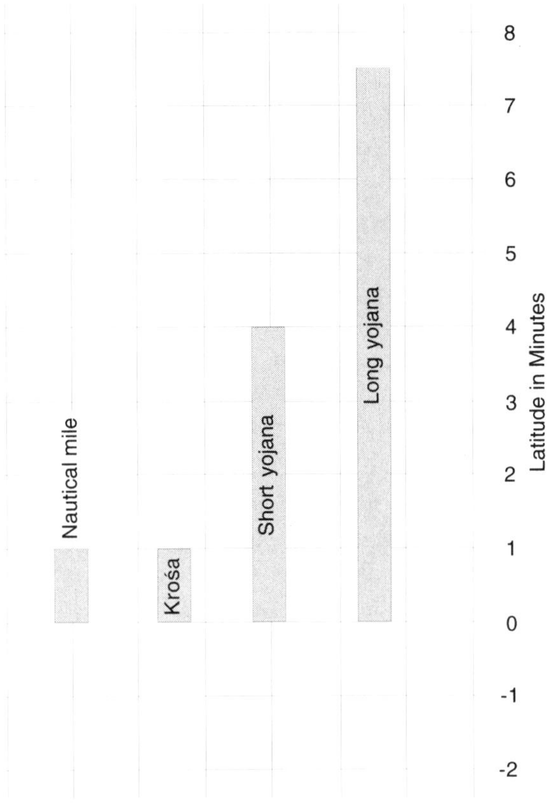

Figure 4.23 The *krośa* of the short *yojana* is one minute of latitude at the equator, and the modern nautical mile is defined in the same way. The short *yojana* is four minutes of latitude, and the long *yojana* is 7.5 minutes of latitude.

Indian tradition, but the measure in customary use equaled thirty *li,* and the measure given in sacred texts was only sixteen (Burgess, 1860, p. 43). The *li* has taken on many values during China's history. But using values for the Thang dynasty (when Hiuen Thsang lived), we can compute that the *yojana* of sixteen *li* matches the small *yojana* of 4.6 miles.

Could the *yojana* of thirty *li* match the larger *yojana* of 32,000 *hastas*? If it does, then the larger *yojana* has to use a slightly smaller *hasta*, $^{30}/_{32}$ as long as the *hasta* in the shorter *yojana*. Multiplying our *hasta* of 460.7 millimeters by $^{30}/_{32}$, we get a smaller *hasta* of 431.9 millimeters. The larger *yojana* of 32,000 *hastas* then comes to 8.59 miles. At the equator, that is $^{1}/_{8}$ of a degree of latitude.

In the illustration above, the short and long *yojanas* are plotted in minutes of latitude at the equator. The *krośa* of the short *yojana* is one minute of latitude, and the modern nautical mile is defined in the same way. Thus the short *yojana* is four minutes of latitude and the long *yojana* is seven and a half minutes of latitude.

In Section 4.4, above, we point out that the geocentric orbits of the planets Mercury, Venus, Mars, Jupiter, and Saturn align closely with the dimensions of the circular features of Bhū-maṇḍala. To align planetary orbits with these features we need to be able to convert the *yojanas* used in the *Bhāgavatam* into the miles or kilometers of modern astronomy. The alignment of orbits and features works well if we assume about eight and a half miles per *yojana*.

To compare orbits with the structure of Bhū-maṇḍala, modern ephemeris programs were used for orbital calculations. We ran these calculations for the epoch of about A.D. 500, based on scholarly estimates for the age of the *Bhāgavatam*. (However, this date is not important in the analysis because the calculated results turn out to be nearly independent of the epoch used, from 3000 B.C. to A.D. 2000.)

The calculations show that the planetary orbits align closely with *dvīpas* in Bhū-maṇḍala at a value of 8.49 to 8.53 miles per *yojana*. This is very close to the figure of 8.59 miles based on the *hasta* of 431.9 millimeters. So the value of the *yojana* we get by historical research is confirmed by completely independent calculations having to do with planetary orbits and the astronomy of the *Bhāgavatam*.

4.5.3 Familiar Numbers

As explained above, we get the larger *yojana* of 32,000 *hastas* (and $^1/_8$ of a degree of latitude) by using a *hasta* of 431.9 millimeters. This can be rounded off to 432, a familiar number in Sanskrit literature. An example is 432,000, the number of years in Kali-yuga. In Section 8.4, we show that this number has a long history in Indian and ancient Near Eastern traditions.

One might think that it is wrong to attribute any significance to a figure of 432 millimeters, when the metric system is a recent invention. But it turns out that the appearance of this familiar number may not be simply coincidental.

First of all, the meter itself derives from a measurement of latitude. The meter (one thousand millimeters) was originally defined in 1791 as one ten-millionth of the distance from the equator to the north pole through the meridian of Paris. That distance has been remeasured since then, but the change amounts to a tiny fraction of a percent.

So accepting for the larger *yojana* a *hasta* of 432 millimeters, we find that this *hasta* comes very close to 108 ten-billionths of the circumference of the earth on a great circle through the poles. (This is because 432 = 4 × 108, and there are four quadrants from equator to pole in the complete circumference.) Here Figure 4.24 shows one such great circle.

Another 108 comes up if we consider the mean diameter of the earth, 7917.5 miles, or 1728.5 "small *yojanas*." This is close to 1728, or 16 × 108. (This is reminiscent of the 1,728,000 years of Kṛta-yuga, the first in the cycle of the four ages. See Section 8.4.)

These observations suggest a simple experiment. Try setting the mean diameter of the earth to exactly 1,728 small *yojanas* of 16,000 *hastas*. Suppose that $^{30}/_{32}$ of a *hasta* gives a smaller *hasta* exactly 108 ten-billionths of the circumference of the earth through the poles. If we multiply it all out, we find that the ratio between circumference and mean diameter comes to 3.13967.

This ratio expresses the degree of polar flattening of the earth. If the earth were a perfect sphere, as shown on the left of Figure 4.25, this number would be π—the ratio of the circumference of a circle to its diameter. This is simply $^{C}/_{D}$. In a flattened sphere, we take the ratio between C', the circumference through the poles, and D', the average of the many, slightly differing diameters of the flattened sphere.

Figure 4.24 The *hasta* of the long *yojana* is equal to 108 ten-billionths of the circumference of the earth, measured on a great circle through the poles. Here one polar great circle is shown.

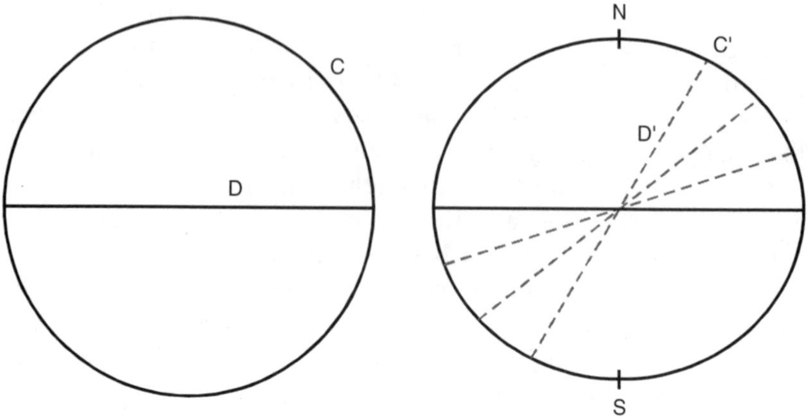

Figure 4.25 The ratio between the circumference C and the diameter D of a circle (shown on the left) is $\pi = 3.1415927$. Since the earth (shown on the right) is flattened at the poles, its diameter varies. The ratio between circumference C' through the poles and the mean diameter D' is 3.13984, within 0.006% of the value calculated on the basis of the *yojana*. (The flattening of the earth is shown greatly exaggerated for clarity.)

As it turns out, 3.13967 is within 0.006% of the actual ratio C'/D', as calculated using modern data. That this calculation works out so well indicates strongly that we are dealing with design rather than coincidence.

The temple of Angkor Wat in Cambodia gives evidence that the *hasta* of 432 millimeters was in use in the Indian cultural area during the medieval period. When measured by the Khmer unit of length called the *hat*, the Angkor Wat complex turns out to be loaded with astronomical relationships relating to the *nakṣatras*, the sun, and the moon (Snodgrass, 1990, pp. 217–224). This unit is 0.43454 meters, which is within 0.6% of the *hasta* of 432 mm. (For a discussion of links between astronomy and Indian temple design, see Section 2.5.)

In summary, simple arguments from the testimony of Megasthenes and Hiuen Thsang enable us to reconstruct two closely related *yojana* values. Both are precisely defined as fractions of a degree of latitude at the equator. Both relate to the earth by multiples of 108 (namely 432 and 1,728), and this relationship gives us a very accurate estimate of the polar flattening of the earth. Also, the length of the larger *yojana* is confirmed independently by an investigation comparing modern

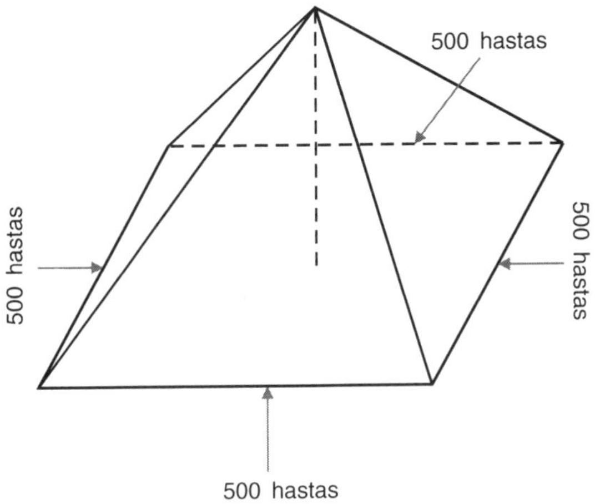

Figure 4.26 Based on accurate measurements made by J. H. Cole in 1925, we calculate that each side of the great pyramid of Egypt is almost exactly 500 *hastas* of the short *yojana*. The perimeter of the pyramid is almost exactly half a *krośa*.

astronomy with the cosmology of the *Bhāgavatam*.

Let us return briefly to our replacement of the Greek cubit with a slightly smaller unit linked to a degree of latitude at the equator. All the calculations above would go through if we used the Greek cubit directly and did not make this substitution. But the errors would be larger. So it is preferable to match the two *yojana* lengths to the equator rather than to Greece.

Curiously, we can find support for this in the design of the great pyramid of Egypt. In 1925 an engineer named J. H. Cole made an accurate survey of the great pyramid using up-to-date instruments. He found that twice the perimeter is 1,842.91 meters (Stecchini, 1971, p. 203). For comparison, a minute of latitude at the equator—or a *krośa* of the small *yojana*—is 1,842.93 meters. In other words, the perimeter of the great pyramid is almost exactly half a *krośa*. Likewise, we find that the *hasta* of the small *yojana* goes almost exactly 500 times into each of the sides of the pyramid.

The Greek cubit and stadium, however, fit the pyramid less closely. (There is a 0.4% error.) So it would seem that the great pyramid was designed using units linked to the degree of latitude at the equator.

4.5.4 Wise Ancients

If the *yojana* was exactly defined as a fraction of the equatorial degree of latitude, then the people who defined it must have known that the earth is a globe. Indeed, they appear to have understood the dimensions of the earth's equatorial bulge.

Who were these people, and when did they live? The evidence considered here puts them at least as far back as the time of the great pyramid in Egypt—a time when Egyptians supposedly believed that the earth is flat. Turning to India, we find evidence that the apparent flat earth of the *Bhāgavatam* represents a sophisticated understanding of the earth and the solar system. The correlation between planetary orbits and features of Bhū-maṇḍala implies an advanced knowledge of astronomical distances that supposedly did not exist until recently. Although one may doubt, on historical grounds, that this correlation could be significant, it is corroborated by the evidence linking the *yojana* with ancient measurements of latitudes and the size of the earth.

The *Bhāgavatam* speaks of an ancient world civilization. Although the evidence we have looked at here does not prove that such a civilization existed, it does indicate that some people in the distant past attained an unexpectedly high level of scientific knowledge. Whether they lived in the East, the West, or both is hard to say. We do know that some evidence for this civilization is preserved in texts from India such as the *Bhāgavatam*, and other evidence may be found in ancient ruins of the West. Perhaps there was an advanced civilization that was worldwide in its influence.

It is worth our while to be on the alert for other evidence that may shed light on this hidden chapter in human history. One body of evidence is found in the study of ancient weights and measures without reference to the *yojana*. This is discussed in Appendix 8.

4.6 HELIOCENTRISM IN THE PURĀṆAS

Although the *Bhāgavatam* does not say that the planets orbit the sun, it does contain references giving the sun a central position in the universe. Indeed, from the point of view of modern astronomy, it could be said that the *Bhāgavatam* goes too far in placing the sun in the center, both in position and in importance. The following are examples of "sun-centered" statements in the *Bhāgavatam*:

1. Verse 5.20.43 says "*aṇḍa-madhya-gataḥ sūryo*," meaning that the sun travels in the middle of the universal egg (*aṇḍa*). It also

says that the distance between the sun and the globe of the universe (*aṇḍa-golayoḥ*) is 250,000,000 *yojanas*, and the sun is in the middle (*madhye*).

Viśvanātha Cakravartī Ṭhākura interprets this verse as referring to the vertical direction (perpendicular to Bhū-maṇḍala), since in the plane of Bhū-maṇḍala, the sun moves in its geocentric orbit and it therefore can't be fixed in the center of the Brahmāṇḍa.

The ratio between the outermost limit of this orbit and the universal sphere is 250,000/15,750, or roughly sixteen. (This orbit has a radius no greater than 15,750,000 *yojanas*, which is the radius of Mānasottara Mountain and the length of the axle of the sun's chariot).

However, Vīrarāghava is not deterred by this point. In his commentary on this text, he fixes the sun precisely in the center of the egg:

> Fixing the sun, the measure of the egg is to be stated. In the middle, between the sun and the egg is 25 *koṭi yojanas*. That means, fixing the sun, from the sun to the egg-wall is 25 *koṭi yojanas*, up, down, and sideways.

Likewise, the commentator Vijayadhvaja says that, "in the middle, between the sun and the egg-ball in all directions together, there should be 25 *koṭi yojanas*." Here he is referring to the ten directions, of which two are up and down and the other eight point sideways (E, NE, N, NW, W, SW, S, SE).

2. Verse 5.21.3 says that the sun is in the middle (*madhya-gataḥ*) of Antarikṣa. The term Antarikṣa literally means the space between earth and heaven (see Section 4.3), and it is technically the space between the plane of Bhū-maṇḍala (earth) and a parallel plane 3,800,000 *yojanas* above Bhū-maṇḍala (the beginning of Svargaloka or heaven).

   Since the sun is said to orbit 100,000 *yojanas* above Bhū-maṇḍala, it is not precisely in the middle of Antarikṣa. Thus there appears to be some tension between the idea of the sun being in the center and the description of the sun's geocentric orbit.

3. Verse 5.20.45 says that the sun divides the directions, suggesting that it occupies a central place. The verse goes on to say that our understanding of the universe depends on the sun, and 5.20.46 says that all living beings are dependent on the sun.

Other *Purāṇas* also include statements ascribing central importance to the sun. For example, the *Vāyu Purāṇa* states, "Thus the bright and sparkling solar zone is described. It is the support and source of origin of the stars, planets and the Moon. All these, the stars, the Moon, and the planets should be known to have originated from the Sun" (Tagare, 1987, p. 364). Modern astronomy would trace the origin of the moon and planets to the sun's primordial gaseous disk. Of course, the *Vāyu Purāṇa* is too heliocentric when it ascribes the origin of the stars to the sun.

Again, the *Vāyu Purāṇa* says that, "There is no doubt that the entire universe, all the worlds including Devas, Asuras and human beings, have their roots in the Sun" (Tagare, 1987, p. 365).

4.7 THE MEANING OF PLANETARY HEIGHTS

In Table 3.5 (p. 68), we listed the heights of different celestial bodies above Bhū-maṇḍala in *yojanas*, as given in the *Bhāgavatam*. These heights make sense in a planisphere model as successive layers in an astrolabelike arrangement (see Section 3.4). The specific magnitudes assigned to these heights are irrelevant from the point of view of such a model. But it turns out that these magnitudes are meaningful if we interpret Bhū-maṇḍala as the ecliptic plane.

Let us sum up the arguments for this interpretation. In Section 4.4, we pointed out that the very large sizes of the *dvīpas* of Bhū-maṇḍala are not appropriate for the planisphere model. But they do make sense if we interpret Bhū-maṇḍala as a map of the solar system. It turns out that the heights of the planets above Bhū-maṇḍala also make sense if we interpret them as part of the solar system map.

The solar system is nearly flat. Therefore, in comparison with the size of their orbits, the planets move relatively small distances away from the plane of the ecliptic. If we surround the solar system by a sphere, we find that it fits into a thin cylinder of space along a plane dividing the sphere into two halves.

We find a similar picture if we turn to Bhū-maṇḍala. In Section 4.3, we showed that Bhū-maṇḍala can be interpreted as a plane parallel to the ecliptic and close to it. We also pointed out that the heights of the planets above Bhū-maṇḍala are small, compared with the diameter of Bhū-maṇḍala (which equals the diameter of the Brahmāṇḍa). Thus, according to the *Bhāgavatam*, the planetary orbits fit into a narrow band which divides the Brahmāṇḍa into two hemispheres.

Since Bhū-maṇḍala represents the plane of the ecliptic, the heights listed in the *Bhāgavatam* should be compared to the furthest distances the planets move perpendicular to the ecliptic plane. These distances are listed in Table 4.3, below, under Height (modern). We added a hundred thousand *yojanas* to compensate for the fact that the sun in the ecliptic plane lies a hundred thousand *yojanas* from Bhū-maṇḍala. For comparison, we list the heights given in the *Bhāgavatam* under Height (*Bhāgavatam*). We also list the mean distances of the sun and planets from the earth, according to modern astronomy. The units in all cases are converted to thousands of *yojanas*, using 8.489 miles/*yojana*.

We see that for the sun, Venus, Mercury, Mars, and Jupiter, the height listed in the *Bhāgavatam* roughly agrees with the modern height. For Saturn, the modern height is about four times too large, but it is still much closer to the *Bhāgavatam* height than the mean distance, which is about seventy-four times too large.

TABLE 4.3
Planetary Heights Compared with Modern Values (In Thousands of Yojanas)

Planet	Height (*Bhāgavatam*)	Height (modern)	Mean Distance
Sun	100	100	10,950
Venus	600	564	10,959
Mercury	800	563	10,951
Mars	1,000	692	16,679
Jupiter	1,200	1,543	56,957
Saturn	1,400	4,907	104,488

Thus the heights listed in the *Bhāgavatam* give a simple estimate of the maximum movement of the planets away from the ecliptic plane.The flatness of the solar system is indicated by the small magnitudes of the *Bhāgavatam* heights in comparison with the radial dimensions of the circular features of Bhū-maṇḍala. Thus, the *Bhāgavatam's* planetary heights are a three-dimensional part of the solar system map represented in two dimensions by Bhū-maṇḍala. However, the fact that the heights are all on one side of the ecliptic, whereas planets move on both sides, is a feature that makes sense only in the planisphere interpretation. We propose that the *Bhāgavatam* is giving a composite presentation of both interpretations.

5

The Earth and Local Geography

5.1 THE HIMALAYAS AND SURROUNDING LANDS

A study of the Purāṇic geography of Jambūdvīpa indicates that Jambūdvīpa can be interpreted as a map of a large region of south-central Asia. This region extends from India in the south to Siberia in the north, and from western China in the east to the Caspian Sea in the west. It is centered approximately on the Pamir Mountains, which

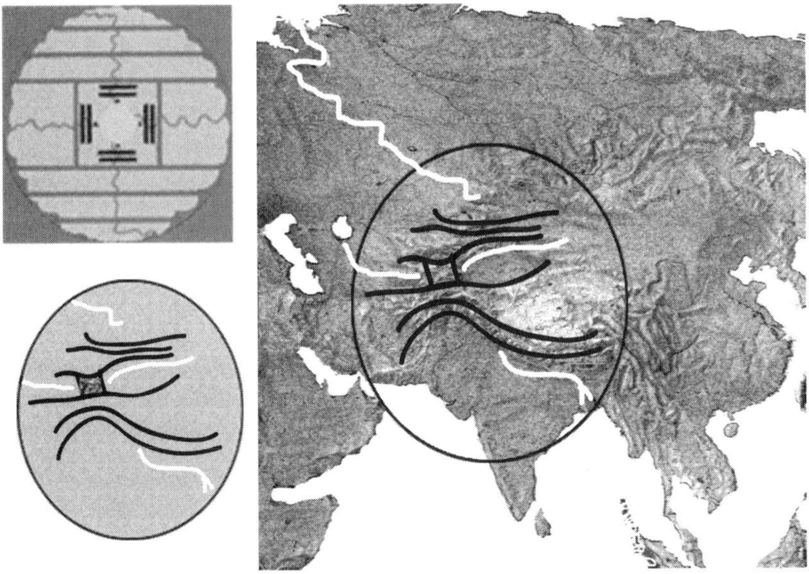

Figure 5.1 The mountains and *varṣas* of Jambūdvīpa can be identified with mountain chains and valleys in a region of south-central Asia, extending from Northern India to Siberia.

correspond to Mount Meru. This interpretation is based on the identification of sites in Asia with geographical features of Jambūdvīpa, and an extensive treatment is given in (Ali, 1966).

We begin with Bhārata-varṣa. It is evident that many sites listed for Bhārata-varṣa in the *Bhāgavatam* are in India, although some identifications are doubtful, and a few Bhārata-varṣa features cannot be identified. On the whole, it is clear that Bhārata-varṣa represents greater India, including territories such as Pakistan and Afghanistan. (For a detailed discussion, see Section 5.1.2, below.)

If Bhārata-varṣa is India, it stands to reason that the eight *varṣas* of Jambūdvīpa other than Bhārata-varṣa must correspond to parts of Asia to the north, northeast, and northwest of India. Here the identifications are weaker. Nonetheless, it seems clear that the mountain ranges centered on Mount Meru in Jambūdvīpa must correspond to the extensive mountainous region north of India, beginning with the Himalayas. In particular, Mount Meru may represent the Pamir Mountains. (See Section 5.1.1, below, for a detailed discussion.)

Ali has tried to identify the six *dvīpas*, Plakṣadvīpa through Puṣkaradvīpa, with various regions of the earth as we know it. However, these identifications seem quite speculative, and we cannot put much confidence in them. It may be that the *dvīpas* did originally refer to regions of irregular shape on the earth globe. Nonetheless, they do not play that role in the *Bhāgavatam* or in other *Purāṇas*. The *dvīpas'* circular shape does not fit our experience of earthly continents, but it does make sense in an astronomical context. Whatever the original role of the *dvīpas* may have been, they play an astronomical role in the existing *Purāṇas*.

We have argued that the *Bhāgavatam* uses the structures of Jambūdvīpa and Bhū-maṇḍala in several different ways, and this inevitably leads to apparent inconsistencies. For example, the following inconsistencies arise if we look at Jambūdvīpa as a local map of part of Asia:

1. In the *Bhāgavatam*, Mount Meru clearly defines the axis around which the stars and other celestial luminaries revolve. But people who explored the countries on all sides of the Pamir Mountains could not have thought that these mountains mark the north pole.

These areas were well traveled, since the famous Silk Road passed through the region north of the Pamirs. Anyone traveling in this area could have seen that the north pole lies to their north.
2. The great size attributed to the features of Jambūdvīpa in the *Bhāgavatam* makes it completely unrealistic as a local map of part of Asia. For example, Bhārata-varṣa (India) is said in the *Bhāgavatam* to be 9,000 *yojanas* from north to south. At roughly eight miles per *yojana*, this comes to 72,000 miles—nearly three times the circumference of the earth.

These inconsistencies can be resolved if we consider that Jambūdvīpa is open to other, equally valid interpretations. Thus Mount Meru plays the role of the polar axis in the planisphere interpretation of Bhūmaṇḍala. (See Section 3.1.) There, Jambūdvīpa and its surrounding *dvīpas* represent a stereographic projection of the earth globe, with Mount Meru at the north pole. One of the main purposes of this interpretation was to explain day, night, and the seasons in relation to the motion of the sun.

The planisphere model places Bhārata-varṣa in the position of India, and this is no doubt an intentional feature of the model. It also places Uttarakuru-varṣa, the most "northern" region, somewhere in Mexico, but this may not have been consciously intended. Broadly speaking, in the planisphere model, Jambūdvīpa represents the lands of the northern hemisphere. Jambūdvīpa has also been interpreted this way in the *Jyotiṣa Śāstras* such as *Sūrya-siddhānta*, which treats the earth as a globe with Jambūdvīpa as the northern hemisphere and Mount Meru as the north pole.

The great size of Jambūdvīpa should not be attributed to ignorance on the part of the Purāṇic geographers. In ancient times and still today, people regularly walked on pilgrimage from one end of India to the other, and this certainly gave them a realistic appreciation of how big India is. The figure of 72,000 miles requires some explanation other than ignorance. Some have suggested that it reflects the crooked roads of rural India, but the roads are not that bad! Our answer is that Jambūdvīpa also represents a map of a heavenly region of demigods, and this accounts for its large dimensions. (This is discussed in Section 6.1.)

Alexander Cunningham remarked, "From the accounts of the Greeks it would appear that the ancient Indians had a very accurate knowledge of the true shape and size of their country" (Cunningham, 1871, p. 1). Cunningham cites figures given by Greek and Roman writers for several important distances in India, and he compares them with modern distance estimates. For example, according to Strabo, Megasthenes "estimated the distance from the southern sea to the Caucasus at 20,000 stadia," or 2,298 British miles. Cunningham notes that by direct measurement on a modern map, the distance from Cape Comorin to the Hindu Kush (which he identifies as the Greek reference points) is about 1,950 miles. If increased by $^1/_6$ to allow for winding roads, this comes to 2,275 miles, or within a few miles of Megasthenes' figure (Cunningham, 1871, p. 4).

It is interesting to note that Cunningham converts stadia into miles on the assumption that the Olympic stadium was $^1/_{600}$ of an equatorial degree of latitude. This is the assumption we made when we used Megasthenes' testimony to estimate the length of the *yojana* (in Section 4.5). Cunningham also said that the well-known inaccuracies in Claudius Ptolemy's map of India were partly due to the fact that Ptolemy used an erroneous value of 500 Olympic stadia for the equatorial degree, rather than 600. This suggests a decline in geographical knowledge between the time of Megasthenes (third century B.C.) and Ptolemy (second century A.D.).

We finally note that throughout the world, people have envisioned local maps in which the cosmic axis, often represented by a mountain or pillar, is identified with a local hill or mountain. These local maps show many resemblances to the Purāṇic Jambūdvīpa, and this suggests that the Purāṇic cosmology in some form was once widely disseminated throughout the world. (This is discussed below in Section 5.2.)

5.1.1 Jambūdvīpa in Asia

The geographer S. M. Ali has offered the following set of tentative identifications for some of the major mountain ranges of Jambūdvīpa (Ali, 1966, pp. 51–53):

TABLE 5.1
Identification of Mountains in Jambūdvīpa

Bhāgavatam	Modern Mountains
Śṛṅgavān	Kara Tau-Kirghiz-Ketman chain
Śveta	Nura Tau-Turkestan-Atbashi chain
Nīla	Zarafshan-Trans-Alai-Tien Shan chain
Meru	Pamir Mountains
Niṣadha	Hindukush-Kunlun chain
Hemakūṭa	Ladakh-Kailash-Trans Himalayan chain
Himālaya	Great Himalayan range

These mountain ranges are fairly close together, and the *varṣas* Hiraṇmaya, Ramyaka, Ilāvṛta, Hari, and Kimpuruṣa are sandwiched between them. Bhārata-varṣa to the south is, of course, India, and Kuru-varṣa to the north corresponds to a vast but thinly populated area "from the Urals and the Caspian to the Yenisei and from the Turkestan, Tien-Shan ranges to the Arctic" (Ali, 1966, p. 87).

Kuru-varṣa is generally referred to as Uttarakuru-varṣa (northern Kuru land) in the *Purāṇas* and the *Mahābhārata*. It is apparently mentioned by ancient western geographers. Erik Seldeslachts of Gent University in Belgium has pointed out on the Internet that

> In Greek and Latin sources Uttarakuru is rendered Ottorokora (and variants). In the *Geography* of Ptolemy, Ottorokora is a city, Ottorokoras is a river and Ottorokorai a people, all of them situated in the southern part of Serike. Serike, which is definitely not China as is often thought, included not only extensive parts of Central Asia including Tibet, but very probably also Assam and adjacent areas.

It is possible that the term Uttarakuru has referred to more than one location in Purāṇic geography.

Ketumāla-varṣa, on the western side of Mount Meru, corresponds to extensive lands in the vicinity of the Āmū Darya (Oxus) river. According to Ali (1966, p. 97),

> Ketumāla signified practically the whole of the ancient Bactria which included the whole of the present Afghan Turkestan (north of Hindukush),

> the lower Hari Rud Valley, the basin of Murghab Kashka system (all south of the old bed of the Āmū Darya) and the basins of the Surkhan, Kafirnigan, Vakhsh and Yakṣu rivers bounded on the north and west by the Hissar-Zarafshan parapet and its south-western extension which touches the Oxus near Kalif.

Bhadrāśva-varṣa, on the eastern side of Mount Meru, is also called Bhadrā-varṣa in the *Purāṇas.* According to Ali (1966, p. 99), this region "was identical with the basins of the Tarim and Hwang Ho rivers, i.e., the whole of Sinkiang and Northern China."

5.1.2 Rivers and Mountains in Bhārata-varṣa

The Purāṇic Bhārata-varṣa is commonly identified as India, and India continues to be known as Bhārata today. This identification is supported by the fact that major rivers in India are referred to in the *Purāṇas* as being in Bhārata-varṣa. The accompanying map illustrates a few of these rivers.

In addition to the Ganges, the following rivers of Bhārata-varṣa are listed in the *Śrīmad Bhāgavatam* 5.19.17–18. The identifications

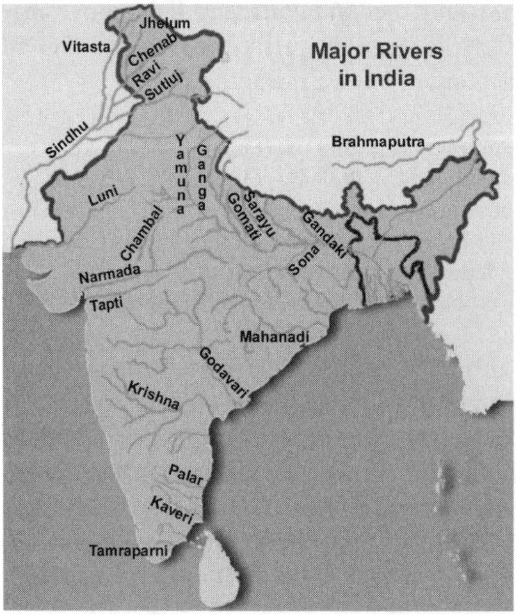

Figure 5.2 A few of the major Indian rivers listed in the *Bhāgavatam.*

with modern rivers in India are taken from the Pargiter (1981) translation of the *Mārkaṇḍeya Purāṇa* and from the geographer S. M. Ali (1966).

Asiknī: a river in the Punjab.
Avaṭodā: unknown.
Bhīmarathī: the present Bhīma, tributary of the Kṛṣṇā, rising near Poona.
Brahmaputra: the famous river that originates in Tibet and flows into the Ganges in Bengal.
Candrabhāgā: the river Chenab in the Punjab, the Greek Acesines.
Candravasā: unknown.
Carmaṇvatī: the river Chambal, the largest tributary of the Yamunā.
Dṛṣadvatī: the famous river between the Sarasvatī and the Yamunā.
Godāvarī: the modern river Godāvarī that enters the Bay of Bengal in Āndhra Pradesh.
Gomatī: the modern Gomatī, which joins the Ganges on the left bank below Benares.
Kauśikī: the river Kosi, which flows into the Ganges on its north bank, through the district of Purnea.
Kāverī: the modern Cavery or Coleroon in South India.
Kṛṣṇāveṇyā: the modern river Kṛṣṇā in South India.
Kṛtamālā: perhaps the Vaigai river having as its source the Kottai-Malai Peak at the junction of the Varushnad and Cardamom Hills.
Mahānadī: flows through Orissa into the Bay of Bengal. Said to be the stream now called Hasdu or Hestho, which rises near the source of the Śoṇe.
Mandākinī: the river Mandākinī, which flows near Mt. Citrakūṭa into the river Paisuni, a tributary of the Yamunā between the Ken and the Tons.
Marudvṛdhā: unknown.
Narmadā: the modern Narbada or Nerbudda, which flows into the Gulf of Cambay.
Nirvindhyā: may be the Pen-gaṅgā, a tributary of the Warda, in the Dekhan.
Payasvinī: same as the Payoṣṇī?
Payoṣṇī: the lower part of the Tāpti.
Revā: a name of the Narmadā.

Rodhasvatī: unknown.
Ṛṣikulyā: said to be the river where Ganjam stands, with the same name at present.
Saptavatī: unknown.
Sarasvatī: thought to be the modern Sarasvatī (Sursooty)-Ghaggar-Hakra-Nara in the desert region of Rajasthana, which in ancient times formed a large river.
Sarayū: the modern Gogra(?), which joins the Ganges below the Gomatī.
Śarkarāvartā: unknown.
Śatadrū: the river Sutlej, the Greek Hyphasis.
Śoṇa: the river Śoṇe which rises near the source of the Narbada and flows into the Ganges above Pātnā.
Surasā: unknown.
Suṣomā: unknown—from *Ṛg Veda.*
Tāpī: the upper part of the Tāpti, before it joins the Pūrṇa.
Tāmraparṇī: the river Chittar of Tinnevelly.
Trisāmā: unknown—from *Ṛg Veda.*
Tuṅgabhadrā: the river Tumbhudra, the large southern tributary of the Kistna, consisting of the combined streams of the Tuṅga and Bhadrā.
Vaihāyasī: unknown.
Vedasmṛti: the modern Banās.
Veṇī: a river Vena is identified as the modern Wain-gaṅgā and its continuation, the Pranhita. Or is it the river Penner, between the Kistna and Kāverī?
Viśvā: unknown.
Vitastā: the river Jhelam in Punjab, the Greek Hydaspes.
Yamunā: the river passing through Vṛndāvana.

The identifications make it clear that Bhārata-varṣa can be interpreted as India (although this is not its only possible interpretation—see Section 6.1). Many additional identifiable rivers are mentioned in the *Mārkaṇḍeya* and other *Purāṇas.*

Of course, by India, we do not mean the land bounded by the present boundaries of India. The India of ancient times had different boundaries, and in some historical periods it included the present-day

Pakistan and neighboring areas.

The *Bhāgavatam* also lists mountains of Bhārata-varṣa. In addition to the Himalayas, which form the northern boundary of Bhārata-varṣa, text 5.19.16 lists the following mountains. As with the rivers, the identifications with modern mountains in India are taken from the Pargiter (1981) translation of the *Mārkaṇḍeya Purāṇa* and from Ali (1966).

Citrakūṭa: a mountain about sixty miles southwest of Allahabad.
Devagiri: between Ujjain and Mandasar near Chambal.
Droṇa: unknown.
Gokāmukha: unknown.
Govardhana: the mountain near Mathurā lifted by Lord Kṛṣṇa.
Indrakīla: also called Mandarācala.
Kakubha: unknown.
Kollaka: there is a hill called Kolla in Mewat.
Kāmagiri: unknown.
Kūṭaka: unknown.
Mahendra: chain of hills that extends from Orissa and the northern Circars to Gondwana, part of which, near Ganjam, is still called Mahindra Malai.
Maināka: mountain of gold north of Kailāsa; mountain where the river Śoṇa begins.
Maṅgala-prastha: unknown.
Malaya: the southern portion of the western Ghats.
Nīla: unknown.
Pāriyātra: the western portion of the modern Vindhya range, west of Bhopal, and extending into Gujarat.
Raivataka: near Dvārakā or Kuśasthalī, capital of Ānarta in Gujarat. Perhaps the Barada Hills in Halar.
Ṛkṣagiri: the mountains of Gondwana.
Ṛṣabha: unknown.
Ṛṣyamūka: in the Dekhan, but the exact site is unclear; a mountain near lake Pampā where Rāma and Sugrīva stayed.
Sahya: the northern portion of the western Ghats, the mountains of Konkan.
Śrī-śaila: a lofty rock overhanging the river Kṛṣṇā in Kurnool District.

Śuktimān: possibly the Garo, Khāsi, and Tipperah Hills which bound Bengal.

Trikūṭa: mountain (in Ceylon?) on which Laṅkā was built.

Vāridhāra: unknown.

Veṅkaṭa: mountain where the temple of Śrī Veṅkaṭeśvara is located, near Madras.

Vindhya: the general name of the mountain chain that stretches across central India.

5.2 CROSS-CULTURAL THEMES IN COSMOLOGY

The identification of Mount Meru with an earthly mountain range may represent a general cultural phenomenon, in which a cosmological structure, in this case the axis of universal rotation, is identified with some geographical feature on the earth. In this section, we will give many examples from around the world in which a cosmological system broadly similar to that of the *Purāṇas* is identified with local geography.

As we have seen, the *Bhāgavata Purāṇa* describes a land called Jambūdvīpa in the middle of the lotus whorl of the Bhūloka planetary system. In the center of this land stands the golden Sumeru mountain, which is shaped like a pillar wider at the top than at the bottom. The city of Lord Brahmā and eight cities of the planetary lords occupy the top of this pillar. The celestial Ganges strikes Brahmā's city and cascades from Sumeru in the form of four rivers flowing in the four cardinal directions.

Mount Sumeru is surrounded by four great mountains surmounted by four gigantic trees. These include the Jambū tree after which Jambūdvīpa is named. Four huge lakes of milk, honey, sugarcane juice, and pure water are located between the four mountains, and these lakes confer mystic powers on the celestial beings who bathe in them. There are also four celestial gardens near these lakes.

From the foot of each of the four trees, there flows a river that either emerges from the tree itself or from the fruits of the tree. These rivers of honey and different kinds of juice flow throughout the region of Ilāvṛta-varṣa surrounding Mount Sumeru, and they confer freedom from fatigue, disease, and old age on the inhabitants of that region (*Bhāgavatam* 5.16.5–25, 5.17.5).

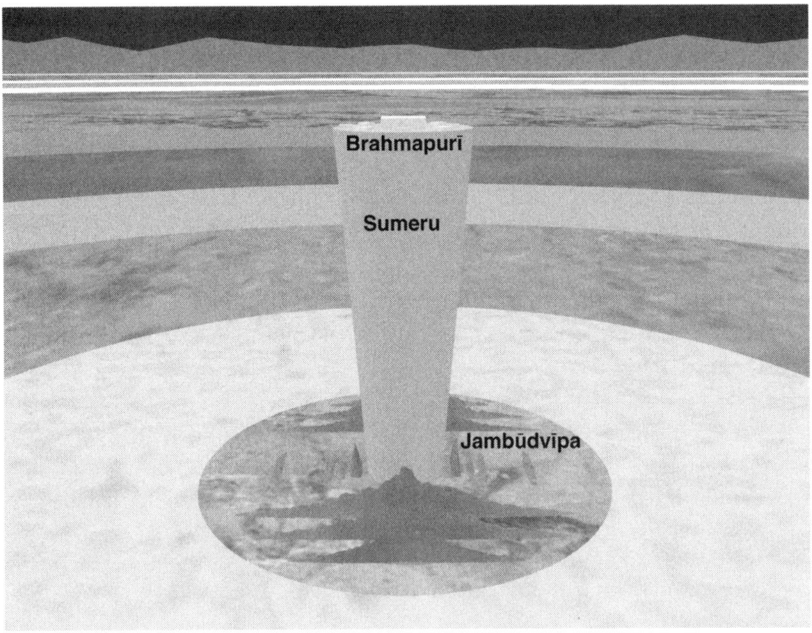

Figure 5.3 Jambūdvīpa with Mount Sumeru, Brahmapurī, and surrounding oceans and *dvīpas.*

Stories similar to these have played an important role in the cosmological thinking of people in many cultures (Hooper). Indeed, the available evidence suggests that in ancient times a cosmology very similar to that of the *Bhāgavata Purāṇa* was widely distributed throughout the world. If this is true, then *Bhāgavata* cosmology is highly relevant to our understanding of ancient history. It tells us something about how ancient peoples understood the world, and it may tell us something about patterns of communication linking ancient societies.

One might shrug off broad similarities between the cosmologies of different cultures by saying that people with similar genes living in similar environments are likely to come up with similar ideas. But people do not inherit detailed ideas from their parents, comparable to the web-building instincts of spiders. If certain specific ideas crop up repeatedly in widely separated cultures, then it is natural to surmise that transcontinental communication was widespread before the modern era.

It turns out that many specific details of *Bhāgavata* cosmology can be found in cultures around the world. We will first discuss some of these details and then return to the question of how they attained world-wide distribution. Here is a partial list:

First, the earth is described as a disk surrounded by an ocean and sometimes by other ring-shaped continents and oceans. There are three worlds, upper, middle, and lower, and the earth is identified as the middle world.

In their study of world mythology, de Santillana and von Dechend arrived "roughly and most inaccurately" at the following conception of the three worlds:

> (a) the sky north of the Tropic of Cancer, i.e., the sky proper, domain of the gods
> (b) the 'inhabited world' of the zodiac between the Tropics, the domain of the 'living'
> (c) the sky south from the Tropic of Capricorn, alias the Sweet Water Ocean, the realm of the dead (de Santillana, 1969, p. 234).

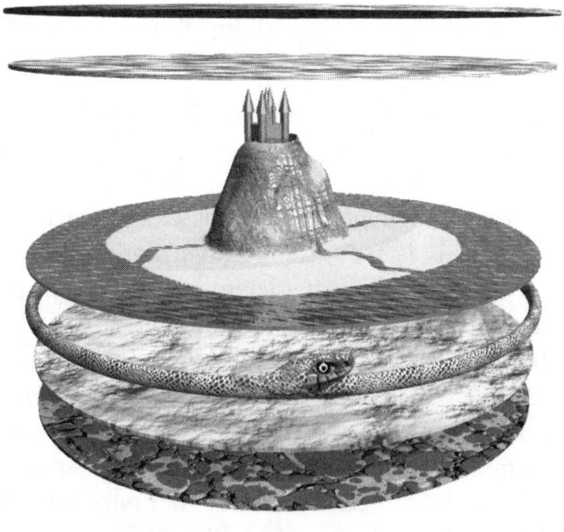

Figure 5.4 The generic world disk found in cultures all over the world. It includes the central continent, four directional rivers, the cosmic mountain surmounted by the abode of the gods, the ring-ocean, upper and lower worlds, and the world-girdling serpent of the underworld.

This general conception agrees, in particular, with the interpretations of Bhū-maṇḍala (literally "earth-disk") both as the ecliptic plane and as a planisphere. In the planisphere interpretation, the Tropic of Capricorn corresponds to Mānasottara mountain, and the Sweet Water Ocean (Svādūdaka) lies just beyond this ring-shaped mountain.

In Purāṇic tradition, the south is taken as the realm of Yamarāja, the Lord of the dead, and the north consists of the path of the gods (*deva-yāna*) and the region of Viṣṇu. If we take the "inhabited world" to represent the ecliptic (running through the zodiac), then Bhū-maṇḍala as the ecliptic plane corresponds to the middle world. The upper and lower worlds are then the regions to the celestial north and celestial south of the ecliptic. In the interpretation of Jambūdvīpa as a region of south-central Asia, heaven is brought down to the earth and cosmic elements such as the polar axis are identified with local earthly features. This identification of earth with heaven is a general cultural phenomenon.

In different traditions, the upper and lower worlds may be divided into several levels (often seven or nine). In the center of the earth-disk there is a world mountain or world pillar that links middle earth to the lower and upper worlds. The world mountain represents the polar axis, and the dwellings of great demigods are located on its summit.

The world mountain may be surrounded by other mountains that define the cardinal directions, and these directions may be associated with certain colors. Four sacred rivers may also flow from the world mountain in the four cardinal directions.

There is a world tree that is often situated on the world mountain (or four world trees may be located on the neighboring directional mountains). The world tree extends from the earth to the heavens, and it is nearly immortal. It is the source of rivers of nectar or pure water that give health and longevity to those who drink them. The tree stands in an earthly paradise where there are celestial gardens and rivers of various substances, such as milk, oil, and honey. The tree or world pillar is often associated with a great eaglelike bird that is the enemy of great serpents dwelling in the lower world.

Although the *Bhāgavatam* features four world trees in the cardinal directions around Mount Sumeru, some Asian traditions place a single tree on the summit of this mountain. For example, the CD

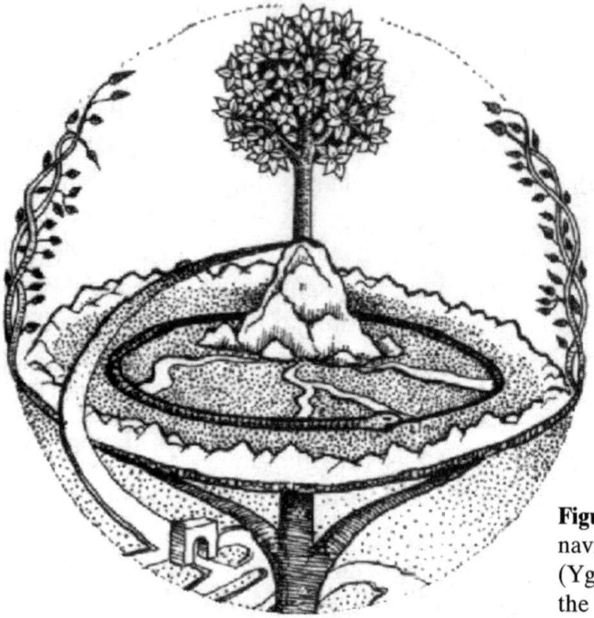

Figure 5.5 The Scandinavian tree of life (Yggdrasil), growing on the cosmic mountain.

includes a picture of East Asian origin that is painted on a long vertical strip, representing the vertical dimension of the universe. It shows the seven *dvīpas* and oceans of Sapta-dvīpa, surmounted by Meru and a single sacred tree.

This idea may be rooted in the *Vedas*. The Vedic scholar F. B. J. Kuiper concluded that the *Vedas* support a conception of a single world tree growing from the Vedic equivalent of Mount Meru: "The tree rises up from the primordial hill and supports the roof of heaven as the world-pillar. Its roots, however, reach through the mountain into the primeval water, on which the earth rests, and thence they bring upwards the *amṛta* (the essence of these waters)" (Kuiper, 1983, p. 39). This sounds very much like the Scandinavian Yggdrasil tree, illustrated above. The primeval waters correspond to the Garbhodaka Ocean, lying beneath Bhū-maṇḍala.

Table 5.2 lists traditions with world mountains or world pillars. The table is self-explanatory, but I will comment on a few of the items in it. Full references for items in this table and Tables 5.3 and 5.4 can be found in the CD.

TABLE 5.2
Examples of World Mountains or Pillars

Tradition	World mountain or pillar	Comment
Purāṇic	Mt. Sumeru	Site of Brahmapurī and the cities of eight Loka-pālas.
Vedic	"Primordial Hill"	This was dug up out of the primeval waters by the cosmogonal boar, who therefore corresponds to the Purāṇic Lord Varāha.
Ancient Iran	Mount Hara Berezaiti (identified as Mt. Albôrz)	With a celestial spring on its highest peak in the realm of the stars.
Zoroastrians of Sogdiana	Girnagar	There is also a world-encircling mountain, called Ardiyā, that corresponds to Lokāloka mountain. Alberuni says that this is called Kāf by the people of his country.
Jain	Mt. Meru	The Jains describe a continent of Jambūdvīpa that is similar to its Purāṇic counterpart, but more complex.
Buddhist	Mt. Meru	Buddhism widely disseminated the Indian traditions of Mount Meru.
China	Mt. Khun-Lun	With dwellings of immortals and the bronze Pillar of Heaven on its summit.
Turkmen tribes of southern Turkestan	Copper pillar	Marking the "navel of the earth."
Altai Tatars	Golden mountain	Seat of Bai Ülgän in the middle of the sky.
Mongols	Mt. Sumber or Sumer	With Zambu tree on its summit.

TABLE 5.2 (*continued*)

Tradition	World mountain or pillar	Comment
Buryats of Siberia	Mt. Sumur	With polestar fastened to its summit.
Kalmucks of Siberia	Mt. Sumer	Used as a stick to stir the ocean and create the sun, moon, and stars.
Egyptian	Mound of the First Time	This is the first land to appear from the Waters and the dwelling place of the High God, the source of light. Its location is said to be Heliopolis. It was the model for the royal tombs at Memphis.
N. Asian, African, and American tribes	World pillar symbolized by central post of dwelling	Often with seven divisions and associated with the polestar.
Navajos	Encircled Mountain	Surrounded by four directional mountains.
Dogon of Nigeria	Cosmic pillar, spanning 14 worlds	The roof-post of the house of the high-god Amma.
Finns	Sampo, the cosmic mill	Said to be derived from Sanskrit. *stambha*, pillar.
Ancient Greeks	Mount Olympus	Home of the gods.
Lapps	Veralden Tshuold (World Pillar)	Their name for the polestar.
Ancient Germans	Irminsūl, the universal column which sustains everything	Charlemagne destroyed an image of this in A.D. 772.

TABLE 5.2 (*continued*)

Tradition	World mountain or pillar	Comment
Norse Edda	Asgard, the burgh of the gods	Rising in the center of Midgard, the circular earth.
Romania	Coloana Ceriului	Sky Pillar.
Venerable Bede (English historian, c. A.D. 800)	Olympus	The third of seven heavens, above Air and Aether.
Medieval Europe	Mons Coelius (Celestial Mountain)	Whence the polestar is called Tramontane.
Gerhard Mercator, 1569	Mt. called Rupes Nigra et Altissima	At north pole, with four rivers or channels at right angles.

First of all, the two ideas of a world mountain and world pillar are combined in Sumeru, which is referred to in the *Purāṇas* as a mountain but is shaped like a pillar. Often the world pillar is said to be made of a metal such as gold, copper, or iron (e.g. Hara Berezaiti means "iron mountain" (Holmberg, 1964, p. 358)). This concept is extremely common in old traditions throughout Asia and Europe.

The idea of the world mountain as a source of rivers is illustrated by Mount Sumeru, which is the source of the four branches of the celestial Ganges. According to the *Avesta*, the spring on Mount Hara Berezaiti is the source of all earthly waters (Evans-Wentz, 1981, p. 67). The Navajos speak of four rivers flowing in the four directions from the world center, but they place these rivers on a lower level than their world mountain (Alexander, 1916, p. 159). Mount Khun-Lun of the

Chinese was also the source of four rivers flowing in opposite directions (Heinberg, 1989, p. 58), and the Siberian Kalmucks spoke of a mountain lake from which four rivers flow to the points of the compass (Holmberg, 1964, p. 359).

The theme of a mountain and four rivers is also illustrated by the curious map of Gerardus Mercator mentioned in the last line of Table 5.2. In 1569 Mercator published a map of the arctic region showing a circular continent in the middle of the Arctic Ocean (Campbell, 1981, p. 22). In the center of this continent, at the north pole, Mercator placed a mountain that is "said to be the highest in the world" (Hues, 1638, pp. 8, 10). Four rivers or ocean channels extend at right angles from this mountain to the coast of the circular continent. It looks as though Mercator placed a small version of Jambūdvīpa in the middle of his arctic map. The question is: why?

The accepted explanation makes no reference to India. It is said that Mercator based his polar map on the *Inventio Fortunata*, a lost manuscript describing the supposed journey of an English monk to the northern regions. Scholars have generally rejected the idea that this journey took place as described, but some claim that the *Inventio Fortunata* was "the principal vehicle by which the medieval Scandinavian view of the North was incorporated into European geographical ideas and cartography of the Renaissance" (Skelton *et al.*, 1965, p. 179). This is consistent with the traditional Scandinavian geography illustrated in Figure 5.5, above, which is strongly reminiscent of Jambūdvīpa.

The cosmologies of some Central Asian peoples show unmistakable signs of Indian influence, and a number of scholars attribute this to relatively recent Buddhist preaching. For example, the Mongols, Buryats, and Kalmucks called their world mountains Sumber, Sumur, and Sumer. The Zambu tree stood on Mount Sumer (Eliade, 1964, p. 271) and can be compared with the Jambū tree of Jambūdvīpa. Mount Sumer was said to be 80,000 leagues high (Holmberg, 1964, p. 346), and, for comparison, Mount Sumeru is 84,000 *yojanas* high.

Mircea Eliade, a well-known scholar of comparative religion, offers the following account of the historical development of these world mountain traditions:

> The idea of a Cosmic Mountain as Center of the World is not necessarily of Oriental origin, for, as we have seen, the symbolism of the

> "Center" seems to have preceded the rise of the paleo-Oriental civilizations. But the ancient traditions of the peoples of Central and North Asia —who doubtless knew the image of a "Center of the World" and of the Cosmic Axis—were modified by the continual influx of Oriental religious ideas, whether Mesopotamian in origin (and disseminated through Iran) or Indian (disseminated through Lamaism) (Eliade, 1964, p. 266).

It is plausible that recent influences from India (or Mesopotamia) may overlay older core beliefs. However, world mountain traditions, with details reminiscent of Indian cosmology, are also found among people living outside the generally accepted sphere of Buddhist preaching. Mercator's map is an example of this. Another instance is provided by the Dogon tribe of Nigeria, whose cosmic pillar is the axis of rotation for fourteen worlds, including a disk-shaped earth (Corliss, 1991, p. 1). Influences from India may well have been transmitted independently of Buddhism, and this may have been going on long before the Buddhist period.

The Warao Indians of the Orinoco Delta in Venezuela also envision a cosmic axis extending above the center of their earth disk. But

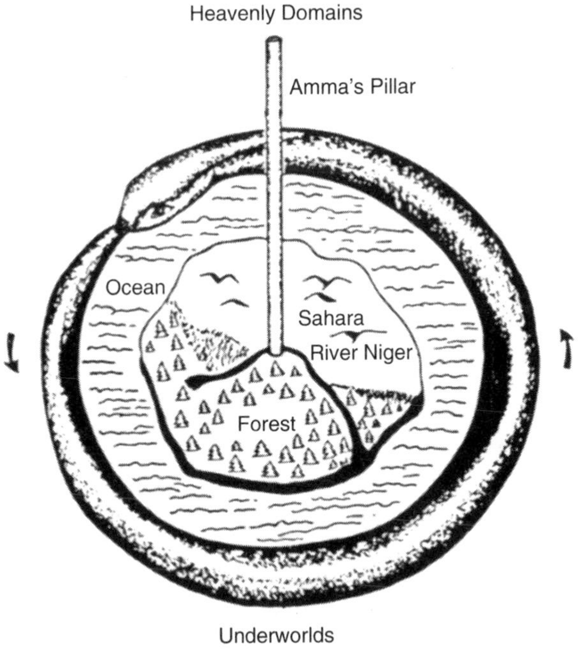

Figure 5.6 The world of the Dogon tribe of Africa, showing the cosmic pillar and the world-girdling serpent (after Corliss, 1991, p. 1).

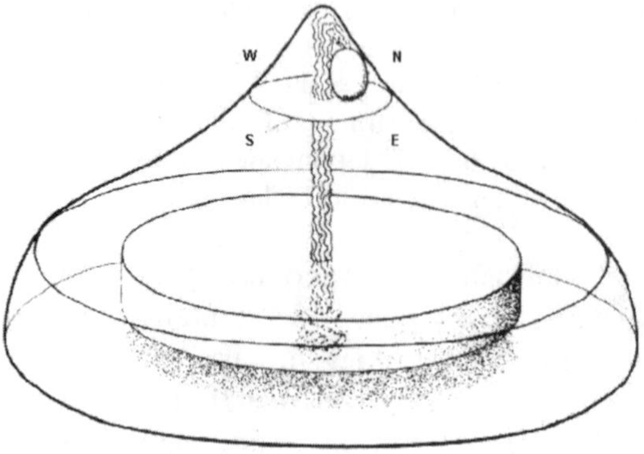

Figure 5.7 The cosmic axis, as portrayed by the Warao tribe of the Orinoco Delta in Venezuela (Krupp, 1983, p. 320).

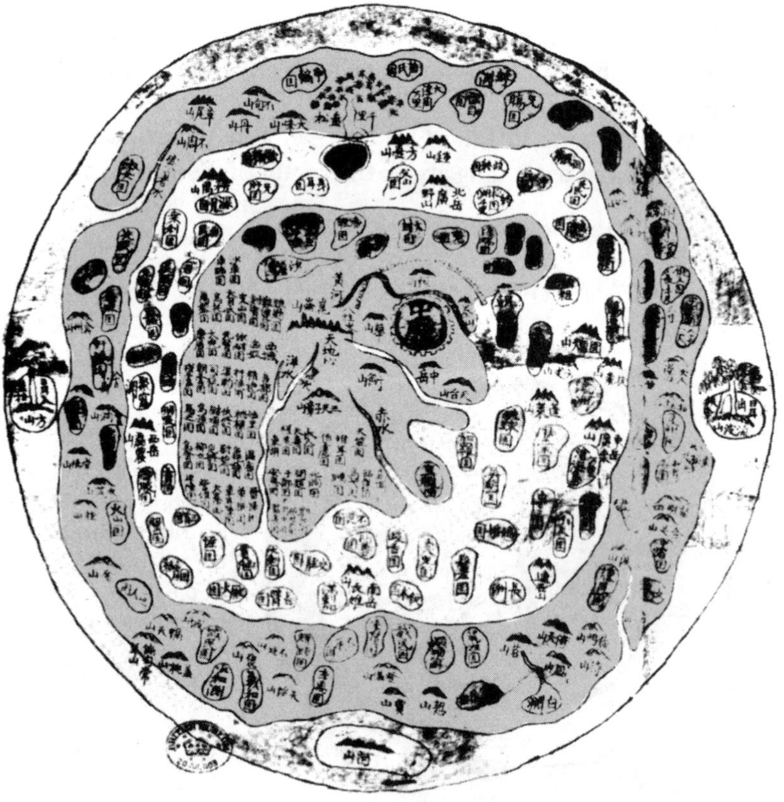

Figure 5.8 A Korean wheel map, showing the central continent surrounded by a ring-ocean, a ring-continent, and a further ring-ocean (Needham, 1959, fig. 242).

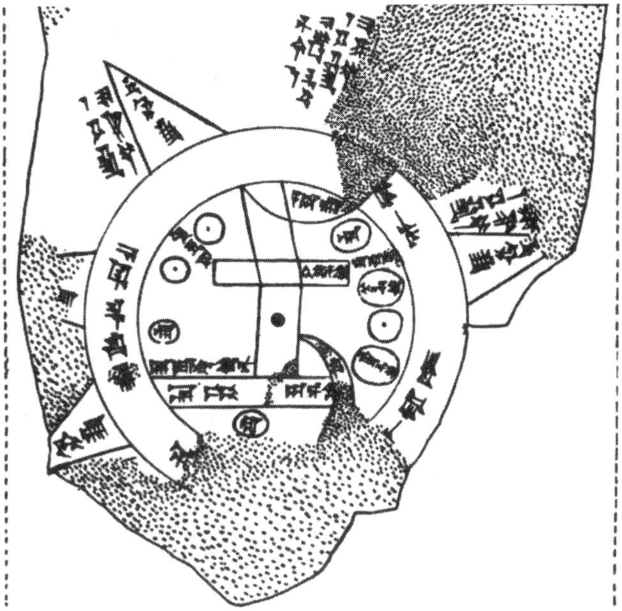

Figure 5.9 A wheel map from Babylon, said to show a central continent surrounded by ocean (Needham, 1959, fig. 254).

they see this as being made of the tobacco smoke used by their shamans to enter into trance and ascend into the heavens.

Joseph Needham, a prominent student of ancient China, connects the Chinese Buddhist tradition of Mount Khun-Lun with "wheel maps" showing a circular continent surrounded by an ocean. Figure 5.8 is a wheel map from eighteenth-century Korea showing a central continent, surrounded by an ocean and another ring-shaped continent (Needham, 1959, fig. 242). North is to the top, and we can see the Great Wall of China crossing the Yellow river in the central continent. Needham traces these wheel maps to India and, ultimately, to an earlier origin in Babylon (Needham, 1959, p. 568). However, he also wonders if their ultimate origin may have been from pre-Buddhist India (Needham, 1959, p. 590).

Figure 5.9 shows a wheel map from Babylon. Wheel maps featuring a circular continent surrounded by ocean were also made in medieval Europe. These were centered on Jerusalem, which was regarded as the cosmic axis and world center in medieval Christianity.

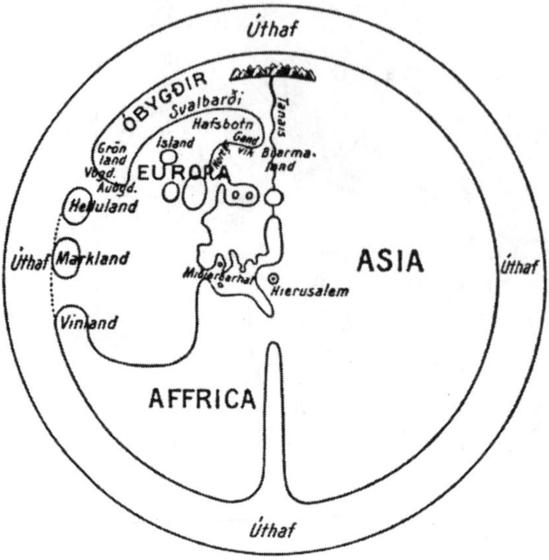

Figure 5.10 A Norse wheel map from the Middle Ages, showing Vinland as part of a central continent surrounded by ocean (Skelton *et al.*, 1965, p. 174).

The medieval Norse example in Figure 5.10 shows Vinland, which may have represented lands in North America visited by the Vikings.

Some of the traditions of North America suggest links with India that are difficult to reconcile with accepted ideas about transcontinental travel—Buddhist or otherwise. Table 5.3 lists five traditions in which certain colors (generally red, white, black, and yellow) are associated with the four cardinal directions.

TABLE 5.3
Colors Associated with the Cardinal Directions in Five Cultures

Tradition	Mountain	East	South	West	North
Purāṇas	Mt. Sumeru	white	yellow	black	red
East Asian Buddhists	Mt. Sumeru	white	blue	red	yellow
Kalmucks	Mt. Sumer	white	blue	red	yellow
Navajos	Encircled Mountain	white	blue	yellow-red	black
Mayans	?	red	yellow	black	white

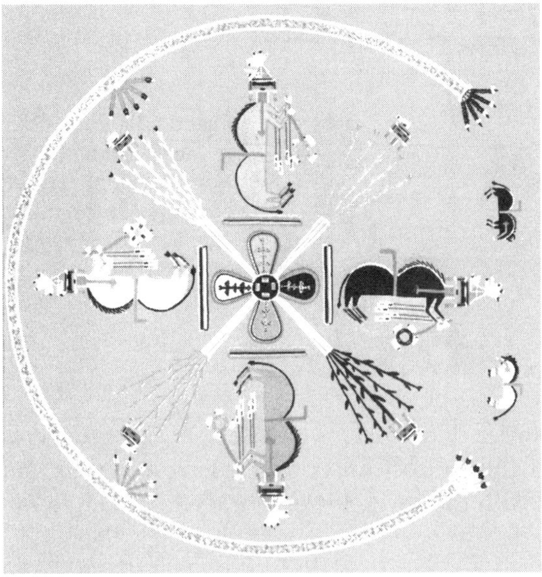

Figure 5.11 Navajo sand painting showing four directional mountains surrounding the central world mountain (Evans-Wentz, 1981, p. 76).

Four of these traditions, the *Purāṇas,* the East Asian Buddhists, the Kalmucks, and the Navajos, assign four colors to the four sides of a world mountain, and these sides face in the four cardinal directions. The Navajos also have four mountains, surrounding the central mountain and colored with the same colors. For the Mayans, I have not seen any reference to a world mountain. However, the Mayan *Book of Chilam Balam of Chumayel* refers to four cosmic Ceiba trees situated in the four directions, east, south, west, and north, and having the four colors red, yellow, black, and white, respectively (Leon-Portilla, 1980, pp. 237–38).

Although the five traditions assign the colors to directions in different permutations, they all use nearly the same colors. In the *Vāyu Purāṇa*, the colors of Sumeru are associated with the four *varṇas*, *brāhmaṇa* (white), *vaiśya* (yellow), *śūdra* (black), and *kṣatriya* (red) (Tagare, 1987, 34.17–19). These are also the colors of the incarnations of Kṛṣṇa mentioned by Gargamuni (*Bhāgavatam* 10.8.13). The question is: How did these colors come to be connected with the four directions in North American traditions?

The Navajos refer to their system of four directional mountains as a four-petaled flower centered on their world mountain (Evans-Wentz, 1981, p. 78). Likewise, Jambūdvīpa is described as a lotus with

Figure 5.12 Phoenician carving showing the world mountain in personified form, with four directional rivers (Clifford, 1972, p. 96).

Mount Sumeru in the center. The Navajos also describe four levels of lower worlds from which their ancestors are said to have emerged, and these can be compared with the seven lower worlds described in the *Purāṇas.*

If we turn to the Near East, we find that the idea of the world mountain appears in Semitic traditions and here too we find a number of explicit parallels with *Bhāgavata* cosmology. Some of the evidence for this is summarized in Table 5.4.

In many traditions, the world mountain is identified symbolically with some local mountain. This is illustrated by Mount Olympus of the Greeks, Mount Alborz of the Iranians, and Mount Khun-Lun of the Chinese. In Near Eastern tradition, the world mountain is the small hill in Jerusalem known as Mount Zion (Clifford, 1972, p. 3). Thus the circular continent centered on Jerusalem in medieval maps also possessed a symbolic world mountain.

This may correspond to the Babylonian tradition of making circular maps centered on Babylon, where the seven-tiered Ziggurat of Marduk represented the world mountain linking earth with heaven (Clifford, 1972, p. 21). We should note that the scholar Richard Clifford states that the Weltberg or world mountain does not exist in Mesopotamian tradition (Clifford, 1972, p. 2). But Eliade cites several world-mountain names for Mesopotamian ziggurats (Eliade, 1964, p. 267), and Clifford himself points out the cosmic meaning of the seven-tiered Ziggurat of Marduk (Clifford, 1972, p. 21).

Jambūdvīpa can be interpreted as a map of a region of Asia extending from India in the south to parts of Siberia in the north, and

TABLE 5.4
The World Mountain and Paradise in Semitic Traditions

Semitic Source	World Mountain or Related Region	Comment
Isaiah	Mount Zion in Jerusalem	God's dwelling, to be set above all other mountains.
Mesopotamia	Mount of the lands	Symbolized by the seven-tiered ziggurat.
Ancient Canaan	Gūri 'ili; the mountain of El	Dwelling of creator El and place of assembly of the gods.
Phoenician ivory carving (1–1000 B.C.)	Deity dressed to represent a mountain	With four streams emerging at right angles.
Assyrian seal	Sacred tree on cosmic mountain (c. 1000 B.C.)	With hands from sky pouring two streams.
Isaiah	The mountain where the gods meet	In the far recesses of the north.
Ezekiel	The mountain of God	The location of Eden.
Genesis	Eden	Source of four rivers.
Enoch	Third heaven	Four rivers, of honey, milk, oil, and wine, from tree of life.
Mohammed	Heaven called Sidre-i Munteha	Four rivers and a divine tree.

extending from China in the east to the general area of Afghanistan and Turkestan to the west (see Section 5.1, above). According to this interpretation, Mount Meru corresponds to the Pamir mountains. Thus Purāṇic tradition also assigns the world axis to a local mountain range which is far from the true north pole.

Richard Clifford has pointed out that Gūri 'ili, the mountain of El, "seems to be the paradisiac source of water that gives fertility" (Clifford, 1972, p. 97). This is consistent with an ancient Phoenician carving showing four streams emerging from a personified mountain and an Assyrian seal showing celestial streams and a sacred mountain (see Table 5.4). Of course, it is also consistent with the account in the *Bhāgavatam* of the four branches of the celestial Ganges flowing out from Brahmapurī on top of Mount Sumeru. El is said to be the progenitor of the gods (Clifford, 1972, p. 44) and the creator of the Earth (Clifford, 1972, p. 45), and thus he is comparable to Brahmā. A parallel can also be seen between the cities of the eight Loka-pālas surrounding Brahmapurī and the assembly of the gods on Gūri 'ili.

Table 5.4 lists three references in the Bible that refer to (1) a mountain in the far north where the gods meet, (2) a mountain of God that is the location of Eden, and (3) four rivers that flow out of Eden. The first century Jewish historian Flavius Josephus identified one of the four rivers flowing from Eden as the Ganges, the others being the Nile, the Tigris, and the Euphrates (Heinberg, 1989, p. 164). This suggests that the story connecting the Ganges with Mount Sumeru, located on the polar axis, may have reached the Mediterranean area by the time of Josephus.

However, there may also be a parallel between the four rivers of Eden and four other rivers associated with Mount Sumeru. This is suggested by information found in the apocryphal *Book of the Secrets of Enoch*. This book has come down to us only in Slavonic manuscripts found recently in Russia and Serbia. However, scholars maintain that its Greek original was highly influential in the early days of Christianity (Lost Books, 1963, p. 81).

The book describes how the patriarch Enoch was taken by angels on a tour of the seven heavens. In the third heaven Enoch saw the fragrant and colorful tree of life that "covers all" and produces wonderful fruits (Lost Books, 1963, p. 83). Next to the tree he saw springs producing honey, milk, oil, and wine, which formed four rivers flowing down into the paradise of Eden. This paradise was described as a place prepared for pious people who had served the Lord and performed acts of goodness (Lost Books, 1963, p. 84).

This account can be compared with the story of the four trees in Ilāvṛta-varṣa that stand on great mountains and produce rivers of nectar and honey, conferring health and youthful vitality on those who drink from them. In particular, the Jambū tree is said to have branches of pleasing colors and to be always bedecked with fruits and flowers (Tagare, 1987, 35.27). It is said to rise to a height of thousands of *yojanas*, and "it seems to cover all the heavens" (Taluqdar, 1916, 114.76).

The Jambū tree is typical of the trees of life found in traditions from around the world. For comparison, consider the world tree of the Yakut people of northeastern Siberia (Holmberg, 1964, p. 353). Like the Jambū tree, it is said to be of immeasurable age, and its crown pierces the heavens (Tagare, 1987, 46.24–26). Its cones are said to be nine fathoms long, while the Jambū tree's fruits are "the size of elephants" (*Bhāgavatam* 5.16.19). Its sap forms a "brawling stream," and when aged or weary animals drink from it, they regain their "youth and overflowingness." Near the tree, there is a lake of milk (Holmberg, 1964, p. 352), a feature also shared by the Jambū tree. As in many traditions, the Yakut tree of life is said to be located at the navel of the earth (Holmberg, 1964, p. 351). For comparison, Mount Sumeru is "born of the umbilical knot of Brahmā" (Tagare, 1987, 34.16).

Although one might suppose that the Yakut story is simply a product of local imagination, a study of the details of many traditions suggests that this is not the case. The anthropologist Uno Holmberg compared the Yakut story with Semitic, Egyptian, Scandinavian, Iranian, Indian, and North Asian traditions. He concluded, "From the fact that the ancient Babylonians already in olden times knew of the paradise-mountain of the gods, the tree, and the water of life, we may conclude that this belief, relics of which have come down to us from ancient times, is of extreme age among the civilized peoples of Nearer Asia" (Holmberg, 1964, p. 355).

In Central and North Asian cultures, the tree of life is typically depicted both as a physically real tree connected with the structure of the universe and as an allegorical tree representing the universe as the reservoir of life (Eliade, 1964, p. 271). We see the same thing in Indian tradition. Thus in *Bhagavad-gītā* 15.1–4, the metaphor of an inverted

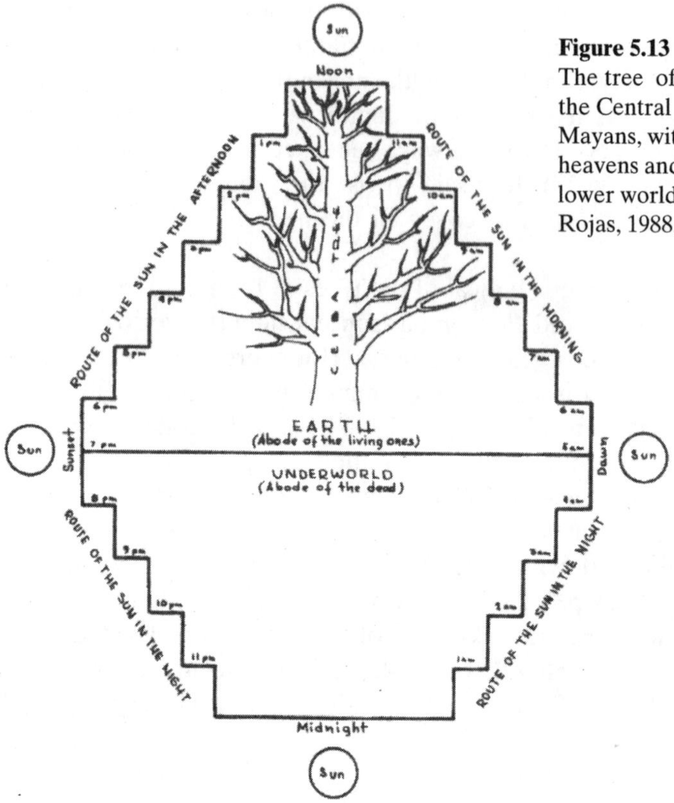

Figure 5.13
The tree of life of the Central American Mayans, with seven heavens and five lower worlds (Villa Rojas, 1988, p. 141).

tree is used to show how the material universe is a reflection of the spiritual world.

The tree of life also is found in the new world, along with other features typical of *Bhāgavata* cosmology. In addition to their four directional trees (mentioned above), the Mayans also spoke of a central green Ceiba tree called *yaax-chel-cab*, meaning "the first tree of the world," and also called "the tree of life" (Villa Rojas, 1988, p. 139). The contemporary Yucatec Mayans describe seven celestial planes, each with a central hole through which the cosmic Ceiba tree extends its branches (Villa Rojas, 1988, p. 136).

The Lenni Lenape Indians, who lived along the Delaware river before being displaced to Oklahoma, performed religious ceremonies in a Big House with a central post made of an entire tree. This post

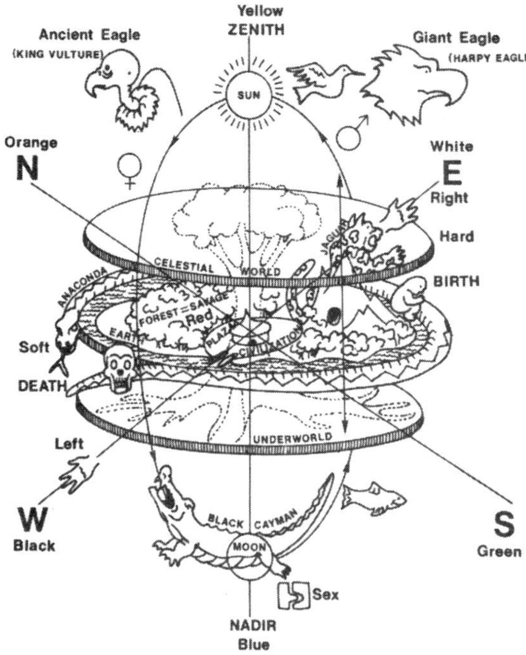

Figure 5.14
The cosmology of the Shipibo tribe of Peru, showing the world tree, upper and lower worlds, and the world-girdling serpent (Roe, 1982, p. 128).

represents "the World Tree that ascended to heaven from soil deposited on the back of a great turtle to form the earth" (Spirit, 1992, p. 164).

We may also note that the Lenni Lenape and other east-coast Native Americans regarded the Big Dipper as a bear being chased by hunters (Rall, 1998, p. 15). This, of course, matches this constellation's designation as Ursa Major, or the Great Bear. Curiously, the Seven Sages (*sapta-ṛṣayaḥ*) which represent the Big Dipper in Sanskrit were once called "bears" (*ṛkṣāḥ*)—another hint of ancient international communication (Eggeling, 1900, 2.1.2.4).

The anthropologist Peter Roe made a study of 105 South American forest peoples, with focus on the Shipibos of the Peruvian Montaya (Roe, 1982, p. 26). He summed up the cosmology of these people as follows: There is a disk-shaped earth surrounded by ocean. This disk is sandwiched between upper and lower worlds which are often subdivided into several levels. There is also a world tree with its roots in the underworld and its crown in the heavens (Roe, 1982, pp. 127–38).

The world tree is associated with a harpy eagle (a large South American raptor) who is the enemy of enormous serpentine beings connected with the underworld. To illustrate this, Roe recounts a story in which the "eagles add their feathers to the arms of a human culture hero and fly with him to steal medicine from the withholding and threatening Poison Anaconda. After the successful theft the hero conveniently . . . turns into a bird" (Roe, 1982, p. 258).

Naturally, the theme of cosmic tree, bird, and serpent is not limited to South America. Mircea Eliade made an observation about this theme that is worth quoting in full: "The cosmological schema Tree-Bird (= Eagle), or Tree with a Bird at its top and a Snake at its roots, although typical of the peoples of Central Asia and the ancient Germans, is presumably of Oriental origin, but the same symbolism is already formulated on prehistoric monuments" (Eliade, 1964, p. 273). This statement pushes the presumed Oriental origins back to the time of the prehistoric monuments, or before.

In the *Purāṇas,* we see the tree-bird-serpent theme in Garuḍa, who lives in a gigantic *śālmalī* tree (*Bhāgavatam* 5.20.8) and who is the traditional enemy of the Nāgas. The Nāgas are intelligent serpentine beings who live in the lower worlds called Mahātala and Pātāla (*Bhāgavatam* 5.24.29–31). We can draw a parallel between the story of the Shipibo hero and the *Mahābhārata* story in which Garuḍa stole the nectar of immortality in an effort to release his mother from the clutches of the Nāgas (van Buitenen, 1973, pp. 89–91).

Although most of the Nāgas are described as poisonous and angry, there is an exceptional Nāga named Ananta Śeṣa who is an *avatāra* of Viṣṇu. The *Mahābhārata* says that He supports the earth by "encircling her entire with endless coils." He also "carries Goddess Earth on his head, encompassing all around the felly [wheel rim] of the ocean" (van Buitenen, 1973, p. 93). Ananta Śeṣa lies on the Garbhodaka Ocean below the lower worlds.

If we turn to the Norse Eddas, we learn of the Midgard serpent (shown in Figure 5.5, p. 136) who "lies in the midst of the ocean encompassing all the land and bites upon his own tail" (Sturluson, 1929, p. 42). Unlike Ananta Śeṣa, the Midgard serpent is described as inimical.

Roe portrays the Shipibo's earth disk as being surrounded by an anaconda (Roe, 1982, p. 134). The Warao tribe of the Orinoco delta

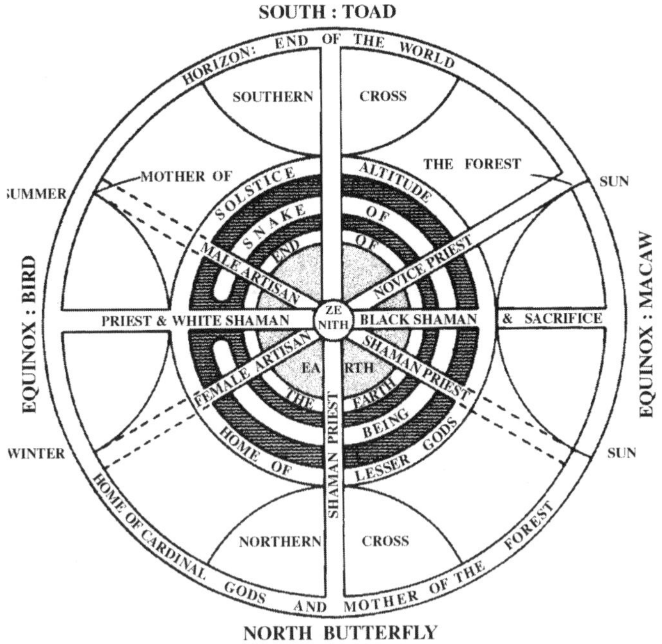

Figure 5.15 The cosmology of the Warao tribe, showing the "Snake of Being" surrounding the earth (Krupp, 1983, p. 321).

have a similar cosmology in which the "Snake of Being" lies below the surface of the encircling ocean, with its tail meeting its head (Krupp, 1983, p. 321). The Warao myths treat this snake as the source of all life. The Dogon tribe of Nigeria, whose cosmic pillar was mentioned above, also describe a serpent who lies in the ocean, encircles the earth disk, and holds its tail in its mouth (Corliss, 1991, p. 1).

The Mongols tell of the evil snake named Losy who lived in the ocean under the earth. By squirting poison on the earth, this serpent tried to crush out all life. The hero Otshirvani tried to kill it and failed. He then ascended the Sumer mountain, transformed himself into the Garide bird, wrapped the snake three times around the mountain, and smashed its head (Holmberg, 1964, p. 345).

Uno Holmberg states that Otshirvani is the Buddhist Bodhisattva Vairapani, but he regards this as only a recent addition to an ancient story (Holmberg, 1964, p. 346). Clearly the Garide bird (Garuḍa) and the Sumer mountain (Sumeru) derive from India. But what can we say about the world-girdling serpents, the multilevel universes, and the world trees and mountains that appear over and over again in widely separated traditions?

There are three basic hypothesis to explain this widespread appearance of similar cosmological themes:

1. Independent invention influenced by environmental and psychological factors common to all humans.
2. Cultural diffusion due to migration, trade and colonization, or the activity of traveling religious preachers.
3. Direct experience of higher realms of being by humans living in different parts of the world.

Although independent invention undoubtedly explains some features of the world's cosmological systems, the many shared details appearing in these systems make it seem doubtful that this could provide a complete explanation. Eliade and Holmberg both tend to prefer cultural diffusion. However, this hypothesis involves a number of controversial topics, such as the debate regarding pre-Columbian transoceanic contact between the Old and New Worlds.

It is clear that the observed parallels to *Bhāgavata* cosmology in various traditions cannot be attributed to recent direct borrowing from the *Bhāgavatam* and related Sanskrit texts. The differences between the traditions and the texts are too great for this to be plausible. However, it is possible that the *Bhāgavata* cosmology was spread around the world thousands of years ago and that modifications have separately accumulated in various parts of the world since that time.

The hypothesis of cultural diffusion requires some original cultural center which was the source of the diffusing elements. The *Mahābhārata* and *Purāṇas* such as the *Bhāgavatam* describe an ancient and highly influential civilization centered in greater India. It is possible that this civilization may have been an important center of cultural influence, if not the original center. Other ancient centers of civilization may have also played an important role, and the level of international communication in ancient times may have been greater than we commonly suppose.

The third hypothesis introduces another factor that should be taken into account in such investigations. In nearly all of the cultures mentioned in this survey, it was once believed that humans can gain direct access to the "mythological" regions and beings described in their cosmological systems. The modern enlightened thinker will tend to reject this. But our present knowledge is far from perfect or complete, and it may be that there is some truth to the old beliefs of nearly all human societies. The possibility of direct access to higher realms should therefore also be considered in efforts to understand our origins and fundamental nature.

6

The Realm of the Demigods

6.1 THE EARTHLY HEAVEN

In earlier chapters, we have shown that Jambūdvīpa can be interpreted either as the northern hemisphere (roughly) or as a region in Asia including India and adjacent lands. In the former interpretation, Jambūdvīpa is part of a planisphere map, with Mount Meru as the polar axis (see Chapter 3). In the latter, Mount Meru corresponds to the Pamir mountain range north of India (see Section 5.1). In the orbital map discussed in Chapter 4, Jambūdvīpa simply serves as the center and thus it represents the earth in this geocentric system.

Yet Mount Meru is described in the *Bhāgavatam* as an inverted cone 84,000 *yojanas* high and 32,000 *yojanas* across at the top. The summit of Mount Meru is said to be occupied by the golden city of Lord Brahmā, which is surrounded by the cities of the eight Loka-pālas or Guardians of the Worlds. This is not something we would expect to find anywhere on the earth.

Our thesis is that this description pertains to another important interpretation of Jambūdvīpa that was intended in the original text of the *Bhāgavatam*. Jambūdvīpa was regarded as a heavenly region, and this must be distinguished from Jambūdvīpa as a region of this earth. We get a hint of this in our cross-cultural study (Section 5.2), in which we repeatedly see things belonging to heaven associated with localized earthly regions.

6.1.1 Jambūdvīpa as the Earthly Heaven

According to the *Bhāgavatam*, Jambūdvīpa is divided into nine *varṣas*, or continents. Of these, only one—called Bhārata-varṣa—is inhabited by ordinary human beings. The other eight *varṣas* constitute a heavenly region. This is described in verse 5.17.11:

> Among the nine *varṣas*, the tract of land known as Bhārata-varṣa is understood to be the field of fruitive activities. Learned scholars and saintly persons declare the other eight *varṣas* to be meant for very highly elevated pious persons. After returning from the heavenly worlds, they enjoy the remaining results of their pious activities in these eight earthly *varṣas*.

In the Sanskrit text, the other eight *varṣas* are called "*bhaumāni svarga-padāni*," or the heavenly places on earth. In 5.17.12 it is said that the inhabitants of these eight *varṣas* live for 10,000 years and are almost like demigods. They have the strength of 10,000 elephants, and their bodies are like thunderbolts. They engage in sexual union until one year of life remains, at which point the wife conceives a child. (This system is standard for demigods, and the child attains adulthood without a prolonged period of growth.)

In Ilāvṛta-varṣa, the centermost of these eight regions, the inhabitants are consistently described as heavenly beings. In verses 5.16.13–14, four lakes surrounding Mount Sumeru in Ilāvṛta-varṣa are mentioned and it is said that,

> The celestial beings [such as the Siddhas, Cāraṇas and Gandharvas] who are also known as *upadevas*, enjoy the facilities of those four lakes. Consequently they have the natural perfections of mystic yoga [such as the power to become smaller than the smallest or greater than the greatest].

Four celestial gardens are near these lakes, and according to verse 5.16.15,

> The best of the demigods, along with their wives, who are like ornaments of heavenly beauty, meet together and enjoy within those gardens, while their glories are sung by lesser demigods known as Gandharvas.

In the same region, a river of mango juice called Aruṇodā is described. It is said in 5.16.18 that the wives of the Yakṣas act as maidservants to Bhavānī, the wife of Lord Śiva, and they become fragrant by drinking the water of this river. According to 5.17.15, no male person other than Lord Śiva is allowed in one part of Ilāvṛta-varṣa, and any man who enters this region is turned into a woman by Bhavānī (the goddess Durgā).

Another river is produced from the broken fruits of the Jambū (Rose Apple) tree, after which Jambūdvīpa is named. This river generates a kind of gold which is said in verses 5.16.20–21 to be enjoyed by the great demigods and their youthful wives.

Verse 5.16.25 sums up the situation in Ilāvṛta-varṣa:

> The residents of the material world who enjoy the products of these flowing rivers have no wrinkles on their bodies and no grey hair. They never feel fatigue, and perspiration does not give their bodies a bad odor. They are not afflicted by old age, disease or untimely death, they do not suffer from chilly cold or scorching heat, nor do their bodies lose their luster. They all live very happily, without anxieties until death.

The sharp distinction between these eight *varṣas* and Bhārata-varṣa is shown by verse 5.19.19, which says that in Bhārata-varṣa,

> The people who take birth in this tract of land are divided according to the qualities of material nature—the modes of goodness, passion, and ignorance. Some of them are born as exalted personalities, some are ordinary human beings, and some are extremely abominable, for in Bhārata-varṣa one takes birth exactly according to one's past karma.

This and similar verses are the only references to ordinary human beings (*manuṣya*) in the entire discussion of Bhū-maṇḍala in the *Bhāgavatam*. In particular, verse 5.19.21 states that human beings living in Bhārata-varṣa are extremely fortunate because of the unique spiritual opportunities which exist there. These opportunities are not available in the heavenly regions, and therefore the demigods are said to aspire to take birth in Bhārata-varṣa.

Thus, according to the *Bhāgavatam*, the eight *varṣas* or continents of Jambūdvīpa outside Bhārata-varṣa constitute a heavenly region, with inhabitants that live for 10,000 years, free of all bodily inebrieties. In contrast, Bhārata-varṣa is the place of karma, where people suffer the vicissitudes of ordinary human life but also have the advantage of being able to quickly attain spiritual liberation. At the same time,

Bhārata-varṣa also has a parallel, heavenly aspect, and thus Jambūdvīpa can be seen fully as a heavenly region (see Section 6.1.2).

At first glance, the account of heavenly life in Jambūdvīpa conveys the impression that Purāṇic geographers regarded countries outside of India as idyllic earthly paradises. Thus Joseph Schwartzberg says that

> A remarkable aspect of many Indian cosmographies is that they do not perceive distant realms as less glorious than their own revered home region. . . . In this they differ from the cosmographies of most other cultures (Schwartzberg, 1987, p. 336).

However, the *Bhāgavatam* verse 2.4.18 refers to races "addicted to sinful acts," including Hūṇas, Pulindas, Yavanas, and Khasas. These have been identified respectively as Huns, Greeks, Turks, and Mongolians—all peoples living outside of India in distinctly unheavenly

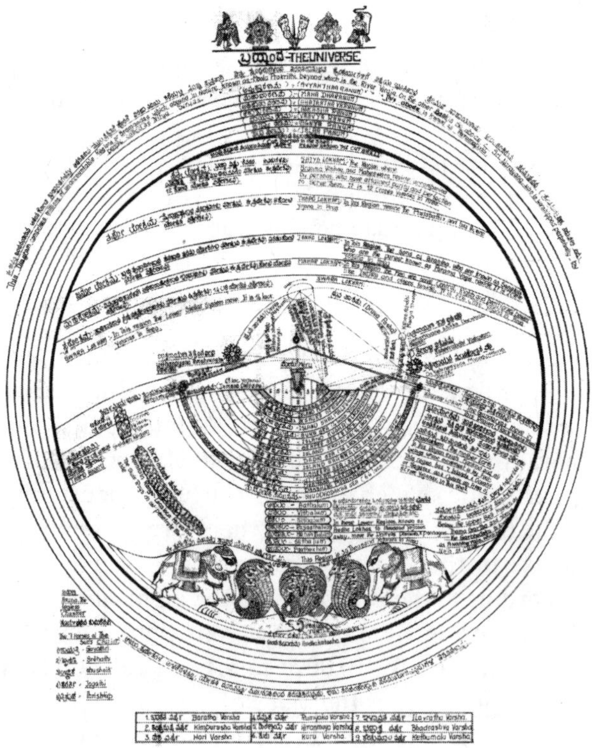

Figure 6.1 Śrī Tiruveṅkaṭa Rāmānuja Jīyar Swami's diagram.

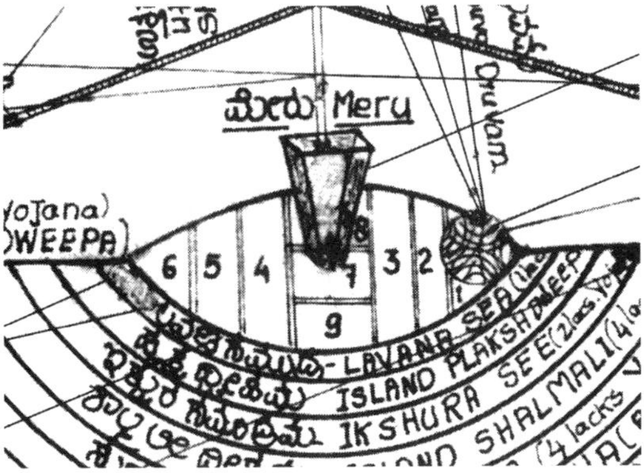

Figure 6.2
In Tiruveṅkaṭa's diagram, the *varṣas* of Jambūdvīpa are numbered 1 through 9. Note that the earth globe is placed in Bhārata-varṣa (number 1).

conditions. It would seem that Indian cosmography may, in fact, agree with other cultures in assigning degraded or barbaric peoples to outlying regions. But this implies that these neighboring regions must be included in Bhārata-varṣa itself. Indeed, it follows from this line of reasoning that all lands of the earth populated with suffering, short-lived people must be part of Bhārata-varṣa.

This idea has been widely accepted in India. For example, here are two Indian examples of nineteenth-century cosmological diagrams portraying the entire earth globe as part of Bhārata-varṣa:

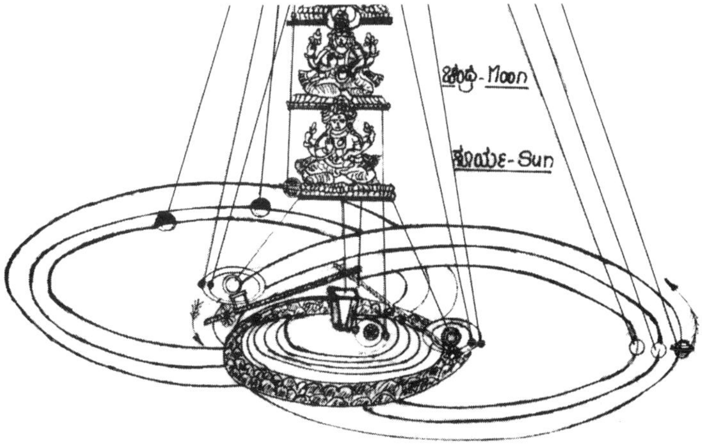

Figure 6.3 The solar system superimposed over Bhū-maṇḍala. Note that the sun is shown orbiting the earth and moon, which are shown next to Mount Meru. Mercury and Venus are shown closely orbiting the sun, and Mars, Jupiter, and Saturn are orbiting further out. This is shown for two positions of the sun simultaneously.

1. A South Indian Cosmological Diagram

The nineteenth-century South Indian *sannyāsi*, Śrī Tiruveṅkaṭa Rāmānuja Jīyar Swami, produced a diagram (partly shown in Figures 6.1–3), showing the relation between Purāṇic cosmology and the solar system of modern astronomy. The original diagram is in the Academy of Sanskrit Research, Melkote, India. It was apparently reworked in this century, and labels in English were added to the original labels in Tamil. The CD includes the diagram, along with several blow-ups showing parts of it in greater detail.

One of these blow-ups, reproduced here in Figure 6.2, shows the earth globe superimposed over Bhārata-varṣa in Tiruveṅkaṭa's rendering of Jambūdvīpa. In this way, he identifies the entire earth globe as Bhārata-varṣa.

It is noteworthy that Tiruveṅkaṭa Swami's solar system model is the same as that of the famous Danish astronomer, Tycho Brahe. (See

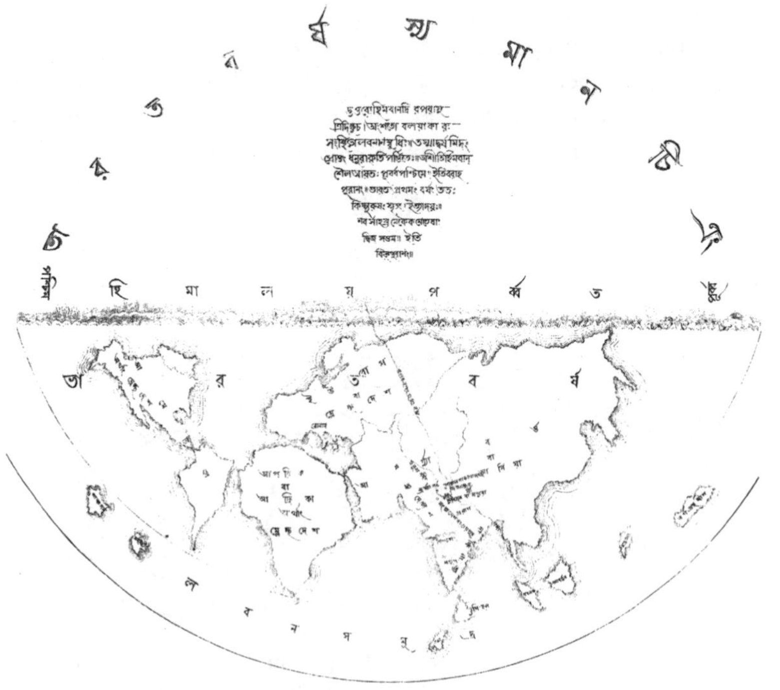

Figure 6.4 Maldah's map, showing Bhārata-varṣa equated with a modern world map. Note the greater "Himalayas" to the north of the arctic region.

Figure 4.8, p. 95). In this model, all of the planets except the earth, orbit the sun, and the sun orbits the earth. This model exactly reproduces the relative motions of the planets, while leaving the earth at the center. This is the natural interpretation of Bhū-maṇḍala in relation with the solar system, and we have argued that it is built into the dimensions of Bhū-maṇḍala, as given in the *Bhāgavatam*. (See Section 4.4.)

2. Recent Cosmological Maps from Bengal

Figure 6.4 reproduces one of several nineteenth-century cosmological maps made by Braja Soonder Moitreya Maldah, a police inspector and a native of Koocha-morah Nundenpore in Zillah Pubnah, Bengal. His maps are dated August, 1871, and he has also written a book in Bengali presenting his cosmological views. Here we see a map of the world superimposed on a diagram of Bhārata-varṣa. Note the Himalayan mountain range which extends across the upper border of the world map. This represents the Himalayas mentioned in the *Bhāgavatam* as the northern boundary of Bhārata-varṣa, and it gives

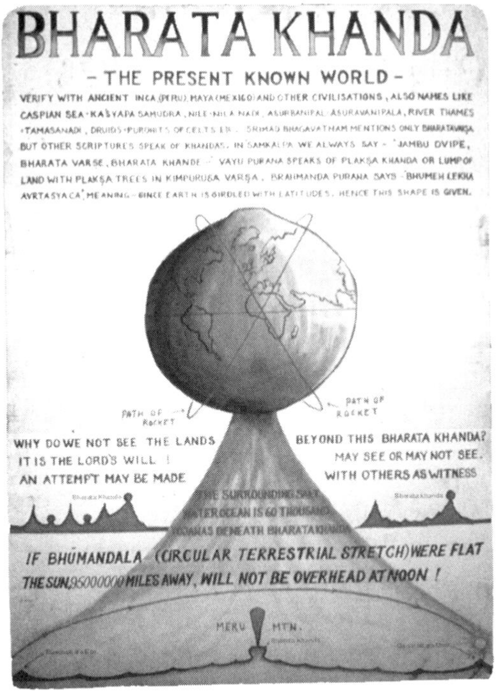

Figure 6.5
This drawing by Badanarayana Murthy of South India shows the earth globe mounted on a mountain extending up from Bhārata-varṣa. It was done in the 1970s.

rise to the problem that now there are two sets of Himalayan mountains to account for.

Figure 6.5 is another diagram from South India, dating to the 1970s, which tries to attach the earth globe to a mountain extending up from Bhārata-varṣa on a literal Bhū-maṇḍala disk. The fine details in this diagram can be seen in color in the CD.

The literal approach clearly runs into irreconcilable contradictions. However, this problem can be avoided by viewing Jambūdvīpa as a map of a heavenly region. We must distinguish this from Jambūdvīpa as a planisphere map or Jambūdvīpa as a local map of Asia. Our thesis is that the heavenly Jambūdvīpa belongs to another interpretation intended by the author of the *Bhāgavatam*.

If this is correct, then it is natural to ask what this heavenly realm is supposed to be made of, where it is, and how it relates to the earthly regions represented by other interpretations of the Jambūdvīpa map. Here the large dimensions of the features of Jambūdvīpa may provide a clue.

Jambūdvīpa is said to be 100,000 *yojanas* across (about the size of the sun). It contains mountains, including the Himalayas, which are 10,000 *yojanas* high. There are trees 1,100 *yojanas* tall, such as the Jambū (Rose-Apple) tree, after which Jambūdvīpa is named. The inhabitants are also very large, as we show below in Section 6.1.3. It would seem that everything is on a grand scale in the heavenly realm. The simple message is that we are literally like ants in relation to the demigods and *upadevas*.

We suggest that the originators of the Purāṇic accounts were not simply deluded into thinking that the earth is nearly a hundred times bigger than it actually is. Nor did they think that earthly mountains such as the Himalayas are many thousands of times taller than they actually are. Rather, they intended to convey the idea of a parallel, heavenly earth which is built on the scale of the demigods and is distinct from this small earth globe.

This parallel earth is not accessible to our ordinary senses, and thus we can say in modern language that it is higher-dimensional. Great yogis and sages were said to visit this realm, using mystic powers, or *siddhis*. The connection between the heavenly realm and its earthly counterpart is this: Important sites in the earthly world were regarded as gateways through which empowered persons could easily gain access to the higher regions. In particular, the earthly Himalayas were seen as portals to higher realms.

The *Purāṇas* and related literatures from India make many references to parallel realities that can be accessed by mystic powers. A prime example is Vṛndāvana, where Kṛṣṇa's pastimes are said to take place eternally, even though Vṛndāvana looks to ordinary vision like a mundane Indian town. Kṛṣṇa's pastimes are believed to take place in a parallel Vṛndāvana, which is invisible to ordinary people, but which can be accessed by those who have achieved special spiritual vision. Significantly, this parallel Vṛndāvana is also unlimitedly expansive, even though the Vṛndāvana of this world extends over a few miles. This topic is explored in detail in Section 6.2.

In its simplest form, the relationship between this earth and the heavenly Jambūdvīpa is that an empowered yogi or sage can enter the heavenly continuum, starting from a location on this earth. This is done by using the *siddhis* described in the Eleventh Canto of the *Bhāgavatam* (see 11.15.3–9). In many Purāṇic stories, it superficially appears that such a person simply travels by ordinary means to places on this earth that seem fabulous and impossible. In fact, however, a parallel realm is intended which extends on a cosmic scale and can be reached only by yogic methods of travel.

6.1.2 The Status of Bhārata-varṣa

If the eight *varṣas* of Jambūdvīpa, other than Bhārata-varṣa, were regarded as heavenly, then what is the status of Bhārata-varṣa itself? The answer is that Bhārata-varṣa was apparently regarded in Purāṇic tradition both as an earthly domain and as a higher, heavenly world.

We have seen that ordinary human beings are assigned to Bhārata-varṣa. But the *Bhāgavatam* also contains stories in which demigods are portrayed as living there. For example, in the story of Kapila Muni and Devahūti, it is said that Svāyambhuva Manu ruled the earth with its seven oceans from Brahmāvarta, which is located in India (see 3.21.26). Likewise the sacrifice in which Prajāpati Dakṣa offended Lord Śiva in the presence of many demigods took place at the confluence of the Ganges and the Yamunā (4.2.35).

This tells us that demigods not only visited India in the distant past but were actually based there. In the *Bhāgavatam*, their activities are described from the point of view of the demigods themselves, and thus they are presented as normal, day-to-day affairs. However, the question can be raised as to whether or not ordinary people would have been able to witness these affairs or participate in them.

Of course, one may argue that stories of demigods in India are merely exaggerated versions of stories of ordinary human beings. Be this as it may, our concern here is with how Bhārata-varṣa was understood in the *Bhāgavatam*. Our overriding impression is that it was (and still is) seen as a composite of parallel realms which can be accessed at different levels of sensory functioning.

If we turn to the *Caitanya-caritāmṛta*, which dates back about 500 years, we find evidence indicating that activities involving demigods were thought to take place in India in recent times. For example, the *Caitanya-caritāmṛta* (*Madhya-līlā* 9.175–7) says that Lord Caitanya met Lord Śiva and his wife Durgā on the hill of Śrī Śaila in South India, where they were living dressed as *brāhmaṇas.* The implication is that more was happening on Śrī Śaila hill than can be seen by ordinary vision.

India is full of such stories, even today. For example, the *Bhāgavatam* states that Maru and Devāpi, two ancient royal princes belonging to the Sūrya and Soma dynasties, are still living in the Himalayas in a place called Kalāpa-grāma. By the power of mystic yoga they will prolong their lives until the beginning of the next Satya-yuga and then revive the lost Sūrya and Soma dynasties by begetting children (see verses 9.12.6 and 9.22.17–18). If we go to the Himalayas, we will certainly not be able to perceive Maru and Devāpi using our ordinary senses. However, there are stories of yogis who were able to visit them through mystic powers, and it is significant that the meetings were said to take place in a parallel reality where Maru and Devāpi are residing.

6.1.3 Size of the Inhabitants of Jambūdvīpa

In verses 4.6.32–33, the *Bhāgavatam* gives the following description of Lord Śiva sitting beneath a banyan tree in Kailāsa, which is part of Jambūdvīpa,

> That banyan tree was 100 *yojanas* high, and its branches spread over 75 *yojanas* around. The tree cast a fine shade which permanently cooled

> the temperature, yet there was no noise of birds.
>
> The demigods saw Lord Śiva sitting under that tree, which was competent to give perfection to mystic yogis and deliver all people. As grave as time eternal, he appeared to have given up all anger.

We have 8 miles per *yojana* and a tree 100 *yojanas* tall and 150 *yojanas* in diameter. Our question is: If the tree was this big, how big was Lord Śiva? Consider a person 6 feet tall sitting under a tall tree about 100 feet high. His height is 6% of the height of the tree. Using the same proportion, Lord Śiva must be 6 *yojanas* tall (48 miles). Of course, we don't know the proportions in this case. But it stands to reason that in a landscape with gigantic trees, the people or demigods must be correspondingly large.

According to the *Bhāgavatam* verse 5.16.12, there are four trees 1,100 *yojanas* tall standing on four mountains surrounding Mount Meru in the cardinal directions. The mountains themselves are 10,000 *yojanas* tall. These trees are listed in Table 6.1 (p. 168).

At roughly eight miles per *yojana*, 1,100 *yojanas* is greater than the diameter of the earth. We suggest that the inhabitants living near these

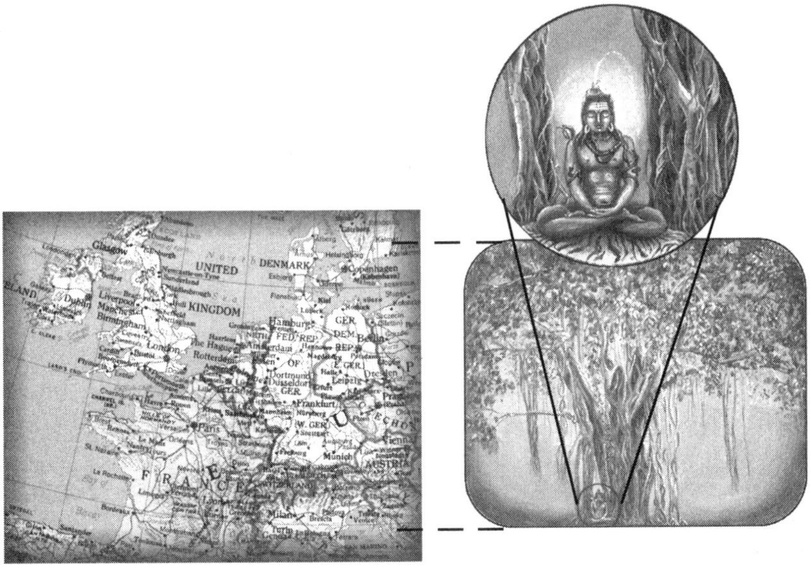

Figure 6.6 Lord Śiva meditating beneath a banyan tree. The tree is placed next to a map of Europe for comparison in size. According to the *Bhāgavatam*, the tree is 800 miles high and 1,200 miles across. Painting by Julia Wilson.

TABLE 6.1
World Trees in Jambūdvīpa

Tree	Type	Mountain	Direction from Meru	Reference
Devacūta	Mango	Mandara	east	5.16.16
Jambū	Rose Apple	Merumandara	south	5.16.19
Mahākadamba	Kadamba	Supārśva	west	5.16.22
Śatavalśa	Banyan	Kumuda	north	5.16.24

trees were also regarded as being extremely large.

The story of Matsya-avatāra, Lord Viṣṇu's fish incarnation, illustrates large sizes for beings entering into the *dvīpas* and oceans of Bhū-maṇḍala, outside of Jambūdvīpa. According to this story, King Satya-vrata of Draviḍadeśa (in South India) was once offering water in a religious ceremony on the bank of the river Kṛtamālā, when a small fish appeared in his palms. The fish asked for protection from aquatic predators, and the king kept him in a jug. Quickly, however, the fish grew, and the king had to place him in larger and larger bodies of water.

After the king transferred the now-gigantic fish to the ocean, the fish revealed himself as an incarnation of the Supreme Lord and warned the king that in seven days the three worlds Bhūḥ, Bhuvaḥ, and Svaḥ would merge in the waters of destruction. The Lord informed the king that He would send a boat, and He said, "Thereafter, O King, you shall collect all types of herbs and seeds and load them on that great boat. Then, accompanied by the seven *ṛṣis* [sages] and surrounded by all kinds of living entities, you shall get aboard that boat, and without moroseness you shall easily travel with your companions on the ocean of inundation, the only illumination being the effulgence of the great *ṛṣis*" (*Bhāgavatam* 8.24.34–35).

In due course, this happened, and the king witnessed the great fish swimming in the ocean. Verse 8.24.44 states,

> Then, while the King constantly meditated upon the Supreme Personality of Godhead, a large golden fish appeared in the ocean of inundation. The fish had one horn and was one million *yojanas* long.

In 8.24.45, it is stated that the king anchored the boat to the fish's horn. For this to be possible, the king must have had a size suitable for dealing with the eight-million-mile fish.

One response to this story is to dismiss it as a ridiculous exaggeration. However, the story is meaningful from the viewpoint of Purāṇic cosmology. In one important interpretation, the "earth" that was inundated corresponds to the plane of the ecliptic, and its illuminated region extends hundreds of millions of miles to the orbit of Saturn (see Section 4.4). This would provide swimming room for the divine fish. The Seven Sages are also celestial. They are said to rule the seven stars of the Big Dipper (Ursa Major).

This particular flood marked the transition from the Cakṣuṣa *manvantara* period to the Vaivasvata *manvantara,* and King Satyavrata became Vaivasvata Manu, the progenitor of mankind in the new age. Although this is extraordinary from a modern standpoint, a basic premise of the *Bhāgavatam* is that human beings can become elevated to divine or transcendental status.

It is interesting to compare this account with the Biblical story of Noah. That story deals with a purely terrestrial flood. However, scholars trace the Biblical story back to the Sumerian legend of Utnapishtim, who was also saved from a deluge on a boat. It is interesting to note that Utnapishtim was later elevated to the status of a demigod, and thus the story may have celestial connections (Sanders, 1972, p. 125).

There may also be a parallel between the story of Satyavrata and that of the "Seven Sages" (*Apkallu*) of Babylonian tradition, who were said to have "lived before the Flood" and to have built the walls of the sacred city of Uruk. The same can be said of the Egyptian "Building Texts" of the second century B.C., which associate Seven Sages with Flood imagery describing the emergence of the "Great Primeval Mound" from the primeval waters (Hancock, 1996, p. 201).

The story of King Satyavrata began along the banks of the river Kṛtamālā in South India (see Section 5.1.2), and the king was presumably of human size at first. Later on, however, we find him coursing through a cosmic ocean and his size must be on the order of thousands of miles. This clearly requires some mode of expansion similar to that of Matsya-avatāra Himself. In fact, this is provided by the *mahimā-siddhi*, the power of unlimited expansion (see 11.15.11).

In addition to *mahimā-siddhi*, there is *aṇimā-siddhi*, the power of becoming smaller than the smallest (see 11.15.10). According to the *Bhāgavatam*, these mystic powers are inherent in God, and by the grace of God, they can be conferred on lesser beings to varying degrees.

It is in relation to this background that we should see the vast distances that the *Bhāgavatam* assigns to Jambūdvīpa. We suggest that demigods were thought to exist naturally on a superhuman scale of size and to use *aṇimā-siddhi* to reduce their size when appearing before ordinary human beings. They then used *mahimā-siddhi* to return to their normal size (or larger).

According to the *Bhāgavatam*, God simultaneously spans all scales of size from largest to smallest. God also defines space rather than existing within it as an object among other objects. The space thus defined involves unlimited scales and dimensions, and it is not limited to the three-dimensional Euclidian continuum. However, it does include this continuum. Indeed, it contains many three-dimensional continua.

This system of thought rules out the kind of comprehensive, model of reality that we are familiar with in the West. Rather, it lends itself to multiple models that represent different aspects of an inconceivable total reality.

Another example illustrating the large size of demigods is the *Bhāgavatam*'s story of the churning of the Milk Ocean. Briefly, the story goes as follows: The Devas and the Asuras held a truce in their celestial battles, and with the encouragement of Lord Viṣṇu, they attempted to churn the Ocean of Milk in Bhū-maṇḍala and thereby produce divine nectar. They used the Mandara Mountain as a churning rod and the serpent Vāsuki as the rope for rotating the mountain. Unfortunately, the mountain sank and became stuck. Lord Viṣṇu responded by appearing as Kūrma-avatāra, the Tortoise incarnation.

Verses 8.7.8–9 state,

> Seeing the situation that had been created by the will of the Supreme, the unlimitedly powerful Lord, whose determination is infallible, took the wonderful shape of a tortoise, entered the water, and lifted the great Mandara Mountain.
>
> When the demigods and demons saw that Mandara Mountain had been lifted, they were enlivened and encouraged to begin churning again.

> The mountain rested on the back of the great tortoise, which extended for one hundred thousand *yojanas* like a large island.

If Kūrma was 100,000 *yojanas* across, then presumably the other participants in the churning of the Milk Ocean were on a scale of hundreds or thousands of *yojanas* in size.

6.2 PARALLEL WORLDS AND YOGIC TRAVEL

The *Purāṇas* make frequent reference to modes of travel which are impossible from the standpoint of our familiar physical conceptions. Here we will survey some accounts of such mystical travel in an effort to understand how physical reality is portrayed in the Purāṇic tradition. These accounts are drawn from the *Bhāgavatam*, the *Mahābhārata*, and recent Indian hagiography.

There is a process of travel, called *vihāyasā*, in which a physical object is moved directly through the ether to another location, without interacting with intervening gross matter. Here the word "ether" is used to translate the Sanskrit word "*ākāśa*." *Ākāśa* is space, but it is considered to be a substance or plenum, rather than a void.

The story of the abduction of Aniruddha in the *Bhāgavatam* (10.62.16–21) contains an example of *vihāyasā* travel. A young princess named Ūṣā was living in the closely guarded inner quarters of her

Figure 6.7
In a story in the *Bhāgavatam*, the *yoginī* Citralekha carries the sleeping Aniruddha through the ether to a distant city. Painting by Julia Wilson.

father's palace in the city of Śoṇitapura. One day, Ūṣā had a vivid dream about a beautiful young man who became her lover. She was certain that the person in her dream really existed, and she engaged her friend, the mystic *yoginī* Citralekhā, to find him for her:

> Citralekhā said, "I will remove your distress. If He is to be found anywhere in the three worlds, I will bring this future husband of yours who has stolen your heart. Please show me who He is."
>
> Saying this, Citralekhā proceeded to draw accurate pictures of various demigods, Gandharvas, Siddhas, Cāraṇas, Pannagas, Daityas, Vidyādharas, Yakṣas and humans.
>
> O King, among the humans, Citralekhā drew pictures of the Vṛṣṇis, including Śūrasena, Ānakadundubhi, Balarāma and Kṛṣṇa. When Ūṣā saw the picture of Pradyumna she became bashful, and when she saw Aniruddha's picture she bent her head down in embarrassment. Smiling, she exclaimed, "He's the one! It's Him!"
>
> Citralekhā, endowed with mystic powers, recognized Him [Aniruddha] as Kṛṣṇa's grandson. My dear King, she then traveled by the mystic skyway [*vihāyasā*] to Dvārakā, the city under Lord Kṛṣṇa's protection.
>
> There she found Pradyumna's son Aniruddha sleeping upon a fine bed. With her yogic power she took Him away to Śoṇitapura, where she presented her girlfriend Ūṣā with her beloved.

This kind of mystic travel is commonplace in the *Bhāgavatam*. It implies that physical entities (e.g. the bodies of Citralekhā and Aniruddha) can be decoupled from other matter and travel directly through the underlying ether.

The *Bhāgavatam* (3.26.34–49) presents an account of the *sāṅkhya* philosophy, in which the elements of gross matter (air, fire, water, and earth) are described as successive transformations of the ether. The sequence of transformation is as follows:

sound, ether, touch, air, form,
fire, taste, water, odor, earth

Each element is regarded as the previous element plus an additional property contributed by a subtle sense element (*tanmātra*). Since the elements are derived from modes of sense perception, they appear to be, in a sense, insubstantial and to be ultimately based on consciousness. Thus from this Purāṇic perspective, the idea of decoupling an object from other matter and moving it through the ether is much more plausible than it is from the standpoint of modern thinking.

In the *Bhāgavatam* verse 11.15.21, a form of mystic travel is described which is based on the mind. Kṛṣṇa says that

> The yogi who completely absorbs his mind in Me, and who then makes use of the wind that follows the mind to absorb the material body in Me, obtains through the potency of meditation on Me the mystic perfection by which his body immediately follows his mind wherever it goes.

This makes sense from the perspective of the *sāṅkhya* philosophy, in which the body is a transformation of subtle sense objects connected with the mind. In this transformation air (wind) is the second gross element, after ether.

If matter and space (ether) are transformations of modes of sense perception, then it would appear that they are not limited to the three-dimensional framework of Euclidian geometry and Cartesian coordinates. Indeed, this is strongly implied by the *siddhi* called *prāpti*, which is said to allow objects to be moved from one point to another without crossing the intervening space.

Śrīla A. C. Bhaktivedanta Swami Prabhupāda recounted a personal story illustrating this *siddhi*:

> In my childhood I had got one tutor. So he was telling about his spiritual master. He was a yogi. . . . He said that when he visited his spiritual master, who was a yogi, his spiritual master asked him, "What do you want to eat?" And because my teacher knew that his spiritual master was a great yogi, he wanted to have a taste of pomegranate of Kabul.
>
> In India pomegranate of Kabul, Afghanistan, that is very famous. So his spiritual master said, "Yes, you will find it in this room. You can see it." So he saw that it has been taken from the tree of pomegranate, and the juice was falling down. You see? So these wonders can be played by a yogi.

The idea can be illustrated by considering travel on a two- dimensional surface. If we are allowed to create short tubes linking distant points on the surface, then we can move from one point to another (e.g. Kabul to Calcutta) without crossing the intervening space along the surface. But to create such tubes we must go outside the framework of two-dimensional Euclidian space, perhaps by bending the surface in three-dimensional space. Likewise, to jump between points in three-dimensional space, we would have to go outside the Euclidian, three-dimensional framework.

This way of understanding *prāpti siddhi* is based on an extension of the familiar system of Euclidian geometry, which forms the basis of modern conceptions of space. The *Bhāgavatam*, however, explains *prāpti siddhi*, or "the power of mystic acquisition," in terms of sense perception rather than geometry. Thus in verse 11.15.13, Kṛṣṇa says that

> Fixing his mind completely in Me within the element of false ego generated from the mode of goodness, the yogī obtains the power of mystic acquisition, by which he becomes the proprietor of the senses of all living entities. He obtains such perfection because his mind is absorbed in Me.

This suggests an entirely novel approach to space: Consciousness is taken as the basis of reality, and space is understood as a coordinated system of sense perceptions. By systematically changing the sense perceptions, one can move or transform things in space, or even enter into different realms of experience.

In many Purāṇic stories, a person leaves this world and enters into a parallel reality—a material domain that is decoupled from this world, but is still accessible by mystical modes of travel. An example is the story of Arjuna and Ulūpī (see Appendix 13), where the hero Arjuna is pulled down into the Ganges by a Nāga woman named Ulūpī. Instead of hitting the bottom of the river, Arjuna finds himself in the kingdom of the Nāgas. This kingdom is accessible from this world, but it is not directly in this three-dimensional continuum.

In some stories, it appears at first glance that mystical travel proceeds in three-dimensions, just like ordinary travel. But on closer inspection, one can see that a shift to another continuum has taken place. An example is Madhvācārya's visit to Vyāsadeva (Appendix 14), in which the thirteenth-century religious reformer Madhvācārya is said to have flown like Hanumān from Badarikāśrama in the Himalayas to Uttarā-badarikāśrama, the residence of the sage Vedavyāsa. Although it may appear that Madhvācārya simply jumped over some mountains (a considerable feat in itself), closer examination of the story shows that Uttarā-badarikāśrama is not of this world.

Finally, there are stories that explicitly posit a parallel reality. An example is the story of Duḥkhī Kṛṣṇa Dāsa (Appendix 15), which took place in Vṛndāvana, near modern New Delhi. In this story, the sixteenth-century saint Duḥkhī Kṛṣṇa Dāsa (later Śyāmānanda Pandit) met a *gopī* from Kṛṣṇa's transcendental Vṛndāvana, and later entered this transcendental realm in meditation.

6.3 THE VERTICAL DIMENSION

The plane of Bhū-maṇḍala nearly bisects the sphere of the Brahmāṇḍa, and the axis perpendicular to this plane can be called the vertical dimension of the Brahmāṇḍa. The positions along this axis assigned to the sun, moon, *nakṣatras*, and five traditional planets are discussed in previous sections (3.4, 4.3, and 4.7). Additional features of the Brahmāṇḍa are distributed along the vertical axis, and these are part of a map of the heavenly regions of the demigods.

Some of these additional features are assigned heights above Bhū-maṇḍala. These are listed in the table on the next page, which expands on Table 3.5 in Chapter 3 (p. 68).

The *Viṣṇu Purāṇa* concludes its description of the planets and stars up to the polestar, Dhruvaloka, by saying, "Such, Maitreya, is the elevation of the three spheres (Bhūr, Bhuvar, Svar) which form the region of the consequences of works." This indicates that Svargaloka, which includes the kingdom of Indra, begins at the level of Dhruvaloka. Bhuvarloka is the region between Bhū-maṇḍala and Dhruvaloka.

Maharloka (also called Ṛṣi-loka), Janaloka, and Tapoloka are described in the *Bhāgavatam* as higher systems reserved for great sages. Satyaloka is the abode of Lord Brahmā, the creator of the worlds. The heights of these systems above Bhū-maṇḍala are not given in the *Bhāgavatam*, but they are listed in the *Viṣṇu Purāṇa* (Wilson, 1980, p. 308). The commentator Viśvanātha Cakravartī Ṭhākura combined the heights for Maharloka through Satyaloka in the *Viṣṇu Purāṇa* with the planetary heights given in the *Bhāgavatam*. This is not entirely consistent, since the *Viṣṇu Purāṇa* gives somewhat smaller planetary heights than the *Bhāgavatam*. Nonetheless, we have reproduced his figures in the table.

TABLE 6.2
Heights Relative to Bhū-maṇḍala in Yojanas

Body	Interval	Height
Satyaloka	120,000,000	233,800,000
Tapoloka	80,000,000	113,800,000
Janaloka	20,000,000	33,800,000
Maharloka	10,000,000	13,800,000
Dhruvaloka	1,300,000	3,800,000
Sapta-ṛṣi	1,100,000	2,500,000
Saturn	200,000	1,400,000
Jupiter	200,000	1,200,000
Mars	200,000	1,000,000
Mercury	200,000	800,000
Venus	200,000	600,000
28 Nakṣatras	200,000*	400,000
Moon	100,000	200,000
Sun	10,000	100,000
Rāhu/Ketu	10,000	90,000
Siddhaloka, etc.	79,900	80,000
Yakṣas, etc.	100	100
Bhū-maṇḍala	0	0
Lower worlds	-70,000	-70,000
Śeṣa Nāga	-30,000	-100,000

*Note: A textual variant assigns 300,000 *yojanas* to the distance from the moon to the 28 *nakṣatras*.

If we understand Bhū-maṇḍala as representing a plane closely parallel to the ecliptic, then the planets and systems "above" Bhū-maṇḍala are on the northern side of this plane (in the sense of celestial north). Likewise, systems "below" Bhū-maṇḍala are on the southern side of this plane.

Height relative to Bhū-maṇḍala is used to signify degree of divine quality. Thus the highest system is the most "elevated" in the spiritual sense. Likewise, there are lower systems beneath Bhū-maṇḍala whose inhabitants are said to be highly materialistic or unspiritual (see Figure 6.9). But divinity again appears when we descend below the lowest of these systems and reach Garbhodakaśāyī Viṣṇu and Ananta Śeṣa.

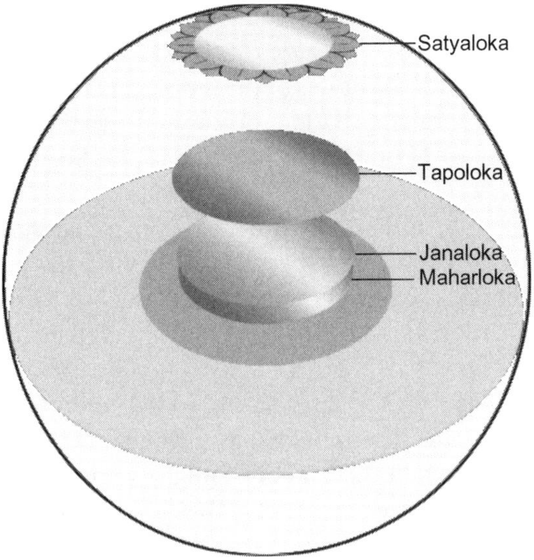

Figure 6.8
Brahmāṇḍa diagram, showing the location of the higher worlds, from Maharloka to Satyaloka.

The heights of the different systems above and below Bhū-maṇḍala may not be intended as literal distances. We have observed that the heights of the planets above Bhū-maṇḍala figure in two interpretations—the planisphere model and the ecliptic plane model. In the former, the heights of the planets define different planes of projection in an astrolabelike model, and they do not refer to physical distances. Similarly, the heights of the higher *lokas* might refer to different levels of spiritual status, rather than to different distances in ordinary space.

The *Bhāgavatam* says relatively little about the higher systems, starting with Maharloka. However, life in these systems is described in detail in the sixteenth-century work *Sri Brihat Bhāgavatāmritam* by Sanātana Goswāmi (1975). There it is indicated that each of these systems is invisible and nearly inaccessible to the inhabitants of the systems below it. Satyaloka, the topmost system, is described as *ā-vāk-manasam* or "beyond the description of mind and words" in verse 5.1.21 of the *Bhāgavatam*, and thus it is clearly not an object in our three-dimensional continuum.

In addition to the higher worlds, our height table has a number of entries beneath the sun. The first of these is the planet Rāhu, which is 10,000 *yojanas* below the sun and is said to be responsible for solar and lunar eclipses. In many *Purāṇas,* Rāhu has a counterpart called Ketu, but Ketu is not mentioned in the *Bhāgavatam*. In the *Jyotiṣa Śāstras*, Rāhu and Ketu are identified with the nodes of the moon, and in some *Purāṇas* Rāhu is associated with the shadow of the earth (which is therefore implied to be a globe). (For a further discussion, see Section 3.4.)

Beneath Rāhu by 10,000 *yojanas* are the worlds known as Siddhaloka, Cāraṇaloka and Vidyādharaloka (see 5.24.4). These are the abodes of beings called Siddhas, Cāraṇas, and Vidyādharas, who are endowed with mystic powers and are able to fly through the ether on their own power.

In the *Bhāgavatam*, these worlds are simply listed and their geometry is unclear. If we regard Bhū-maṇḍala as a plane extending across the Brahmāṇḍa-sphere, then these abodes might be anything from parallel planes on a higher level, to small globes above Jambūdvīpa. In the planisphere model, they might map to spherical regions surrounding the earth globe.

Below these worlds there are the abodes of the Yakṣas, Rākṣasas, Piśācas, Pretas, and Bhūtas. These regions are said to lie at least 100 *yojanas* above the earth (about 800 miles), and it is also stated that the upper limit of the earth is marked by how high large birds can fly (see 5.24.5–6).

The beings in this list are considered to be demonic or ghostly in nature, and they are also said to be endowed with superhuman mystic

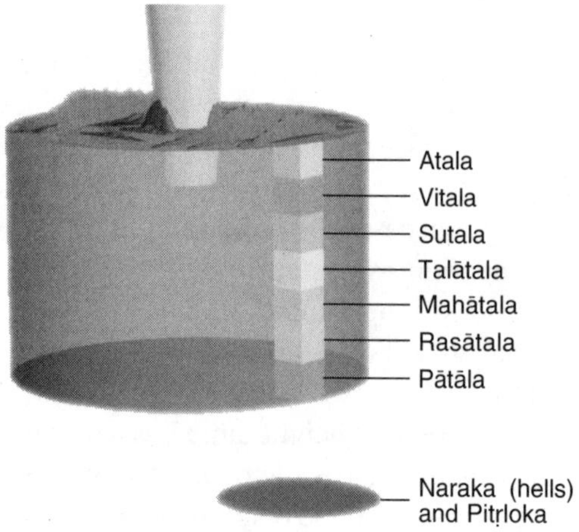

Figure 6.9
The *Bhāgavatam* describes seven cubical chasms in the earth, known collectively as Bila-svarga, or the subterranean heaven. The hells are placed above the Garbhodaka Ocean, 30,000 *yojanas* beneath the lowest of these chasms.

powers. The *Bhāgavatam* seems to be saying that these beings live overhead about 100 or more *yojanas* up, relative to our familiar earth globe. For comparison, the American and Russian manned orbital flights range in altitude from about 100 to 900 miles above the earth, while the highest clouds are observed to lie about 50 miles up (Baker, 1981, pp. 534–536).

There is a possible cultural parallel between this account in the *Bhāgavatam* and the nursery story about Jack and the beanstalk. In this story, Jack meets a giant who lives up in the clouds. The giant is a man-eater, he has magical powers, and he hoards gold. These are precisely the characteristics of the Purāṇic Rākṣasas. Thus the familiar nursery tale may be a cultural fossil—a remnant of past cosmological thinking that has survived in the harmless guise of a children's story.

Directly below Bhū-maṇḍala there are seven lower systems, called Atala, Vitala, Sutala, Talātala, Mahātala, Rasātala and Pātāla (see 5.24.7.) These systems are described as chasms or openings in the earth having a horizontal length and breadth of 10,000 *yojanas*. Each opening is said to lie 10,000 *yojanas* below the one above it, and Atala, the first, lies 10,000 *yojanas* beneath Bhū-maṇḍala. These seven chasms are like a series of subbasements within Bhū-maṇḍala. The *Bhāgavatam* does not say where they are located beneath Bhū-maṇḍala, so we arbitrarily placed them beneath Bhārata-varṣa in the illustration (Figure 6.9).

The seven lower systems are collectively called Bila-svarga, which means the "subterranean heaven." They are described as being more opulent materially than the heavens of the demigods. Like the inhabitants of the heavenly portion of Jambūdvīpa, the inhabitants of Bila-svarga do not experience wrinkles, grey hair, or invalidity (see 5.24.13). However, they are said to be extremely materialistic.

There are seven lower systems, one earth mandala, and six higher systems (from Bhuvarloka to Satyaloka), making fourteen worlds in total. Bhū-maṇḍala is sometimes referred to as the middle system, and thus one can refer to three worlds, lower, middle, and upper. However, in some cases, the phrase "three worlds" refers to Bhū-maṇḍala, Bhuvarloka, and Svargaloka.

Bhū-maṇḍala extends through the heavens and is known as Bhauma-svarga—the earthly heaven. Above it (towards celestial north) is Divya-svarga, the heaven of Indra, and beneath are the cramped subbasements of Bila-svarga, the subterranean heaven.

In the *Jyotiṣa Śāstras* such as *Sūrya-siddhānta*, the lower systems are placed within the concave strata of the earth globe, and this is the natural interpretation according to the planisphere model of Bhū-maṇḍala. This is also consistent with the statement in *Bhāgavatam* verse 5.24.11 that there is no distinction between day and night in Bila-svarga since the sunlight does not reach there.

The idea that there are heavenly regions within the earth can be found in many cultures, and we find stories in the *Mahābhārata* indicating that Bila-svarga can be reached by entering into a hole in the earth (van Buitenen, 1973, p. 51). A cultural parallel from China is discussed in Appendix 11. This example draws attention to the fact that Bila-svarga, like other heavenly regions described in the *Bhāgavatam*, can best be understood as a parallel reality that is not part of our ordinary three-dimensional continuum.

Pātāla is the lowest of the seven lower systems, and it is said to be the abode of the mystical Nāgas, cobra-like serpents that can also assume human forms. The jewels decorating the hoods of these serpents are said to emit an effulgence that illuminates the entire region of Bila-svarga (see 5.24.31).

The Nāgas are generally regarded as being angry and materialistic in nature, but 30,000 *yojanas* beneath Pātāla is the abode of Lord Ananta Śeṣa or Saṅkarṣaṇa. Ananta Śeṣa is described as a multi-headed, cobra-like serpent who is an incarnation of Lord Viṣṇu. He is in charge of material false ego and the *tamo-guṇa*, or mode of darkness (5.25.1). He also destroys the creation at the time of annihilation by manifesting the Rudras in anger.

Saṅkarṣaṇa is said to support Bhū-golam, which is compared with an atom resting on one of His hoods (5.25.12). At the same time, Saṅkarṣaṇa is described as being within the Bhū-golam, or sphere of the Brahmāṇḍa. This is not necessarily a contradiction. Rather, it is a joining together of ideas that have to be viewed separately to be understood (i.e. one must consider that different expansions of Saṅkarṣaṇa are meant). Clearly, Saṅkarṣaṇa is not presented as an inhabitant of our three-dimensional continuum.

Saṅkarṣaṇa is the object of meditation by Lord Śiva and is said to be the root cause of Lord Śiva's existence (5.17.16). Thus the root cause of the material creation in serpent-form is placed beneath the

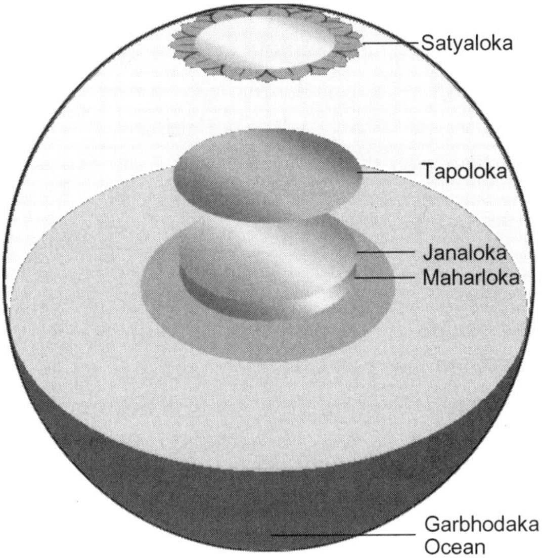

Figure 6.10 The Garbhodaka (Embryonic) Ocean fills the lower half of the Brahmāṇḍa (Brahmā-egg), beneath Bhū-maṇḍala and Bila-svarga.

lowest of the worlds (as well as outside the entire system of worlds).

Another incarnation of Lord Viṣṇu, named Garbhodakaśāyī Viṣṇu, is generally portrayed as resting on the coils of Ananta Śeṣa. Ananta Śeṣa, in turn, floats on the waters of the Garbhodaka (Embryonic) Ocean, which fills the lower hemisphere of the Brahmāṇḍa. According to the *Bhāgavatam*, Garbhodakaśāyī Viṣṇu generates a lotus flower from His navel. Brahmā, the Creator, is born from this lotus, and Brahmā creates the fourteen *lokas*. The lotus stem represents the vertical dimension of the Brahmāṇḍa, along which the *lokas* are situated.

The Brahmāṇḍa is thus portrayed as an egg within which the creation is generated without hatching out. It includes an amniotic region (the Garbhodaka Ocean), an umbilicus (the lotus stem), and a developing embryo (the fourteen *lokas*).

If we look at Bhū-maṇḍala as a three-dimensional model of the solar system, then the Garbhodaka Ocean consists of everything to the celestial south of the ecliptic. This perspective is supported by the analysis given by de Santillana and von Dechend of the cosmology of their "archaic" culture, which supposed a watery region filling the southern celestial hemisphere (see Appendix 3). Of course, Bhū-maṇḍala lies along the ecliptic, rather than the celestial equator, and all stars to the south of the ecliptic must therefore lie within the Garbhodaka Ocean.

It is noteworthy that, according to 3.8.19, Brahmā tried to find the root of the lotus from which he took birth, but he was unable to do so by the power of his senses. This indicates that Ananta Śeṣa and Garbhodakaśāyī Viṣṇu are invisible even to Brahmā, whose own world is said to be beyond mind and words. Thus the two poles of the vertical dimension, Satyaloka and the region of Ananta Śeṣa, are both parallel realities lying beyond the reach of ordinary sense perception.

The lotus of Lord Brahmā corresponds to Satyaloka. An interesting analogy can be drawn between the cosmic axis of the Brahmāṇḍa, with Ananta Śeṣa at the lower end and Satyaloka at the upper end, and the human spinal column, with the *kuṇḍalinī* "serpent" at the base, and the lotuslike *brahma-randhra* at the top of the head. This is discussed below in Section 6.3.1.

We should finally note that the upper and lower parts of the vertical axis are linked by the celestial Ganges river. This river is said to enter the Brahmāṇḍa through the hole kicked by Lord Vāmanadeva, to descend upon the earth, and to finally pass through the lower systems and reach the Garbhodaka Ocean. This topic is discussed in Section 6.3.2.

According to the *Bhāgavatam* 5.26.5, the hells and the region called Pitṛloka are situated between the lower systems and the Garbhodaka Ocean, on the southern side of Bhū-maṇḍala. Pitṛloka is the headquarters of Yamarāja, the lord of the dead, who awards punishment to sinful persons. In verse 5.21.7, Saṁyamanī, the place of Yamarāja, is said to be located on Mānasottara Mountain in the southern direction. However, this is not necessarily the location of Pitṛloka.

In Figure 6.9, Pitṛloka and the hells have been placed above the Garbhodaka Ocean, about 100,000 *yojanas* directly beneath the southernmost *varṣa* of Jambūdvīpa (Bhārata-varṣa). This choice is supported by the statement in verse 3.30.24 that the servants of Yamarāja take souls to the hellish regions along a path that is 99,000 *yojanas* in length.

Horrible tortures are prescribed for different categories of sinners in the various hells, but it is said that internment in hell is not permanent. It is also pointed out that beings suffer hellish punishments in their subtle bodies. Thus, the idea that hell might exist is rendered more plausible by the idea that hell is like a nightmare from which one cannot awaken because one no longer has a gross physical body. The *Bhāgavatam* clearly intends the hells as subtle regions that are not directly manifest to gross vision.

Pitṛloka is a heavenly region to which pious persons may attain after death. These persons then assume the status of *pitṛs* (forefathers), and they are concerned with the well-being of their earthly families. In India and in other parts of the world, offerings have been traditionally made to propitiate the forefathers or ancestral spirits.

According to H. H. Wilson, the *pitṛs* "include a man's ancestors; but the principal members of this order of beings are of a different origin" (Wilson, 1980, p. 463). They fall into seven classes: three classes of beings without form who can assume forms at will, and four classes of beings with fixed bodily forms. They are said to descend from sons of the demigods who gave good instructions to their fathers at a time when the demigods had offended Brahmā. Therefore, they were addressed by their fathers as fathers (*pitṛs*).

It may be relevant to our understanding of Pitṛloka to note that many people in modern America (who are mostly of Christian background) report out-of-body experiences in which they meet departed relatives and "beings of light." The light-beings may be formless, or they may appear as religious figures such as Jesus Christ. Thus Purāṇic ideas concerning Pitṛloka are paralleled by relatively common forms of experience involving altered states of consciousness.

In the *Purāṇas*, the *pitṛs* are assigned a number of different living places, in addition to Pitṛloka proper. For example, the Agniṣvāttas live in Somaloka, which appears to be the moon, and the Haviṣmantas live in the sun (Wilson, 1980, p. 464). The *Bhāgavatam* also connects the *pitṛs* indirectly with the moon, since it says that the two fortnights of the waxing and waning moon constitute the day and night of the *pitṛs* (see 5.22.9).

The *Purāṇas* also give information placing the *pitṛs* in outer space. The *Viṣṇu Purāṇa* states that "On the north of Agastya, and south of the line of the Goat, exterior to the Vaiśvānara path, lies the road of the Pitṛs" (Wilson, 1980, p. 327). According to H. H. Wilson, the line of the Goat, Ajavīthī, comprises the *nakṣatras* Mūlā, Pūrvāṣāḍhā, and Uttarāṣāḍhā, which contain stars in Scorpio and Sagittarius (Wilson,

1980, p. 328). Agastya is the star Canopus in the southern celestial hemisphere. (The terminology used to describe the groups of *nakṣatras* is given in Appendix 1).

This suggests that the road of the *pitṛs* was associated with an area in outer space, including stars in Scorpio and Sagittarius. In Appendix 12, we mention several cultural traditions in which these constellations were connected with the world of the dead. This is consistent with the identification of Bhū-maṇḍala with the ecliptic. Scorpio and Sagittarius are just south of the ecliptic, and Pitṛloka is south of Bhū-maṇḍala.

6.3.1 Macrocosm and Microcosm

In the hermetic philosophy of the West, it is said that the microcosm corresponds to the macrocosm. Purāṇic cosmology expresses a similar idea by viewing the universe as a bodily form of the Supreme Being.

The universal form, or *virāṭ-puruṣa*, is conceived of as the material manifestation of the transcendental Godhead. In the *Bhagavad-gītā*, the universal form is portrayed as a reality that Arjuna was able to perceive through divine vision. In other accounts, it is described by assigning parts of the Lord's body to parts of the universe. In these descrip-

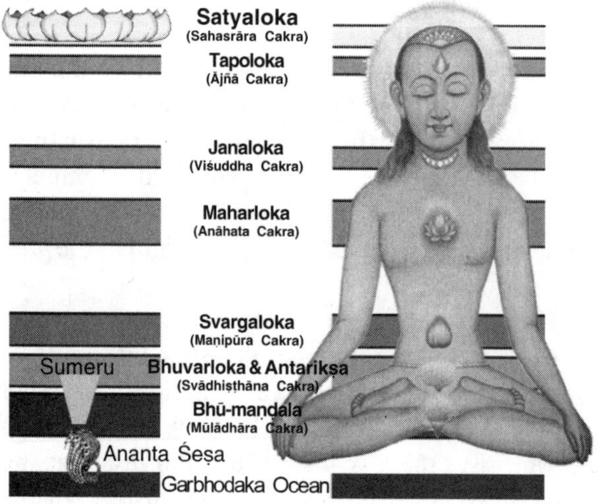

Figure 6.11 The seven upper worlds and the polar axis (aligned along Mount Meru) are compared with the seven spinal *cakras* and the spinal column (*merudaṇḍa*).

tions, the word "imaginary" (*kalpitaḥ*) is sometimes used. This indicates that the particular description of the universal form is intended as an aid to meditation on the Lord, but it is not to be taken literally.

The *Bhāgavatam* verses 2.5.38–41 present one of these imaginary accounts. They associate the fourteen worlds of the universe with parts of the Lord's body as shown in Table 6.3:

TABLE 6.3
Parts of the Universal Form

World	Part of the Lord's Body
Satyaloka	head
Tapoloka	neck
Janaloka	breast (upper chest)
Maharloka	chest
Svarloka	chest
Bhuvarloka	navel
Bhū-maṇḍala	waist
Atala	waist
Vitala	thighs
Sutala	knees
Talātala	shanks
Mahātala	ankles
Rasātala	upper portion of feet
Pātāla	soles of feet

Thus the vertical axis of the universe is made to correspond to the personal form of the Lord. An analogy is sometimes made between this axis, with its graded series of heavens, and the spinal *cakras* on which yogis meditate. In this analogy, Bhū-maṇḍala corresponds to the lowest *cakra* and Satyaloka corresponds to the thousand-petaled *brahma-randhra* at the top of the head. The lower worlds corresponding to the legs of the universal form do not play a role in this analogy, but the serpent Ananta Śeṣa may correspond to the *kuṇḍalinī* at the base of the spine. In the illustration, we have paired the seven *cakras* with the corresponding higher *lokas*, starting at the top with Satyaloka and ending with Bhū-maṇḍala.

In his essay on Indian cartography, Joseph Schwartzberg described one way in which the analogy between the spine and the cosmic axis is used in processes of meditation. By contemplating this analogy, meditators "further the process by which one's self becomes a microcosm that fuses and becomes one with the enveloping macrocosm. One's spine then becomes the Meru or *axis mundi* of both. Arrayed along the spine are various centers of psychic energy that one summons up, in the practice of yoga, in moving toward the supremely illuminated *samādhi* state. These energy centers may be viewed as the psychophysiological analogues of the heavens that the soul traverses on its path to ultimate liberation . . ." (Schwartzberg, 1987, p. 381).

In accordance with this analogy, the spine is called *merudaṇḍa* in Sanskrit texts on yoga. This topic is discussed extensively in Snodgrass (1990, pp. 158–64).

6.3.2 The Descent of the Ganges

The descent of the Ganges river from heaven to earth provides a map of the vertical dimension of the Purāṇic universe. According to the *Bhāgavatam* verse 5.17.1, the Ganges consists of water from the Causal Ocean which entered the upper portion of the universe through a hole kicked in the universal covering by Lord Vāmanadeva. This water is said to take about a thousand *yugas* (*yuga-sahasra-upalakṣanena*) to reach Dhruvaloka (the polestar), which is said to be situated approximately thirty million miles above the sun. Jīva Goswami says that, by the usage of the *Jyoti-śāstra*, *yuga* is to be taken here as five years. This implies that the descent onto Dhruvaloka takes 5,000 years.

From Dhruvaloka, the Ganges reaches the stars of the Seven Sages (Sapta-ṛṣi), and from there it is carried to the moon "through the spaceways of the demigods" (*devayānena*) in billions of celestial airplanes. From the moon it falls down (*nipatati*) to the top of mount Meru, where it divides into four branches in the cardinal directions (5.17.4–5). Finally, the southernmost branch, called the Alakanandā, passes from Brahmapurī over the tops of many mountains and becomes the Ganges of India (5.17.9).

We have the sequence: Dhruvaloka, Sapta-ṛṣi, moon, top of Mount Meru. Since Meru and Dhruvaloka define the polar axis, and the Big Dipper (Sapta-ṛṣi) is a northern constellation, this seems to put the moon close to celestial north. However, the moon stays within about 5° of the ecliptic and therefore is never further north than about 28.5°. The motion ascribed to the descending Ganges clearly does not follow obvious physical principles if we try to understand it in three dimensions.

The Purāṇic star lore may give us some insight into the path of the celestial Ganges. This leads us to seek the Ganges' course across the celestial sphere, where the stars are projected.

First of all, the phrase "spaceways of the demigods" refers to the *deva-yāna* path, which is discussed in Appendix 12. This path is defined roughly in the *Viṣṇu Purāṇa* in terms of star positions ranging from the Sapta-ṛṣi constellation to parts of Aries and Taurus. It lies to the north of the ecliptic plane, and its northernmost terminus, Sapta-ṛṣi, is one of the way stations of the celestial Ganges. Following the celestial sphere, we see that the Ganges might well pass from the north pole (Dhruvaloka) to Sapta-ṛṣi, and from there to the moon's orbit in the vicinity of the ecliptic.

In their comparative study of ancient mythologies, de Santillana and von Dechend commented on "that curious archaic intrication of earth and heaven which has become familiar and which makes great rivers flow from heaven to earth" (de Santillana, 1969, p. 188). The "intrication of earth and heaven" is there in the concept of Bhū-maṇḍala, which is both earth and heaven. Taking the earth as the ecliptic plane, the celestial Ganges falls down to the earth, and taking

Figure 6.12
The fall of the celestial Ganges onto the city of Brahmā on the summit of Mount Meru and its division into four branches.

it as this terrestrial globe, the Ganges flows through India. The link connecting the celestial and terrestrial rivers involves the heavenly *varṣas* of Jambūdvīpa.

First of all, the celestial Ganges is said to fall on the summit of Mount Meru. In Figure 6.12 we show it precipitating on the center of Brahmapurī and dividing into four branches. After falling upon various mountains in Jambūdvīpa, one branch of the Ganges descends onto the head of Lord Śiva in the Himalayas and then enters India as a visible river. This is a classical example of mystical travel, involving a shift from a parallel reality to the world perceived by our ordinary senses.

There are other mystical features of the Ganges. For example, the *Bhāgavatam* verse 3.8.5 describes a visit by Sanāt-kumāra and other sages to Lord Saṅkarṣaṇa, in the region of the Garbhodaka Ocean. Śrīla A. C. Bhaktivedanta Swami Prabhupāda commented as follows on the sages' mode of transportation:

> The Ganges water flows directly from the lotus feet of Viṣṇu, and its course runs from the highest planet of the universe down to the lowest. The sages came down from Satyaloka by taking advantage of the flowing water, a process of transportation made possible by the power of mystic yoga. If a river flows thousands and thousands of miles, a perfect yogi can at once transport himself from one place to another simply by dipping in its water. The Ganges is the only celestial river which flows throughout the universe, and great sages travel all over the universe via this sacred river.

The general rule seems to be that a terrestrial river may have a celestial river as its counterpart. These exist in distinct domains (earth and heaven), and they cannot interconnect by ordinary means. But there is connection involving parallel worlds and mystic *siddhis*.

This applies not only to the Ganges but to other major rivers in India. For example, the *Bhāgavatam* verse 6.10.16 describes a celestial battle between the armies of Indra and those of the demon Vṛtrāsura:

> Thereafter, at the end of Satya-yuga and the beginning of Tretā-yuga, a fierce battle took place between the demigods and the demons on the bank of the Narmadā.

Prabhupāda commented that,

> Herein, the Narmadā does not mean the Narmadā River in India. The five sacred rivers in India—Gaṅgā, Yamunā, Narmadā, Kāverī and Kṛṣṇa—are all celestial. Like the Ganges River, the Narmadā River also flows in the higher planetary systems.

This implies that in addition to the earthly India, with its five sacred rivers, there is also a corresponding celestial India. As we pointed out above, this is required by the interpretation of Jambūdvīpa as a heavenly region. This interpretation implies a heavenly and an earthly Bhārata-varṣa, linked by mystic travel.

6.4 GODS, DEMONS, AND ASTRONOMY

One may ask how scientific information about astronomy can coexist with stories of gods and demons in the *Purāṇas* and in other traditions. The astronomical phenomena are recognized to occur in a regular way. In contrast, the behavior of the gods and demons seems to depend on personal whims and irreproducible events which wouldn't be expected to follow a regulated timetable.

A common explanation is that primitive people saw things as the unpredictable behavior of whimsical gods. Later on, their more scientific descendants recognized lawful patterns in nature, but retained the gods as a matter of tradition. However, whatever the historical steps leading to a tradition may have been, the question remains as to how people reconciled gods and deterministic laws.

Modern philosophy is based on the assumption that only the laws of physics are real, and all other levels of meaning are nothing but combinations of words. In contrast, an older approach to philosophy attributes real existence to many different philosophical categories, including categories involving consciousness and psychology. This approach tends to give meaning to the relation between the individual and the universe, whereas the modern approach sees such meaning simply as a matter of psychological projection.

In one sense, the conflict between whimsical gods and regular laws becomes irreconcilable only when one adopts a purely mechanistic view of cause and effect. Then the gods and the laws become competing

Figure 6.13
The *kīrttimukha* is a monstrous face without a body or lower jaw that decorates doorways and temple towers in South Indian iconography. It has complex symbolic meanings relating to time, creation, and destruction.

systems of mechanical causation, and it is hard to accommodate both of them. But if a richer system of philosophical categories is allowed, the restrictions imposed by strict mechanical causation are relaxed, and attention is focused on a wide variety of meaningful relationships.

The story of the *kīrttimukha* illustrates how this works in Indian cosmology. South Indian temples are typically surmounted by a monstrous visage without a lower jaw that seems to contain within its mouth everything beneath it. This is called the *kīrttimukha* or "Face of Glory," and its origin is recounted in the *Śiva Purāṇa* (Śiva, 1990, pp. 886–90). It seems that the demon Jalandhara, after conquering the three worlds, decided that he should possess Śiva's wife Pārvatī, and he sent Rāhu to Śiva to convey his demand. On hearing this demand, Śiva projected a horrific monster from the space between his eyebrows and it rushed to devour Rāhu. Rāhu begged Śiva for mercy and was spared, but the monster objected that he was tormented by hunger and desperately needed something to eat. On Śiva's order, the being devoured its own body up to the head, and Śiva, being pleased with him, declared that he would be his doorkeeper and would be known as *kīrttimukha*.

How are we to understand this story? According to Snodgrass (1985, pp. 305–9), the *kīrttimukha* involves many levels of symbolic meaning. These include

1. The *kīrttimukha* is also the *kālamukha* or face of time, and to pass beneath his jaws is to be devoured by time.
2. The jaws represent all-devouring death, but they also spew forth foliage representing new life.
3. Rāhu is also a decapitated head, and he is identified with *kīrttimukha*. Here there is a link with the sun, which is also the all-devourer and all-producer.
4. The link with Rāhu also refers to the ascending and descending nodes of the moon. These are connected with Rāhu's role as the eclipse that represents death by covering the light of the sun and moon.
5. The *kīrttimukha* is portrayed as a partly a *makara*, an aquatic monster. This links him with the zodiac and *makara sankranti*, the winter solstice. Thus the theme of creation and destruction is mirrored in the ascending and descending paths of the sun (*udagayana* and *dakṣiṇāyana*).
6. Rāhu was decapitated by Viṣṇu just as he began to taste the *amṛta* produced by the churning of the Milk Ocean. In temple iconography, the dripping down of the *amṛta* from the mouth of the *kīrttimukha* is represented by cascades of jewels. Thus to pass through the doorway beneath the *kīrttimukha* is to be bathed in the rain of *amṛta*.
7. There is an analogy with the yoga system, in which the pairs of opposites represented by *ida* and *pingala* merge in the *coincidentia oppositorum* in the cerebral *cakra* and generate the *amṛta*, which descends through the body and purifies it. The *kīrttimukha*, exuding elixer, is stationed above the lintel of the door, and the channels of *ida* and *pingala* are represented by serpents, wreathed with flames and vegetation, that extend along the doorjambs from its mouth and terminate in *makara* heads.
8. There is a link between the *kīrttimukha* and the *śiśumāra* or "child killer," stationed in the heavens, "who lies in wait with jaws agape and turned counter-current against the river of the sacrificer's path leading to the celestial regions" (Snodgrass, 1985, p. 310). Note that the tail of the *śiśumāra* is Dhruvaloka, the place of Viṣṇu, and note also that the head of the *śiśumāra* was intended to be oriented on the winter solstice (see Section 8.2.1). The basic concept is that "he who would pass beyond the Sun Door must be devoured, his selfhood swallowed, offered in a willing act of sacrifice. Then the other, glorious side of the Mask is revealed. . . . The other side of the monster's mask is the Face of Glory" (Snodgrass, 1985, p. 309).

We can see that the various interpretations of the *kīrttimukha* refer to universal principles, such as time, creation, and destruction, that relate to the universe as a whole and to the individual as a conscious being. Since these principles are regarded as real entities, they cannot be reduced to a linear sequence of mechanical causes and effects. Rather, they lend themselves to a multicontextual view of reality, in which the universe is seen as an ultimately incomprehensible whole with many meaningful aspects. Since the universe is thought to be based on consciousness, Śiva (and even the *kīrttimukha*) are regarded as real, but they are not thought to exist in a simplistic, mechanical way as arrangements of moving parts in space.

This approach may tend to inhibit the development of consistent mechanical models of the modern scientific type. At the same time, it must be said that the effort to impose a single mechanical model on all of reality (a TOE or "theory of everything") may be unrealistic in its own right. There are phenomena such as consciousness that are notoriously hard to fit into such a scheme, and there is the danger that important aspects of reality may be suppressed or overlooked in an effort to achieve mechanistic consistency. There may still be room for a multicontextual approach.

7

The Greater Universe

7.1 DISTANCES TO THE STARS

In the *Bhāgavatam*, there are relatively few references to stars. The twenty-eight *nakṣatras* are mentioned in 5.22.11 and are said to be 200,000 *yojanas* above the moon (300,000 in some texts). In Section 3.4, we argue that this statement does not give a literal distance to the *nakṣatra* stars. Rather, it places the *nakṣatra* plane above the moon's plane in a planisphere model. This is appropriate, since the *nakṣatras* are stations marking the daily motion of the moon in its orbit. (They are therefore sometimes called lunar mansions. See Appendix 1.)

In some Indian systems, the ecliptic is divided into twenty-seven equal *nakṣatra* intervals, and the moon stays a little over a day in each one. In another system, a smaller interval is assigned to a twenty-eighth *nakṣatra* (Abhijit), so that the moon stays one day in each of twenty-seven *nakṣatras* and about .3 days in the twenty-eighth (Dikshit, 1888).

This means that the *nakṣatras* serve as a system of markers that can be used to measure time using the motion of the moon. The *nakṣatra* intervals are associated with star constellations, and one can determine what *nakṣatra* the moon is in by observing the stars near the moon.

In this application, the distances to the *nakṣatra* stars in three-dimensional space are not important. What is important is that the *nakṣatras* form a backdrop in 2-D against which the motion of the moon can be measured. Therefore, it is significant that the *nakṣatras* are placed in the layer just above the moon in 5.22.11. This is like placing the plate with hour markings just behind the hands of a clock.

The stars called the Seven Sages (Sapta-ṛṣi) are placed 1,100,000 *yojanas* above Saturn in 5.22.17, and the polestar Dhruvaloka is placed 1,300,000 *yojanas* above the Seven Sages in 5.23.1. These locations can also be understood in terms of the planisphere model. According to the

Viṣṇu Purāṇa, Dhruvaloka also marks the upper boundary of Antarikṣa (the "inner space" in which the sun, moon, and planets orbit) and the lower boundary of Svargaloka (Wilson, 1980, p. 307).

The Seven Sages, Dhruvaloka, and the stars making up the Śiśumāra constellation are treated in the *Bhāgavatam* as markers indicating the passage of time. The daily rotation of the stars and planets around the polestar, Dhruvaloka, is strongly stressed in 5.23.2 and 5.23.3. We can directly see this rotation at night, and it is compared to the turning of a great wheel (the *kāla-cakra*), measuring time. The Śiśumāra is referred to as an incarnation of Kṛṣṇa (who says "Time I am"), and it is an object of meditation by yogis. Thus the Śiśumāra is like a great clock representing Kṛṣṇa as the time factor.

The *Bhāgavatam* does not refer to stellar distances of many light-years, as understood by modern astronomy. Specific references to stellar distances are part of an astrolabelike structure in which stars play the roles of markers in a cosmic clock. Apart from this, the *Purāṇas* indicate that the stars are nearby and that they shine by the reflected light of the sun. In this sense, it could be said that the *Purāṇas* are too heliocentric (see Section 4.6).

7.1.1 Distant Stars in the Mahābhārata

However, we do find indications in traditional Sanskrit literature that the stars are far away—so far that, if we traveled to the stars, we could not see the sun or the moon due to their great distance. For example, the *Mahābhārata* tells how the hero Arjuna traveled to the kingdom of Indra to obtain celestial weapons. On the way there, he passes through the region of the stars:

> And on this sunlike, divine, wonder-working chariot the wise scion of Kuru flew joyously upward. While becoming invisible to the mortals who walk on earth, he saw wondrous airborne chariots by the thousands. No sun shone there, or moon, or fire, but they shone with a light of their own acquired by their merits. Those lights that are seen as the stars look tiny like oil flames because of the distance, but they are very large. The Pāṇḍava saw them bright and beautiful, burning on their own hearths with a fire of their own. There are the perfected royal seers, the heroes cut down in war, who, having won heaven with their austerities, gather in hundreds of groups. So do thousands of Gandharvas with a glow like the

> sun's or the fire's, and of Guhyakas and seers and the hosts of Apsarās.
> Beholding those self-luminous worlds, Phālguna [Arjuna], astonished, questioned Mātali in a friendly manner, and the other said to him, 'Those are men of saintly deeds, ablaze on their own hearths, whom you saw there, my lord, looking like stars from earth below.' Then he saw standing at the gateway the victorious white elephant, four-tusked Airāvata, towering like peaked Kailāsa. Driving on the roadway of the Siddhas, that most excellent Kuru Pāṇḍava shone forth as of old the great king Māndhātar. The lotus-eyed prince passed by the worlds of the kings, then looked upon Amarāvatī, the city of Indra (van Buitenen, 1975, p. 308).

One important thing to notice about this passage is that Arjuna entered a region of stars where there was no light from the sun, the moon, or fire. This is what we would expect to find if we did travel among the stars. It is also stated that the stars are very large, but they seem small due to distance when seen from the earth. This also agrees with modern ideas.

In that region, Arjuna saw that the stars were self-luminous worlds, and that they were inhabited by various kinds of beings. The stars themselves are spoken of as aerial chariots, and this is reminiscent of the "billions of celestial airplanes" (*vimāna-anīka*) that carry the water of the celestial Ganges (see 5.17.4–5). Thus we see modern-sounding ideas combined with expressions of the Purāṇic picture of a universe thronging with life.

7.1.2 Expanding the Brahmāṇḍa

We find quantitative indications of vast stellar distances in the *Jyotiṣa Śāstras*, which are generally assigned by scholars to the medieval period. For example, the *Sūrya-siddhānta* 12.90 says that "The circumference of the sphere of the Brahmandee in which the sun's rays spread is 18,712,080,864,000,000 *yojanas*" (Sāstri, 1860, p. 87). Likewise, the *Siddhānta-śiromaṇi*, Golādhyāya Bhuvana-kośa, states:

> Some astronomers have asserted the circumference of the circle of heaven to be 18,712,069,200,000,000 *yojanas* in length. Some say this is the length of the zone binding the two hemispheres of the Brahmāṇḍa. Some Paurāṇikas say that this is the length of the circumference of the Lokāloka Parvata [adṛśya-dṛśyaka-girim] (Wilkinson, 1861, p. 126).

The circumference of 18,712,069,200,000,000 *yojanas* corresponds to a diameter of 5,956,200,000,000,000 *yojanas*. Arguments based on the earth's diameter show that the *Sūrya-siddhānta* and the *Siddhānta-śiromaṇi* use a *yojana* of about five miles (see Section 3.4.2), and therefore these figures can be converted into miles by multiplying by five.

According to the *Bhāgavatam* 5.20.37, the circular Lokāloka Mountain is the outer limit of the rays of the luminaries, including the sun. This explains why some Paurāṇikas (expounders of the *Purāṇas*) would say that the eighteen quadrillion *yojanas* refer to the circumference of Lokāloka Mountain. Since Lokāloka Mountain has half the diameter of the Brahmāṇḍa, the radius of the Brahmāṇḍa comes to $5 \times 5.956 = 29.78$ quadrillion miles, or about 5,065 light years.

According to modern astronomers, the Milky Way galaxy is about 100,000 light years across. It follows that the sphere of the Brahmāṇḍa has a diameter about 1/10 that of the Milky Way galaxy, with room for large numbers of stars. In the illustration, this is shown by the sphere superimposed on a galaxy representing the Milky Way.

The eighteen-quadrillion-*yojana* figure is computed as the orbital distance traveled by the moon in a day of Brahmā, which lasts 4,320,000,000 years. We do not need to take this speculative calculation seriously. But it is worth noting that Indian astronomers were discussing distances equivalent to thousands of light years at a time when European astronomy assigned the fixed stars to a shell lying just outside the orbit of Saturn.

In the twentieth century, some Vaiṣṇava commentators have invoked the *Sūrya-siddhānta* and *Siddhānta-śiromaṇi* to revise the

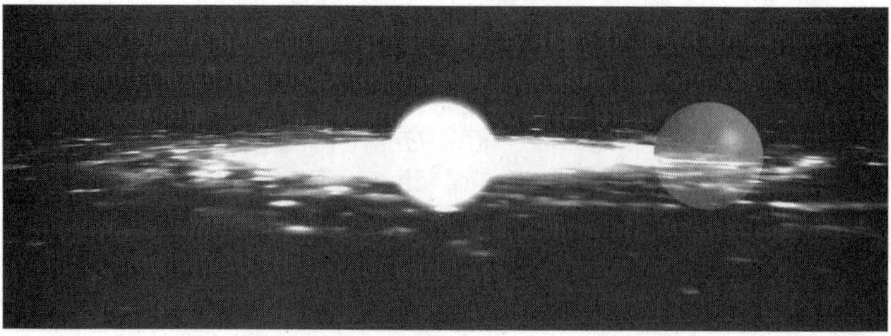

Figure 7.1 The enlarged Brahmāṇḍa of the *Sūrya-siddhānta*, shown as a gray sphere in comparison with the Milky Way galaxy.

diameter of the Brahmāṇḍa given in the *Bhāgavatam*. The *Caitanya-caritāmṛta* is the biography of the sixteenth-century saint Caitanya Mahāprabhu, written by Kṛṣṇadāsa Kavirāja. According to text 21.84 of the *Madhya-līlā* section of this work, Kṛṣṇa said to Brahmā:

> Your particular universe extends four billion miles; therefore it is the smallest of all the universes. Consequently, you have only four heads.

In his commentary written in the 1970s, Śrīla A. C. Bhaktivedanta Swami Prabhupāda remarked:

> Śrīla Bhaktisiddhānta Sarasvatī Ṭhākura, one of the greatest astrologers of his time, gives information from *Siddhānta-śiromaṇi* that this universe measures 18,712,069,200,000,000×8 miles. This is the circumference of this universe. According to some, this is only half the circumference.

This refers to the *Anubhāṣya* commentary on *Caitanya-caritāmṛta* by Śrīla Bhaktisiddhānta Sarasvatī, in which he cites the verses from *Sūrya-siddhānta* and *Siddhānta-śiromaṇi* quoted above. Evidently, Śrīla Bhaktisiddhānta thought it was admissible to attribute a greatly enlarged size to the Brahmāṇḍa, using the expanded distances given in *Jyotiṣa Śāstras*. Note that "according to some" the indicated figure is only half the circumference. This is clearly a reference to Lokāloka mountain, as mentioned in the text of the *Siddhānta-śiromaṇi* quoted above. Thus the 18-quadrillion-*yojana* figure refers to the Brahmāṇḍa itself and not to its coverings, as some have supposed.

7.2 THE UNIVERSAL GLOBE AND BEYOND

According to the *Bhāgavatam*, the Brahmāṇḍa consists of a spherical inner portion 500 million *yojanas* in diameter, enclosed in a series of seven coverings made from the material elements described in *sāṅkhya* philosophy. The inner portion extends to about twice the orbit of Saturn, and the covering shells are said to be surrounded by a purely spiritual region known as the Causal Ocean.

This arrangement can be compared with Renaissance and medieval cosmological diagrams from Europe, in which the sphere of the fixed stars lies just outside the orbit of Saturn, the most distant known planet. Beyond the fixed stars, lies the sphere of the Prime Mover and

Figure 7.2 A typical diagram of the medieval Ptolemaic universe, in which the sphere of the fixed stars lies just outside the orbit of Saturn (Heninger, 1977, p. 38, fig. 28).

then the unlimited empyrean realm (believed in ancient times to be made of the pure fire element).

The Purāṇic Brahmāṇḍa can be seen as a system of higher-dimensional heavenly worlds, combined with an astronomically reasonable model of the solar system. Unlike the medieval European system, the Brahmāṇḍa is large enough to accommodate the orbit of Saturn, which lies near the circular Lokāloka Mountain, the outer limit of the luminaries.

As we have seen, much larger distances—up to a tenth of the radius of the Milky Way galaxy—have been contemplated by Indian astronomers and seriously considered by modern commentators on the *Bhāgavatam*. However, the general view of followers of the *Bhāgavatam* is that all visible bodies in the universe lie within the 500-million-*yojana* sphere of the Brahmāṇḍa.

The *Bhāgavatam* does not give a systematic explanation of the seven shells covering the Brahmāṇḍa. It makes passing references to them in a number of places, but it does not mention them in the main cosmological discussion in the Fifth Canto. This conveys the impression that the coverings were taken for granted as common knowledge in the *Bhāgavatam*, but they were not considered to be an integral part of the cosmology of the Brahmāṇḍa.

In 2.1.25, 3.26.51–2, 3.29.43, 3.32.9, and 6.16.37, there are references to seven shells, but these are not actually enumerated anywhere in the text. In 6.16.37, the shells are said to start with earth, but in 3.26.52 they are said to go from water to *pradhāna*, the undifferentiated material energy.

In 3.32.9, the coverings are listed as earth, water, fire, air, ether, mind, senses (*indriya*), sense objects (*artha*), ego, etc. However, this list of at least nine elements does not clearly refer to geometrical shells covering the Brahmāṇḍa. It may also refer to the material elements covering conscious souls within the Brahmāṇḍa. (The role of these *sāṅkhya* elements within the Brahmāṇḍa is discussed in Section 6.2.)

In the sixteenth-century work *Sri Brihat Bhāgavatāmritam*, the coverings are listed as being made of earth, water, light, air, ether, ego, *mahat-tattva*, and *prakṛti*, coming to eight in total (Goswāmi, 1975, p. 135). There it is stated that variegated activities take place within each shell. Each shell is presided over by a demigoddess, beginning with the earth goddess, Bhūmi, in the first shell and ending with Prakṛti, the personified material energy, in the last. A yogi who is trying to attain liberation by leaving the material universe is presented with temptations within each shell, which he must overcome in order to continue his journey.

In 2.2.28, it is explained that a yogi leaving the material world may pass through stages described as earthly, watery, fiery, airy, and ethereal. It is noteworthy that the *sāṅkhya* philosophy holds that these elements are created in the reverse order, and each successive element is defined by a new quality that was not present in the element before it. Thus the yogi, in effect, reverses the creation as he frees himself from the material elements.

The *sāṅkhya* theory of creation implies that the shells of the Brahmāṇḍa can be seen as nested spheres. Within a sphere of ether, a smaller sphere is given an additional quality (touch or *sparśa tanmātra*), and this produces a sphere of air. Within this sphere, a still smaller sphere is given an additional quality (form), and this produces a sphere of fire. In this way, a series of shells is produced, surrounding an inner sphere of earth, in which all of the qualities of matter are manifested. The Brahmāṇḍa lies within this sphere.

In 3.11.41, 3.26.52, and 6.16.37, it is mentioned that each successive shell is ten times as thick as the shell within it. The thickness of the

Figure 7.3 Innumerable Brahmāṇḍas, each surrounded by its elemental shells, are said to float in the Causal Ocean.

first shell is not mentioned, but A. C. Bhaktivedanta Swami Prabhupāda comments on 3.11.41 that its thickness is ten times the diameter of the Brahmāṇḍa. If this is so, and the Brahmāṇḍa has a diameter of D, then the outer radius of the seventh shell comes to D times 11,111,110.5. Thus if the outermost shell is scaled to the size of the earth, the sphere of the Brahmāṇḍa will be about four feet across.

From a modern point of view, there is something attractive about the idea of successive condensations of elements within a nested series of spheres. It is reminiscent of the big bang theory, in which a series of symmetry breakings brings about the physical world as we know it. We can think of the successive manifestations of the *sāṅkhya* elements as a series of symmetry breakings in which successive properties are added to material nature. Thus there are parallels between modern cosmological speculation and Purāṇic cosmology.

Large though the shells of the Brahmāṇḍa may be, they are minute compared with the larger world lying outside. There are many Brahmāṇḍas, and 3.11.41 compares them with "atoms in a huge combination." In 6.16.37, they are likewise compared with atoms, and they are said to number in the ten millions of ten millions (*aṇḍa koṭi koṭibhiḥ*).

These universes are floating in the Causal Ocean (*kāraṇārṇavaḥ jala*), and they emanated from the pores and breathing of Mahā-Viṣṇu. This same Causal Ocean is said to be the source of the celestial Ganges, which enters the Brahmāṇḍa through a hole kicked in the shells by Lord Vāmanadeva (see 5.17.1).

We may observe that in recent years modern cosmologists have contemplated a multiplicity of universes. This idea has come up in the context of the big bang theory and the inflationary universe scenario. For example, the Russian physicist Andrei Linde has proposed a theory in which universes are continuously being born from quantum fluctuations in the underlying "space-time foam." The main difference between Linde's ideas and *Bhāgavata* cosmology is that the latter attributes the seed-universes to a divine source, while Linde's theory attributes them to random fluctuations based on the quantum mechanical uncertainty principle. Thus *Bhāgavata* cosmology is driven by an underlying theological world view, whereas modern cosmology is driven by an underlying theory of physics.

8

Notes on Time and Chronology

8.1 PRECESSION AND THE POLESTAR

The theory of precession of the equinoxes states that the spin axis of the earth moves slowly around in a conical path, centered on the pole of the ecliptic. At present, the spin axis is nearly pointing at the star Polaris, which we call the polestar. However, prior to a few centuries ago, Polaris was not near the north celestial pole. Within the last few thousand years, the last time there was a notable polestar was about 2500 B.C., when Thuban (Alpha Draconis) was near the north pole.

Thus Hipparchus, in about 150 B.C., said that "As regards the north pole, Eudoxus is in error in stating that 'there is a certain star which always remains at the same spot'" (Kay, 1981, p. 13). There was no polestar in the time of Hipparchus, but Eudoxus may have

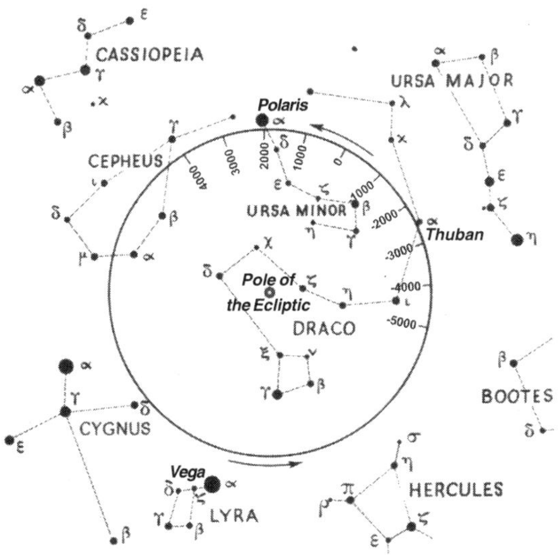

Figure 8.1
The polar axis moves around a circular path in about 26,000 years. Occasionally it points at a star, which becomes the polestar for that time period (Flammarion, 1964, p. 43).

been following a tradition dating back to the time when Thuban was at the pole.

In India, there are strong traditions of a fixed polestar which may also date back to this period. For example, the *Sūrya-siddhānta* advocates a theory of trepidation, in which the equinoxes shift slowly back and forth by plus or minus 27° (see Appendix 16). However, it does not say what effect these oscillations might have on the polestar, and it defines two fixed polestars (*dhruvatārā*) on the northern and southern ends of the Meru axis (Burgess, 1860, p. 286).

The *Bhāgavatam* verse 5.23.3 states that the planets and stars revolve around Dhruvaloka, the polestar, until the end of the creation (*ā-kalpa-antam*). "Dhruva" literally means "fixed" in Sanskrit, and thus precession is not recognized in the *Bhāgavatam*. This assumes, of course, that the tradition of a fixed polestar was based originally on observable stars and not simply on the abstract idea of a celestial body marking the cosmic axis. If Dhruvaloka were simply defined as the polar axis, then by definition, it would always be perfectly fixed.

Although the *Bhāgavatam* does not recognize smooth precession of the equinoxes, the idea of an abrupt displacement of the polestar is present in Indian tradition. For example, the modern poet and spiritual teacher, Bhaktivinoda Ṭhākura, used the shifting of the polestar to illustrate the transitory nature of material existence:

> Beings still greater than these have passed away—vast oceans have dried, mountains have been thrown down, the polar star displaced, the cords that bind the planets rent asunder, the whole earth deluged with flood—in such a world what relish can there be in fleeting enjoyments? (Bhaktivinoda, 1968, p. 18)

This is reminiscent of a passage in the *Mārkaṇḍeya Purāṇa*, in which the sun is being pared down on a kind of celestial lathe because he has become unbearably brilliant:

> And Viśvakarman, being permitted by the Sun in Śākadvīpa, mounted the Sun on his chariot wheel and set to work to pare down his glory. While the Sun, which was the center of all the worlds, was whirling around, the earth with its oceans, mountains and forests mounted up into the sky, and the whole heavens with the moon, planets and stars went downward, and were tossed together and confused.... And all creatures also were

> scattered about with the waters out of the ocean; lofty hills were shattered to pieces, their summits and roots were torn asunder. The supports of the pole, all the asterisms, O best of munis, with their bands and foundations splitting, went downwards in thousands (Pargiter, 1981, pp. 569–70).

These stories bring to mind a theory propounded by the scholars Giorgio de Santillana and Hertha von Dechend. They maintain that precession of the equinoxes was known in ancient times, but it was expressed in terms of violent catastrophes, rather than being viewed as a gradual process (de Santillana, 1969). Their prime example of such a catastrophe is the universal Flood, which is mentioned in traditions from all over the world. They argue that the end of an age, marked by the shifting of the equinox into a new sign of the zodiac, was believed to end in such a universal Deluge.

The steady shifting of the equinox by about 1° in seventy-two years hardly seems violent, and it certainly doesn't bring about flooding on earth. However, the slow catastrophes of de Santillana and von Dechend take place not on the earth, but in the heavens. The link between precession and flooding is the cosmic ocean, defined as occupying the space south of the plane of the celestial equator. As the equinoxes shift, one constellation of the zodiac will gradually rise from this ocean on the side of the vernal equinox, and another will gradually sink into the ocean on the side of the autumnal equinox. This sinking is the cosmic Flood, and although it is almost imperceptibly slow, it eventually results in a complete change in what people would see in the morning sky at particular times of the year.

Since agriculture depended on using stars to time the planting and harvesting of crops, a complete change of the morning constellations in relation to the seasons would have had a significant impact on the long-entrenched customs of ancient agricultural peoples. This leads to two possibilities: One is that people remained unaware of the idea of precession, but that they unavoidably became aware at certain points in history that their old customs were out of sync with the seasons. Then they made drastic reforms and spoke of an abrupt transition to a new age. Another possibility, favored by de Santillana and von Dechend, is that real knowledge of precession did exist in an intellectual elite in ancient times, but they expressed it in terms of catastrophic upheaval of the world order.

Myths of cosmic catastrophe are often so vivid and dramatic that it is enough to make one wonder whether literal "dis-asters" have actually happened here on earth. The statements of Bhaktivinoda Ṭhākura and the *Mārkaṇḍeya Purāṇa* can be compared with the following flood story from China, reported by the pioneer British Indologist Sir William Jones in 1801:

> The Chinese believe the Earth to have been wholly covered with water, which, in works of undisputed authenticity, they describe as flowing abundantly, then subsiding and separating the higher from the lower ages of mankind. . . . The pillars of heaven were broken; the earth shook to its very foundations; the heavens sunk lower to the north; the Sun, the Moon, and the stars changed their motions; the Earth fell to pieces, and the waters enclosed within its bosom burst forth with violence and overflowed it. Man having rebelled against Heaven, the system of the Universe was totally disordered. The Sun was eclipsed, the planets altered their course, and the grand harmony of nature was destroyed (Jones, 1801).

8.2 PRECESSION AND THE DATING OF TEXTS

The *Bhāgavata Purāṇa* 5.21.4 states that "When the sun passes through Meṣa and Tulā, the durations of day and night are equal." Likewise, the *Viṣṇu Purāṇa* [II.8.70–73] states that the equinoxes take place when the sun enters the first degrees of Meṣa and Tulā (Wilson, 1980, p. 325). Meṣa and Tulā are Sanskrit names for the signs of the zodiac called Aries and Libra, respectively (see Section 3.3).

Due to precession, the equinoxes slowly shift relative to the constellations of the zodiac. However, they may not shift relative to the *signs* of the zodiac. In the tropical zodiac, the beginning of the sign Aries is defined to be the vernal equinox and the signs therefore move with the equinoxes. In a sidereal zodiac, the signs are fixed to the constellations.

Historically, the twelve constellations of the zodiac were named first and the signs were chosen as 30° divisions of the ecliptic corresponding to these constellations. These developments are thought to have taken place in the Near East. Initially, the signs were fixed to the constellations, but after Hipparchus discovered precession of the equinoxes, Greek astronomers invented a tropical zodiac. This is still used today in Western countries, and the zodiacal signs are gradually shifting further and further relative to the original zodiacal constellations.

We can estimate the earliest date for the adoption of the tropical zodiac by asking when the 30° signs line up with the constellations which were their original inspiration. For example, Leo is a well-defined constellation stretching about 30° from the star Regulus to the star Denebola. If this constellation is required to line up with the fifth 30° sign, then the equinox was in the beginning of Aries between A.D. 100 and 100 B.C. If we do the same experiment with constellation Scorpio, we get similar results.

This agrees reasonably well with the date of about 150 B.C. for Hipparchus. The tropical zodiac used in the *Bhāgavatam* could be this old but not much older. The reason is that as we move back in time before 100 B.C., the signs, shifting in reverse, gradually move ahead of the constellations that they are named after. This means that each sign would have a name that would become appropriate only in the future, when the sign lined up with its constellation.

It may be that the *Bhāgavata* and *Viṣṇu Purāṇas* (or their underlying traditions) were updated astronomically at some time near the beginning of the Christian era by introduction of the tropical zodiac inherited from Hipparchus. Their statements about the zodiac cannot date back much earlier, due to the problem of misalignment of signs and constellations. However, these *Purāṇas* also contain much older material. For example, the *Viṣṇu Purāṇa* states that

> When the sun, most excellent sage, is in the first degree of the lunar mansion, Kṛttikā, and the moon is in the fourth of Vishākhā; or when the sun is in the third degree of Vishākhā, and the moon is in the head of Kṛttikā (these positions being contemporary with the equinoxes), that equinoctial season is holy (and is styled the Mahāvishubha, or the great equinox) (Wilson, 1980, p. 325).

The vernal equinox was at the principal star of Kṛttikā (Alcyone in the Pleiades) in about 2222 B.C., and the autumnal equinox was at the principal star of Viśākhā (thought to be Iota Librae) in about 1635 B.C. So the statement from *Viṣṇu Purāṇa* appears to refer to a time period somewhere in this range of dates. (We use star positions and not *nakṣatra* intervals in these calculations because we do not know how *nakṣatra* intervals would have been defined before the current era. The difference between the two dates may be partly due to the choice of intervals.)

At first glance, this seems strange, since the *Viṣṇu Purāṇa's* statement about the equinoxes in Kṛttikā and Viśākhā directly follows the statement putting them in Meṣa and Tulā. It appears that the person who wrote this thought that Meṣa should begin near Kṛttikā (the Pleiades), but the constellation of the Ram (Meṣa) certainly never began there.

It may be that Indian astronomers adopted the Greek tropical zodiac—defined as starting with the vernal equinox in the beginning of the sign Aries—and they were never concerned with zodiacal constellations. An editor of the *Viṣṇu Purāṇa* may have thought, on the basis of old texts, that the vernal equinox was in Kṛttikā, and he naturally assumed that Aries starts there.

Later on, around A.D. 500, the authors of *Jyotiṣa Śāstras* brought things up to date and fixed Meṣa (Aries) to the star Revatī (Zeta Piscium) in Pisces. This created the modern Indian sidereal zodiac, which is slightly skewed relative to the constellations, due to the precession between the second century B.C. and the fifth century A.D.

We note that some authors cast doubt on dates derived from texts that place an equinox or solstice near a particular constellation. They say that, gross errors could have been made in solstice or equinox measurements, and such errors invalidate precessional dates. For example, David Pingree pushed forward the precessional date of the *Jyotiṣavedāṅga* by several centuries on the plea that there easily could have been an error of 10 days in determining the winter solstice (Pingree, 1973, p. 10). In another context, Willy Hartner said that "without instruments (gnomon), the determination of the solstices will needs be affected with an uncertainty of ± eight days or more" (Hartner, 1965, p. 13).

In view of the statements found in the *Viṣṇu Purāṇa*, let us consider the effect of such errors in determining an equinox. An error of ±10 days results in an error of about ±720 years in precessional dating. If we reduce the date when Viśākhā was at the vernal equinox by 720 years (assuming that the error is negative), we get 915 B.C. Likewise, the date when the Pleiades fell on the vernal equinox is reduced to 1502 B.C. So even if a gross, 10-day error fell consistently in the right direction to make things look too old, the *Viṣṇu Purāṇa's* statement about the Mahāvishubha is still of considerable antiquity. Precessional dating is crude due to the possibility of various errors, but it may still give us a "ball park" figure. We should consider, of course, that errors may also fall in such a way as to make things look too young.

8.2.1 Dating by the Śiśumāra Constellation

The Śiśumāra constellation is described in verses 5.23.4, 5.23.5, and 5.23.6–7 of the *Bhāgavatam*. This constellation includes all of the twenty-eight *nakṣatras*, as well as additional stars to the north of the ecliptic. It is sometimes considered an incarnation of Kṛṣṇa, Vāsudeva, and it is meditated upon by yogis.

The Śiśumāra constellation includes the stars listed in Table 8.1. These star assignments produce a somewhat irregular figure of an

TABLE 8.1
The Śiśumāra Constellation

Text	Feature	Constellation
5.23.5	end of tail	Dhruvaloka
	body of tail	Prajāpati, Agni, Indra, and Dharma
	base of tail	Dhātā and Vidhātā
	hips	the Seven Sages (Sapta-ṛṣi)
	right side	*nakṣatras* marking *udagayana*
	left side	*nakṣatras* marking *dakṣiṇāyana*
	back	Ajavīthī (Mūlā, Uttarāṣāḍhā, and Pūrvāṣāḍhā)
5.23.6	abdomen	*ākāśa* Ganges (the Milky Way)
	right and left loins	Punarvasu and Puṣyā
	right and left feet	Ārdrā and Āśleṣā
	right and left nostrils	Abhijit and Uttarāṣāḍhā
	right and left eyes	Śravaṇā and Pūrvāṣāḍhā
	right and left ears	Dhaniṣṭhā and Mūlā
	ribs on the left side	8 *nakṣatras:* Maghā to Anurādhā
	ribs on the right side	8 *nakṣatras*: Mṛgaśīrṣā to Pūrvabhādra
	right and left shoulders	Śatabhiṣā and Jyeṣṭhā

animal, typical of star constellations. This figure is shown in Figure 8.2 for A.D. 1000. Its head is pointing down, towards the winter solstice.

In the figure, the positive x-axis marks the vernal equinox, and the negative x-axis marks the autumnal equinox. The positive y-axis marks the summer solstice, and the negative y-axis marks the winter solstice. Due to precession of the equinoxes, the Śiśumāra figure rotates clockwise or counterclockwise when the date is changed.

The straight, dark gray lines connect pairs of *nakṣatras* corresponding to the bodily parts listed above under 5.23.6. They include a line connecting Maghā to Anurādhā. In Figure 8.2, dating to A.D. 1000, this is the nearly vertical straight line on the left hand side. Maghā is the *nakṣatra* at the top of this line, and Anurādhā is at the bottom. The southern course of the sun (*dakṣiṇāyana*) goes down the left-hand side of the diagram from summer solstice to autumnal equinox to winter solstice. It is appropriate for the Maghā/Anurādhā line to fall in this interval, since according to 5.23.6, the stars from Maghā to Anurādhā mark the southern course.

Figure 8.3 shows the Śiśumāra in 3000 B.C., and the situations for intermediate dates are shown in the CD. For dates back to 1000 B.C., the Maghā/Anurādhā line reasonably represents *dakṣiṇāyana*. But in

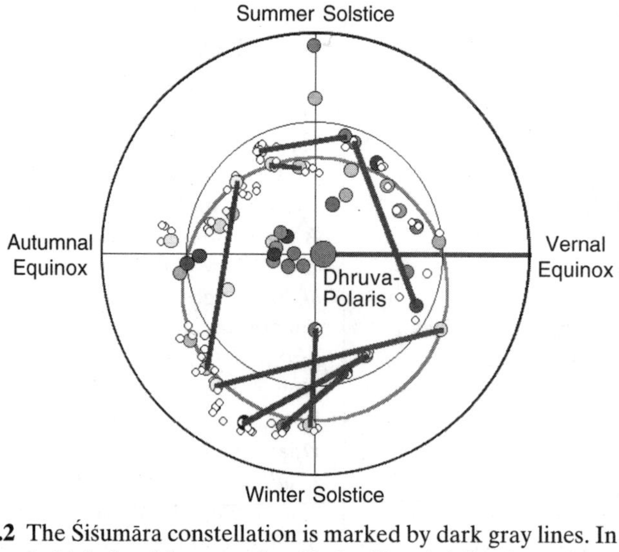

Figure 8.2 The Śiśumāra constellation is marked by dark gray lines. In A.D. 1000 it is oriented with its head downward and its bodily axis is lined-up with the solstices.

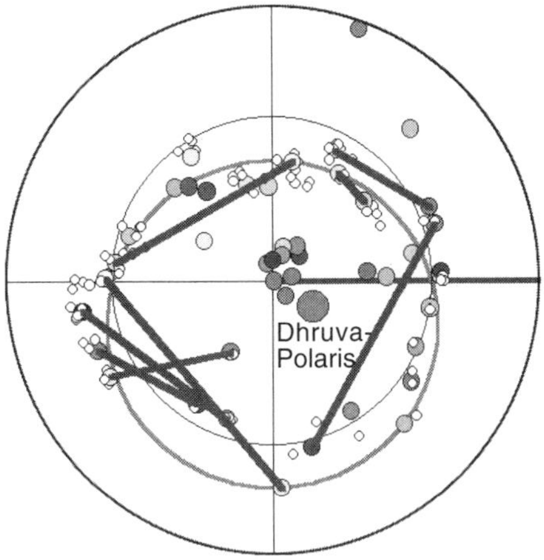

Figure 8.3 The Śiśumāra constellation is marked by dark gray lines. In 3000 B.C. it is not aligned with the solstices and its sides do not correspond to the northward and southward paths of the sun.

3000 B.C., it so greatly tilted that this assignment is no longer reasonable.

The same thing can be said of the line from Pūrvabhādra to Mṛgaśīrṣā on the right-hand side. These stars are said in 5.23.6 to represent *udagayana*, but they cease to do so if we go back as far as 3000 B.C. In general, the Śiśumāra is constructed with an axis of symmetry that should align with the axis from the winter solstice to the summer solstice. Between 1000 B.C. and A.D. 1000, it lines up with this axis reasonably well. But if we go back to 3000 B.C., it no longer does so.

Therefore, the *Bhāgavatam's* account of the Śiśumāra constellation supports a precessional date in the range of 1000 B.C. to A.D. 1000. This is contrary to the traditional date of about 3100 B.C. for the *Bhāgavatam*, but it may represent a relatively recent astronomical update to the old text (see Section 8.3, below). Unlike the statement putting the equinoxes in Meṣa and Tulā, this update seems to involve strictly Indian material. However, it may have taken place at about the same time.

In his commentary on 5.23.5, Śrīdhara Swami says that *dakṣiṇa-āyanāni* refers to the fourteen *nakṣatras*, Puṣyā through Uttarāṣāḍhā, on the left side of the Śiśumāra. This statement gives us a precessional date range from 790 B.C. to A.D. 1111, since this is the period when these stars lie in the *dakṣiṇāyana* interval.

8.3 THE MYSTERIOUS EPOCH OF 3102 B.C.

The traditional date in India for the beginning of Kali-yuga is February 18, 3102 B.C., as measured by the Gregorian calendar. According to the *Purāṇas,* Lord Kṛṣṇa departed from the earth at this time. Thus it is the closing date for the main events of the *Mahābhārata*, in which Kṛṣṇa was a major participant.

According to Indologists, 3102 B.C. is far too early for the events of the *Mahābhārata*, which portray an Iron Age civilization in the Ganges basin of India. Some archaeologists place the advent of the Indian Iron Age in about 1000–700 B.C. (Agrawal, 1974, p. 147), and others push it back to the second half of the second millenium B.C. or somewhat earlier (Shaffer, 1984). So how did people arrive at 3102 B.C. in the first place? There is an interesting story behind this, which we present in this section.

We begin with the astronomical tables produced for Alfonso X of Castile, which list the date of Noah's Flood as February 17, 3102 B.C. Similar Flood dates were produced by many medieval and renaissance Christian chronologists, but this one turns out to be exactly one day earlier than the traditional Indian date for the beginning of Kali-yuga (North, 1977, p. 317). This date was widely reproduced in medieval Western astronomical works. But it belongs to the *yuga* system of India, and in that system Kali-yuga does not begin with a flood. So how did it find its way into European literature?

It turns out that this date can be traced back to the *Book of Thousands* written by Abu Ma'shar al-Balkhi in the ninth century. Abu Ma'shar taught that planetary motions repeat with a period of 360,000 years and that a deluge occurs every 180,000 years. According to his calculations, the last deluge occurred on February 17, 3102 B.C., and it was marked by a conjunction of all the planets in the beginning of Aries, the first sign of the zodiac (van der Waerden, 1987, p. 539). This combines a typical date for what looks like the Biblical Flood with huge periods not at all in line with Biblical thinking. This is puzzling, and we still have to explain the connection with the floodless Kali-yuga of India.

The mathematician B. L. van der Waerden offered a speculative reconstruction, in which Hellenistic astronomers living somewhere in the Near East developed methods for theoretically computing planetary conjunctions by about 200 B.C. (van der Waerden, 1987). These astronomers were inspired by the idea of a deluge that would occur when all of the planets lined up at the beginning of the zodiac. They may have based their ideas directly on Babylonian traditions of the deluge, bypassing the Bible. Thus the Babylonian priest Berossus in about 300 B.C. is said to have connected the deluge with a conjunction of all the planets in Capricorn, and the Hellenistic astronomers may have followed this tradition.

According to van der Waerden, these astronomers worked backwards in time using conjunctions of Jupiter and Saturn in an effort to calculate the time of the most recent mean alignment of planets. The result, using their data, was February 17, 3102 B.C.

Later on, astronomers in this school developed "eternal tables," based on the assumption that all planets return to their starting points in a great year of 360,000 years. Their work filtered into Persia and then India, where it was taken up by the astronomer Āryabhaṭa in the fifth century. Āryabhaṭa multiplied the length of the great year by 12, yielding a period of 4,320,000 years. He also replaced the deluge with the beginning of Kali-yuga. Subsequently, Āryabhaṭa's calculations were used in the revised Persian Tables of the Shah, ordered in A.D. 556 by King Khosro Anoshirvan. Abu Ma'shar's work made use of the Tables of the Shah.

8.3.1 Conjunctions of Jupiter and Saturn

Let us examine how a conjunction of the planets can be calculated using conjunctions of Jupiter and Saturn. First of all, since the period of Jupiter is about twelve years and the period of Saturn about thirty, Jupiter slowly catches up with Saturn and overtakes it about once every twenty years. This means that if you are looking for a conjunction of all the planets, it is convenient to go backwards in time by the twenty-year periods of Jupiter-Saturn conjunctions and search for additional planetary alignments.

Islamic astronomers in the ninth to the twelfth centuries were doing this kind of calculation in an effort to date the deluge (van der Waerden, 1980, p. 122). They looked at mean motions of Jupiter and Saturn, in which the planets are assumed to move at a steady, average pace (disregarding retrograde motion). They called a twenty-year conjunction of Jupiter and Saturn a small conjunction. Three successive small conjugations formed a near-equilateral triangle called a trigon, as shown in Figure 8.4.

The system starts in the beginning of Aries. The first trigon falls in the signs Aries, Leo, and Sagittarius, called the fire triplicity. Each successive trigon shifts forward slightly, but the first four all fall in this triplicity. In aggregate, they are called a middle conjunction (de Santillana, 1969, p. 400).

The next four trigons fall in the earth triplicity, consisting of Taurus, Capricorn, and Virgo. Next comes the air triplicity of Gemini, Aquarius, and Libra, followed by the water triplicity of Cancer, Pisces, and Scorpio. Four middle conjunctions carry one through all the signs of the zodiac and are called a big conjunction. However, a big conjunction leaves one about four signs ahead of one's starting point (assumed here to be the beginning of Aries). To return to the starting point, three big conjunctions are required, and this is called a mighty conjunction.

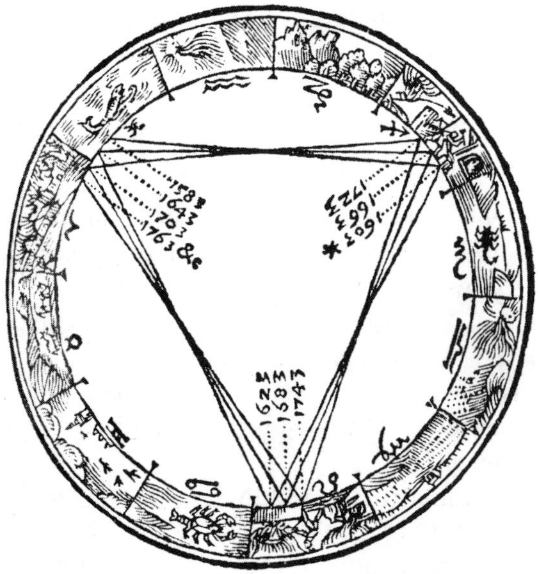

Figure 8.4
Three successive conjunctions of Jupiter and Saturn mark out an equilateral triangle, as shown here. As time passes, the successive triangles slowly rotate around the ecliptic, spending time in successive triplicities, or groups of three zodiacal signs (de Santillana and von Dechend, 1969, opposite p. 268).

8.3.2 Computing the Deluge

Van der Waerden proposed that Hellenistic astronomers computed the deluge date by using this system of Jupiter-Saturn conjunctions (see Appendix 17).

To find out about conjunctions near 3102 B.C., it is necessary to work backwards. To illustrate this process, suppose that some Hellenistic astronomer tried to do this on January 1, 1 A.D. He would have known the mean positions of Jupiter and Saturn at this time. From this, he could easily have computed the date for the most recent small conjunction. To get back from then to 3102 B.C., it is necessary to subtract about 156 small conjunctions (of about twenty years apiece).

This procedure inevitably introduces errors. The length of a small conjunction depends on the numbers used for the motion of Jupiter and Saturn. If we use Abu Ma'shar's numbers, a small conjunction takes 19.8478 years. If we use modern numbers, it takes 19.8585 years. The difference is small, but it adds up over thirty-one centuries to about 1.67 years. So we conclude that if our astronomer hit the date of February 17, 3102 B.C., he did so by chance. Ancient astronomers made mistakes in their measurements, and this is likely to have produced errors of a year or so in their deluge calculations.

8.3.3 Modern Calculations

So why couldn't the date be a product of chance? As van der Waerden points out, "According to modern calculation, no conjunction took place in 3102 B.C." (van der Waerden, 1980, p. 119). This is what we would expect, given the random errors affecting astronomical back-calculations in ancient times. But it turns out that a *near* conjunction of all the planets did take place precisely on the Kali-yuga date of February 18, 3102 B.C.

To evaluate such conjunctions, we used an up-to-date ephemeris program written by S. L. Moshier, based on algorithms from the Astronomical Almanac. With this program, we examined the positions of the planets for every day from January 1, 4000 B.C. to January 1, 2000 A.D.

In that entire period of time, there are no alignments of planets that come even close to being exact. But there are many approximate alignments, and one of the closest in this entire period occurs exactly on the Kali-yuga starting date.

This alignment involves thirteen astronomical longitudes, and it is presented in the table below. The astronomical objects in the alignment are listed in the second column. The numbers in the third column are the ecliptic longitudes of the objects in degrees for the Julian day 588465.5, corresponding to February 18, 3102 B.C. These longitudes average out to 306.42 degrees[1]. The numbers in the fourth column are the differences between the individual longitudes and the average longitude. Although there is considerable spread in these differences, this spread is nearly at a minimum for the entire 6,000 year period from 4000 B.C. to the year 2000.

This table requires some explanation. First of all, we should consider what is meant by a Julian day. In astronomy, time is measured

TABLE 8.2
The Alignment of February 18, 3102 B.C.

Number	Object	Longitude	Difference
1	Sun	303.84	-2.58
2	Moon	304.44	-1.98
3	Mercury	288.36	-18.06
4	Venus	316.37	9.95
5	Mars	300.61	-5.81
6	Jupiter	317.43	11.01
7	Saturn	276.51	-29.91
8	Uranus	340.73	34.31
9	Neptune	250.31	-56.11
10	Pluto	308.60	2.18
11	Ketu	327.21	20.79
12	Ceres	328.56	22.14
13	Citra + 180°	313.41	6.99

[1]When averaging angles, there is the problem that, to give one example, the average of 1° and 359° is 180°, even though we want 0°. To avoid this, we average over vectors pointing to the desired angles in the x,y plane. This method gives us the right averages for general sets of longitudes distributed around the circle.

from the epoch of January 1 of the year 4713 B.C.—a date chosen for technical reasons by Joseph Scaliger of Leyden in 1583 (Neugebauer, 1975, p. 1061). The "Julian day" is the number of days from noon of this date, as measured at the prime meridian at Greenwich. This is converted into day/month/year using the Gregorian calendar. A Julian day ending in .5 corresponds to midnight at Greenwich, since .5 days from noon is midnight. Thus our table is for midnight, the beginning of February 18, at Greenwich.

In Indian astronomy, a similar system was used. Time was expressed by the *ahargana*, or "collection of days," counted from a particular epoch. Typically, this epoch was midnight on the beginning of the first day of Kali-yuga, as measured on the meridian through Ujjain. This city is about 76° east of Greenwich, a difference of about five hours. In Ujjain our date is therefore at about five in the morning of the 18th.

Ancient astronomers referred to seven "planets," consisting of the sun, the moon, and Mercury through Saturn. The outer planets, Uranus, Neptune, and Pluto, were discovered only recently, as far as we can tell from existing records. Nonetheless, Uranus, Neptune, and Pluto are also part of the Kali-yuga alignment. Ceres, the largest asteroid, was discovered in the 19th century, and it is also part of the alignment.

As far as orbital physics is concerned, the fact that the sun, moon, and five planets are partially aligned does not imply that four other planets should also be aligned with these seven. The four additional planets—Uranus, Neptune, Pluto, and Ceres—could be anywhere in

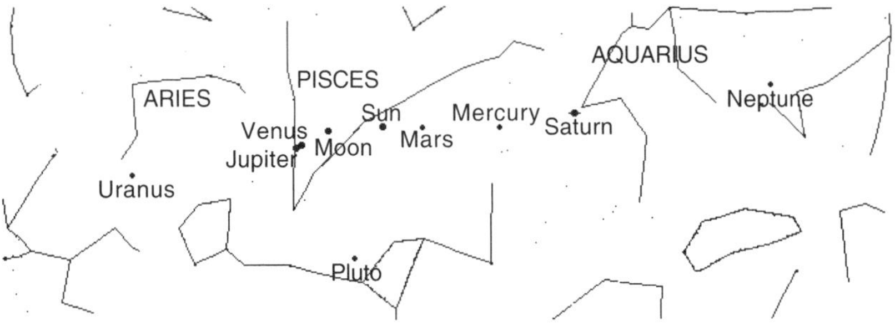

Figure 8.5 The sun, moon, and planets are shown for midnight of February 18, 3102 B.C., according to modern ephemeris calculations (done by the program called SkyGlobe). Note that even Uranus, Neptune, and Pluto are part of the alignment, which covers about 90° of the sky with these planets included.

the 360° of the circle. But on the Kali-yuga date, they were clustered within an arc of 90° along with the seven traditional planets.

In Indian astronomy, the ascending and descending nodes of the moon are treated as planets, called Rāhu and Ketu. These nodes mark the points on the celestial sphere where the plane of the ecliptic intersects the plane of the moon's orbit, and they are connected with solar and lunar eclipses. In Western traditions, they are known as the head and tail of the dragon. According to Indian astronomy, Ketu is part of the Kali-yuga alignment, and we see from the table that this is correct. Rāhu, of course, is always 180° from Ketu, and it is situated opposite to the alignment.

It is often said that the Kali-yuga alignment is in the beginning of Aries, the first sign of the sidereal zodiac. Actually, Venus, Jupiter, and Ketu lie in Aries, if this is defined according to medieval *Jyotiṣa Śāstras* as beginning 10 minutes of arc after the star Zeta Piscium. The sun, moon, Mercury, Mars, and Saturn lie in Pisces, the sign before Aries.

We should note that traditional Indian astronomers used a sidereal zodiac, which is fixed relative to the stars. In contrast, Western astronomy has inherited the tropical zodiac from its Hellenistic forbears. In the tropical zodiac, Aries begins with the vernal equinox, by definition, and it shifts with the precession of the equinoxes. In this zodiac, the Kali-yuga alignment falls in Aquarius and Capricorn, with the midpoint near the beginning of Aquarius.

However, it may be misleading to look at the Kali-yuga alignment from the point of view of the Western zodiac. Interesting insights emerge if we instead consider the Indian *nakṣatra* system.

Consider Citra, the bright star known in the West as Spica (Alpha Virginis). It is one of the twenty-eight *nakṣatras* or "lunar mansions" that mark the ecliptic in Indian astronomy. It is significant that the lunar months of the Indian calendar are named after *nakṣatras*. The first month of the spring season is traditionally Caitra, which is named after Citra.

Lunar months are determined by the phases of the moon, and they can be either *amānta*, meaning from new moon to new moon, or *pūrṇimānta*, meaning from full moon to full moon. Ideally, a lunar month was named after the *nakṣatra* in which the full moon appeared during that month. As with the zodiac, the *nakṣatra* constellations correspond to fixed subdivisions of the ecliptic, and the full moon is "in" a *nakṣatra* if its longitude lies in the appropriate subdivision. In practice, the moon might become full in one of the *nakṣatras* on either side of the one designated by the month's name.

At the time of the Kali-yuga conjunction, the moon was new and it marked the beginning of the *amānta* lunar month of Caitra. According to the SkyGlobe astronomy program, the new moon occurred on about 9:16 p.m., New Delhi time, on February 17, 3102 B.C.—about three hours before midnight of the 18th. At midnight in the beginning of March 5, the moon was full in close conjunction with the star Citra. Thus the Kali-yuga conjunction occurred on the first day of the beginning of Spring, according to the ancient Indian calendar.

8.3.4 High-Precision Conjunctions

To evaluate how close the Kali-yuga alignment is, we need a single number to represent the spreading out of the planets and other objects along the ecliptic. For any given date, we use Moshier's ephemeris program to calculate the longitudes of the thirteen astronomical objects. We then compute the root-mean-square difference between the thirteen longitudes and their average. This tells us how far the individual longitudes spread out around their average. For the Kali-yuga alignment, this spread factor comes to 22.85°.

We evaluated the spread factor for every day from 4000 B.C. to A.D. 2000 and looked for days when it dipped down to a minimum (meaning that it was higher the day before and the day after). These can be called minimal alignments. In this entire 6,000-year period, there were only three minimal alignments in which the spread of the thirteen objects was no greater than it was on February 18, 3102 B.C. These appear in Table 8.3.

What we see is that the alignment of 3102 B.C. is not exact, but it is one of the three closest alignments in the last 6,000 years.

We should emphasize that although these numbers reflect up-to-date astronomical knowledge, they are also subject to error. We do not know by observation what the planets were doing thousands of years ago, and no two modern ephemeris programs will give exactly the same answers. However, given uniformitarian assumptions, these calculations are probably not very far off.

If the date of February 18, 3102 B.C. was obtained by astronomical calculation between 2,200 and 1,500 years ago, then it would have

TABLE 8.3
Alternate Alignments Since 4000 B.C.

Date	Julian Day	Spread in Degrees
Feb. 18, 3102 B.C.	588465.5	22.85
Mar. 1, 1597 B.C.	1138178.5	21.58
Mar. 28, 1597 B.C.	1138205.5	22.08

been affected by random errors in the astronomical parameters used by astronomers in that period. These errors certainly should be greater than the corresponding modern ones. Yet the date agrees to the day with one of the best astronomical alignments in a 6,000 year period, as determined by modern calculations. This is quite improbable.

One might anticipate that more alignments will show up if we limit ourselves to a smaller set of objects. In fact, if we use the sun, the moon, and the five planets Mercury through Saturn, we find 324 minimal alignments in the 6,000 year period with a spread no greater than the spread of 13.56° that occurs on the Kali-yuga date. If we add Ketu to the list of objects, the number of minimal alignments no worse than the Kali-yuga alignment goes down to fifty-two. If we add Citra plus 180°, it goes down to ten. In each of these cases, the Kali-yuga alignment is minimal in the sense that the spread dips down to a minimum on February 18, 3102 B.C.

The uniqueness of the Kali-yuga alignment depends on the contribution of all of the astronomical objects that make it up. In particular, if we look at the positions of Jupiter and Saturn in the alignment, we see that they are separated by nearly 41°. They do not line up at all well, and therefore the Kali-yuga alignment would not be found by someone looking at Jupiter-Saturn conjunctions with accurate data.

But it so happens that Islamic astronomers such as Abu Ma'shar had inaccurate parameters for Jupiter and Saturn that just happened to give a conjunction of these planets at the Kali-yuga date. How did this happen? The most plausible answer is that they followed Āryabhaṭa, who *assumed* an exact conjunction of planets on this date.

Let us examine this matter more closely. First of all, we can not trace these parameters back to Claudius Ptolemy. According to his data, the mean positions of Jupiter and Saturn on that date were about 325° and 291°. If Ptolemy had searched for Jupiter-Saturn conjunctions, he would have missed the Kali-yuga date.

On this date, the best alignment of the thirteen objects occurred at about 4:48 a.m. on the 18th, Greenwich time, or about 9:52 a.m. in Ujjain. It would have been 6:48 a.m. in Alexandria. Āryabhaṭa's midnight system put the Kali-yuga date at midnight in the beginning of February 18, and his sunrise system put it roughly at sunrise at 6:00 a.m. on that day. In contrast, Abu Ma'shar and the Tables of the Shah put the Flood date on midnight of February 17, the day before.

Van der Waerden explains this by pointing out that Abu Ma'shar added 1/3600 of a day to the year used in Āryabhaṭa's midnight system (van der Waerden, 1987, p. 537). As we mentioned in Appendix 16, Āryabhaṭa commented that 3,600 years of Kali-yuga had elapsed on his twenty-third birthday. Apparently, Abu Ma'shar and the author of the Persian tables reckoned from Āryabhaṭa's twenty-third birthday, using their slightly longer year. By doing this, they missed the optimal alignment by one day.

Van der Waerden agrees that Abu Ma'shar and the Tables of the Shah depend on the work of Āryabhaṭa (van der Waerden, 1987, p. 538). Āryabhaṭa assumed an exact mean conjunction of all seven planets on the Kali-yuga date, and nearly all medieval Indian astronomers did the same. So it is no coincidence that calculations based on Indian astronomy yield a Jupiter-Saturn conjunction at that date. But the question remains: How was the date selected in the first place?

8.3.5 Alternative Explanations

At present, this remains a mystery. The possible explanations are as follows:

1. Hellenistic astronomers, using erroneous data based on speculation and poor, naked-eye observations, stumbled on the date of the Kali-yuga conjunction by chance. We estimated above that the error in calculating a mean Jupiter/Saturn conjunction in about 3102 B.C. comes to about 1.67 years. (According to SkyGlobe, there

was an actual Jupiter/Saturn conjunction on about Jan. 9, 3104 B.C.) So the chance hypothesis says that an error of about 2 years landed our Hellenistic astronomers on the precise day of an unusual planetary conjunction. A lucky hit!

2. The conjunction of February 18, 3102 B.C. was observed, and the date was preserved in historical records up to the time of Āryabhaṭa (about A.D. 500). At some point in this period, people forgot that an unusual *partial* alignment had occurred, and they imagined an exact alignment on this date.

   For records to be effectively maintained, a well-organized civilization must have existed over this entire span of time. However, well before Āryabhaṭa's time, surviving records may have become fragmentary and poorly understood. As knowledge declined, the growing vacuum was filled by newer developments starting nearly from scratch, but with inspiration from stories of the past. These new developments included the astronomy of the Babylonians and the Hellenistic Greeks.

   In India, Āryabhaṭa combined some of these new materials with surviving ancient fragments and started a new school of thought. By successfully establishing a new standard, he contributed to the neglect of older material, which gradually disappeared completely. In the West, the rise of Babylonian and Greek astronomy had a similar effect.

   This loss of earlier writings is an accepted social phenomenon. For example, Neugebauer pointed out that when new authoritative works on a subject are produced, people may cease to pay attention to older works, which then fall into oblivion. In particular, this process erased much of the history of Greek mathematics and astronomy. He remarked that "The dominating influence of Euclid's Elements succeeded in destroying almost all references to pre-Euclidian writings, and essentially the same effect was produced by Ptolemy's works" (Neugebauer, 1945, p. 16).

3. Another explanation of the Kali-yuga conjunction is that it was found by calculations using advanced astronomical knowledge and mathematical techniques. This hypothesis also implies the existence of an advanced civilization that greatly declined before the advent of the well-known civilizations of classical antiquity.

4. A fourth hypothesis is that people were informed of the significance

of the conjunction of 3102 B.C. through communication from higher beings. Although this is not acceptable from a conventional scientific perspective, it would have seemed perfectly reasonable in ancient times. In India, for example, the *Purāṇas* state that before the advent of Kali-yuga, great saints and sages openly served as intermediaries between human society and higher civilizations within the universe. Other ancient societies, such as the Sumerians, also maintained that their ancestors had learned extensively from higher beings descending from the heavens.

Apart from the theory of pure chance, all of the possible explanations of the Kali-yuga date require the existence of an ancient civilization that was highly advanced. The question remains: Where was this advanced civilization, and when did it exist? At present, this remains a mystery. We note, however, that the evidence for sophisticated astronomical knowledge in the *Bhāgavatam* also implies the existence of advanced scientific knowledge at some time before the modern scientific period. (See Sections 4.4 and 4.5.) For evidence of remnants of advanced astronomy in the *Sūrya-siddhānta*, see Appendix 10.

8.4 THE YUGA SYSTEM

The chronology of the *Purāṇas* consists of a series of time divisions that can collectively be called the *yuga* system. This system is expounded in the *Purāṇas,* in the principal *Jyotiṣa Śāstras*, and in many medieval Sanskrit texts. The *Manu-saṁhitā* and the *Mahābhārata* also define this system, and the four original *Vedas* may allude to it indirectly.

This chronological system is based on four time periods called *yugas*. The *Manu-saṁhitā* describes the lengths of the *yugas* in years as listed in Table 8.4 (Dikshit, 1969a, pp. 103–4).

Each *yuga* begins and ends with intermediate periods, called the *sandhyā* and *sandhyāṁśa*, which are one-tenth as long as the main body of the *yuga*. The total of the four *yugas* is called a divine *yuga* (*divya-yuga*), and it comes to 12,000 years. This period is also called a *mahāyuga*, a *catur-yuga*, or simply a *yuga* in various texts. A day of Brahmā, also known as a *kalpa*, is defined to be 1,000 divine *yugas*, or 12,000,000 years. It is also mentioned that a Patriarchate, or *manvantara*, consists of seventy-one *divya-yugas*.

TABLE 8.4
Yugas in Divine Years

Yuga	Length	Sandhyā	Main Period	Sandhyāṁśa
Kṛta-yuga	4,800	400	4,000	400
Tretā-yuga	3,600	300	3,000	300
Dvāpara-yuga	2,400	200	2,000	200
Kali-yuga	1,200	100	1,000	100

The *yuga* periods are arranged like a set of bowling pins according to the pattern 4+3+2+1 = 10. Each of these numbers is then multiplied by the factors, 100 + 1,000 + 100 = 1,200, which are suggestive of dawn, daytime, and evening.

In *Jyotiṣa Śāstras* such as the *Sūrya-siddhānta*, the *yugas* are explicitly multiplied by 360 to yield the following lengths:

TABLE 8.5
The Yuga System in Human Years

Division	Length (years)
Kṛta-yuga	1,728,000
Tretā-yuga	1,296,000
Dvāpara-yuga	864,000
Kali-yuga	432,000
divya-yuga	4,320,000
manvantara	306,720,000
day of Brahmā	4,320,000,000

The multiplication is done by replacing years in the *Manu-saṁhitā's yuga* definitions by divine years of 360 human years.

The *Bhāgavata Purāṇa* follows the pattern of the *Manu-saṁhitā* by specifying a *divya-yuga* of 12,000 divine years, with Kṛta-yuga and so on as multiples of 1,200 by 4:3:2:1 (*Bhāgavatam* 3.11.18–19). A *manvantara* period of a little more than 71 *divya-yugas* is also defined, as well as a *kalpa*, or day of Brahmā, of 1,000 *divya-yugas* (*Bhāgavatam* 3.11.24).

There is no explicit reference to the span of 4,320,000 years in the *Bhāgavatam*. But this period is implied by the use of the words *divya varṣa* (divine year) in verse 3.11.18. Although the divine year is not defined in the text, verse 5.20.30 says that a day and night of the demigods is one human year. This suggests that a year of the demigods should be 360 years, since the year is assigned 360 days. In the *Vāyu Purāṇa*, this is spelled out by the statement that 360,000 human years equals 1,000 divine years (Tagare, 1987, p. 398).

It is noteworthy that the *Bhāgavatam* gives 360 days as the length of one year and it never explicitly mentions a year of 365¼ days. This gives us a consistent situation in which a divine day is 360 human days and a divine year is 360 human years. However, *Jyotiṣa Śāstras* such as the *Sūrya-siddhānta* use a solar year of 365¼+ days when speaking of the *mahāyuga* of 4,320,000 years. We show below in Section 8.5 that there are good astronomical reasons for using a nominal year of 360 days and that this period was never intended as a literal solar year. But the question remains of whether the *Bhāgavatam* and other *Purāṇas* intended the *mahāyuga* to be composed of 360-day years or of realistic solar years of 365¼+ days.

There is some controversy regarding the history of the *yuga* system. The traditional view in India is that the *yugas* are real and have therefore been going on for millions of years. The view of modern historians is that the *yugas* are mere ideas that developed historically through a series of stages. In particular, the suggestion is often made that the four *yugas* once added up to 12,000 human years and were later expanded to 12,000 divine years of 360 years apiece. We discuss these historical issues below in Section 8.4.1.

In his famous *Cosmos* series, the astronomer Carl Sagan remarked that "The Hindu religion is the only one of the world's great faiths dedicated to the idea that the Cosmos itself undergoes an immense, indeed an infinite, number of deaths and rebirths. It is the only religion in which the time scales correspond, no doubt by accident, to those of modern scientific cosmology" (Sagan, 1980, p. 258). Sagan is referring to the fact that each of the cycles in the *yuga* system ends with some form of *pralaya* or annihilation. Thus the day of Brahmā ends with the destruction of the three worlds, Bhūr,

Bhuvar, and Svar, followed by a night of Brahmā of equal duration. This is followed by a new creation in the next day of Brahmā.

The day of Brahmā lasts 4,320,000,000 years, and this roughly matches the modern scientific estimate of 4.5 billion years for the age of the earth. The *manvantaras* of about 307 million years remind us, even more roughly, of geological periods spanning hundreds of millions of years. Somehow or other, the Purāṇic time scales make sense from the standpoint of modern geology and cosmology. In contrast, Biblical chronology dates the creation of the world to a few thousand years ago—on October 23, 4004 B.C. according to the famous calculations of Archbishop James Ussher (North, 1977, p. 307).

The *yugas* reflect vast cosmic cycles, but they also express a cyclic understanding of human history. According to this concept, life on earth revolves through a sequence of four ages, starting with Kṛta-yuga. This period is also called Satya-yuga, or the age of truth, and it corresponds to the golden age of Greek mythology. In this period, life is idyllic and human beings live tranquilly in a state of pure goodness. The succeeding three *yugas*, corresponding to the ages of silver, bronze, and iron, are marked by increasing degradation in human society. The final age of Kali is a period of darkness and quarrel. But after a great debacle, goodness is restored, and the cycle begins again with Kṛta-yuga.

From the standpoint of modern historical dating, a *divya-yuga* of 12,000 ordinary years fits human history much better than a *divya-yuga* of 12,000 divine years. Could it be that divine and human cycles of 12,000 years are both intended by the *yuga* system—with one representing events on a cosmic scale and the other mirroring the petty pace of human affairs? There is no explicit indication of this in the *Purāṇas* or the *Mahābhārata*. However, the evidence suggesting a historical transition from human to divine *yugas* might also be taken to imply an acceptance of both scales of time.

In Section 5.2, we pointed out that key features of Purāṇic cosmology (such as Mount Meru) have parallels in traditions from around the world. The same is true of the idea of a temporal cycle characterized by advancing corruption and punctuated by annihilation. Thus the Greeks believed that each set of four ages ended in a catastrophe. Norse mythology taught that the destruction of the gods, called *ragnarok,* was followed by a fresh cycle of creation. The Chinese called the interval between world destructions a "great year," and the Hopi spoke of four worlds, with three ended by destruction (Heinberg, 1989, pp. 107–8). Likewise, the Sioux Indians have a close parallel to the Hindu bull of Dharma that loses one leg during each of the four successive *yugas* (see Appendix 18).

The Purāṇic cycle of the *yugas* is associated with Bhārata-varṣa. Thus the *Bhāgavatam* verse 5.17.12 states that conditions like those of Tretā-yuga prevail in the eight *varṣas* of Jambūdvīpa other than Bhārata-varṣa, and the *Vāyu Purāṇa* assigns the four *yugas* to Bhārata-varṣa alone (Tagare, 1987, p. 398). This is consistent with the interpretation of Bhārata-varṣa as the whole earth and the other eight *varṣas* of Jambūdvīpa as heavenly regions (see Section 6.1).

The *Sūrya-siddhānta* gives some details on the *yuga* system that are widely accepted in Hinduism but do not appear in the *Bhāgavatam*. This astronomical text divides the day of Brahmā into fourteen *manvantara* periods of seventy-one *divya-yugas* apiece (Burgess, 1860, p. 11). Each of these is followed by a *sandhyā*, or twilight period, which lasts one Kṛta-yuga. There is also a beginning *sandhyā* before the first *manvantara*. If we combine a *manvantara* with its *sandhyā*, we get 71.4 *divya-yugas*, since a Kṛta-yuga is 0.4 *divya-yugas*. This may be what verse 3.11.24 of the *Bhāgavatam* means when it says that a *manvantara* is a little more than seventy-one *divya-yugas*. The breakdown between *manvantaras* and *sandhyās* is as follows:

$$1{,}000 = 15 \times .4 + 14 \times 71$$

Having defined the *manvantara* and its *sandhyā*, the *Sūrya-siddhānta* goes on to fix its own date. In this day of Brahmā, six *manvantaras* are said to have elapsed with their respective twilights, and twenty-seven *divya-yugas* have elapsed in the seventh *manvantara*, called Vaivasvata (Burgess, 1860, pp. 12–13). The *Sūrya-siddhānta* dates itself to the beginning of Tretā-yuga by stating that Kṛta-yuga has elapsed in the twenty-eighth *divya-yuga*. According to traditional usage in India, the Tretā and Dvāpara-yugas have passed, and we are in about the 5,000th year of Kali-yuga.

This chronology is generally accepted by followers of the *Bhāgavatam* in India. In the *Golokera Gamana* section of the *Brahma-vaivarta Purāṇa*, it is connected with a timetable which indicates that for the first 5,000 years of Kali-yuga, people will be purified from sins by bathing in the Ganges. There is also mention of a 10,000-year period in which people will be purified by contact with the Lord's devotees. By traditional reckoning, the 5000th year of Kali-yuga falls in 1899.

This prophecy is presented in a dialogue between the goddess Gaṅgā and Lord Kṛṣṇa, who was about to depart from this world. Here we present a translation by Robert Woodfield:

> The Ganges said: "O Lord, best of those who are pleasing, You are going to Goloka, that excellent planet of cows. What will be my destiny here in the age of Kali?" (49)
>
> The Supreme Personality of Godhead said: "Remain on this earth for five thousand years of Kali. The sinful people will give you their sins by bathing (in you). (50)
>
> "Just as sins are (destroyed) by bathing (in you) O Gaṅgā, by touching or even seeing one who is dedicated to chanting My mantra, sins are immediately reduced to ashes. (51)
>
> "Wherever the ancient names of the Lord are, going there with care you will hear them along with them (other female river goddesses mentioned earlier). . . . (52)
>
> "My devotees shall be on the earth for ten thousand years of Kali. My devotees being so, they will constitute one caste. (59)
>
> "When the earth is no longer inhabited by My devotees, the earth will be in the grip of the age of Kali." (60)

8.4.1 Age of the Yuga System

Some Indologists maintain that the system of four *yugas* was originally based on a dice game mentioned in Vedic texts and in the *Mahābhārata* (Gonzalez-Reimann, 1989). In this game, there were four throws, called *kṛta*, *tretā*, *dvāpara*, and *kali*. *Kṛta* was the best throw, with a value of 4, and it means "done" in Sanskrit. *Tretā* and *dvāpara* had values of 3 and 2 (*tri* and *dvā* in Sanskrit), and *kali*, with a value of 1, was the worst throw.

The idea is that this game inspired the cyclic system of *yugas* sometime around the fourth century B.C. The *yugas* were first defined as multiples by 4:3:2:1 of a Kali-yuga of 1,200 human years. Later they were expanded by the device of replacing human years by divine years of 360 human years.

Of course, one could argue that the dice game was inspired by the *yuga* system and that it testifies to the existence of this system in the

Vedic period. Of greater weight is the thesis that the *divya-yuga* of 12,000 divine years is a recent expansion of an earlier cycle of as many human years.

In his treatise on Indian astronomy, S. B. Dikshit offered several counterarguments to this theory. First of all, he pointed out that the idea of a divine day dates back to the Vedic period (Dikshit, 1969a, p. 65). This is shown by the following quote from the *Taittirīya Saṁhitā* of the *Vedas*:

> *ekaṁ vā etaddevānāmahaḥ yatsaṁvatsaraḥ* (The year is equivalent to a day of the gods.) (*Te. Bra.* 3.6.22).

One could infer from this that the divine year was also known in the Vedic period. Saṁvatsara generally denotes a nominal year of 360 days, and a year of the gods should therefore be 360 years, or 360 × 360 days.

Dikshit argued that the 12,000-year *divya-yuga* of the *Manu-saṁhitā* must be made of divine years, since otherwise it wouldn't be called divine, or *divya* (Dikshit, 1969a, p. 104). Thus he maintained that the *divya-yuga* of 4,320,000 = 360 × 12,000 human years dates back to the *Manu-saṁhitā* in the second-century A.D., or earlier.

Dikshit also pointed out that the *Nirukta* of Yaska assigns 1,000 *yugas* to the day of Brahmā, without defining what is meant by a *yuga* (Dikshit, 1969a, p. 102). Thus the day of Brahmā was already known as a series of 1,000 lesser cycles in Yaska's time—about 500 B.C. Of course, these might have been cycles of 12,000 ordinary years.

To see if the *Mahābhārata* supports a cycle of 12,000 human years, we consulted Ganguli's translation and compared it with the Sanskrit text of the critical edition (Tokunaga, 1996). The *Mahābhārata* defines the *yugas* in the standard way as 1,200 years times 4:3:2:1. However, in 3.186.18–21, this is done using the word *varṣa* for year without any qualifying term meaning "divine." The same is true of the verses starting with 12.224.191. Just before the latter verse, it is said that a human year is a day and night of the gods. It is further stated that their day is the *udagayana* and their night is the *dakṣiṇāyana* (the northern and southern courses of the sun). There is, however, no mention of a divine year. Ganguli glosses years as "years of the deities" in the *yuga* definitions, but this appears to be based on traditional understanding and not on the literal reading of the text (Ganguli, vol. IX, p. 155).

Either the *Mahābhārata* is defining a *yuga* cycle that sums to 12,000 human years, or it is implicitly following a tradition that assumes divine years made of days and nights of the gods. The latter is quite plausible, since the *Bhāgavatam* itself defines the *divya-yuga* as 12,000 divine years without ever defining the divine year. Moreover, like the *Mahābhārata*, the *Bhāgavatam* defines a divine day as the northern and southern courses of the sun (i.e. one year). Thus we have a pattern in which 12,000-year periods and divine days are mentioned, but divine years of 360 human years are assumed without mention.

Gonzalez-Reimann (1988) has pointed out that numbers related to the *yuga* system are embedded in Vedic texts, and this is also discussed in Kak, (1993a) and (1993b). For example the *Śatapatha Brāhmaṇa* states that the *Ṛg Veda* contains 432,000 syllables. This is expressed as 12,000 verse *bṛhatis*, each of which has thirty-six syllables, or 10,800 verse *panktis*, each composed of forty syllables.

Some of the fire altars described in the *Vedas* are also built with 10,800 bricks (Gonzalez-Reimann, 1988, p. 108). This suggests that the groundwork for *yuga*-cycle calculations was already laid down in the days of the *Śatapatha Brāhmaṇa* and the Vedic fire sacrifices. The *Śatapatha Brāhmaṇa* is dated by some scholars to 1000–800 B.C. (Seidenberg, 1978, 320).

The number 10,800 is easily arrived at, using numbers that were familiar in Vedic times. For example 10,800 is the number of *muhūrtas* (30ths of a day) in a year of 360 days. It also appears in familiar Western calculations. For example, it is the number of minutes in half a circle (180° × 60 minutes/degree).

The numbers used in the *yuga* system are similar in many ways to numbers used in modern astronomy. The factor of 360 is reminiscent of the number of degrees in a circle. The length of Tretā-yuga is 360 × 3,600, which equals the number of arcseconds in a circle. The length of Dvāpara-yuga is 240 × 3,600, and this comes to ten times the number of seconds in a 24-hour day.

There are also many examples of the numbers 10,800 and 432,000 from Europe and the Near East, and some of these refer specifically to long periods of time. According to Censorinus, 10,800 years was given by Heraclitus as the duration of the Aion. In the Icelandic Edda, Valhalla was said to have 540 doors and 800 warriors would issue from each of these doors to fight with the Wolf. The total number of warriors comes to 432,000 (de Santillana, 1969, p. 162). If people in widely separated places were not independently coming up with these numbers, then time must be allowed for them to widely spread out from some original source.

One possible source is Babylon. According to the ninth-century writer Georgius Syncellus, in 280 B.C. the Babylonian priest Berossus gave 120 *saroi* as the time for the reign of the Babylonian kings before the flood. Since a *saros* is 3,600 years, this comes to 432,000 years (North, 1977, p. 315). Berossus also stated that the time elapsed from the creation to the universal catastrophe is 2,160,000 years (with 2,148,000 years from creation to Alexander the Great and 12,000 years from Alexander to the catastrophe). This is half of a *divya-yuga*, and it is also ten "great sars" of the Babylonians (Sellers, 1992, pp. 196, 200).

It is noteworthy that Berossus expressed 432,000 as 120 saroi of 3,600 years apiece, whereas the Kali-yuga is 1,200 divine years of 360 years apiece. Thus even the arithmetic used in Babylon is similar to that used in India. For some, this suggests that these calculations were transmitted into India from Babylon. However, the *Śatapatha Brāhmaṇa* antedates Berossus, and the Indologist Jean Filliozat has suggested that this transmission could have happened in the inverse order—from India to Mesopotamia (Gonzalez-Reimann, 1988, p. 104). This would imply the presence of *yugas* measured in divine years in India before the third century B.C.

Although the *Bhāgavatam* does not mention precession of the equinoxes directly, a number of scholars have seen a connection between the *yuga* system and precession. For example, Stella Kramrisch, in her study of Hindu temple designs, argues that "All the cyclical numbers in Hindu cosmology are essentially based on the period of the precession of the equinoxes" (Kramrisch, 1946, p. 36). Her observation boils down to the fact that a *divya-yuga* is 2,000 × 2,160 years. The latter period is the time for the vernal equinox to pass through one sign of the zodiac, and thus it is the length of the celebrated ages of the signs, such as the Age of Aquarius.

If this is not mere coincidence, it suggests a link between the *yuga* system and Western astrological calculations, which assign great importance to the 2,160-year ages of the zodiacal signs. This link may extend back to the ancient roots of astrology. Thus the Egyptologist

Jane Sellers has argued that numbers such as 2,160 and 432 represented precession in the ancient Near East long before its rediscovery by Hipparchus in the second century B.C. (Sellers, 1992).

By the way, in this scheme, the cycle of precession takes 25,920 years, and this is 432 sixty-year cycles of Jupiter. The sixty-year cycle of Jupiter is discussed below in Section 8.5, and it would have originally been measured in years of 360 days.

Another number which may be related to the *divya-yuga* is the 360,000-year world-year of the Persians. This was used by Abu Ma'shar of Balkh and traced by B. L. van der Waerden to the sixth-century Persian Tables of the Shah and to earlier Persian sources. It is 1/12 of a *divya-yuga*. Van der Waerden argues that the sixth-century Indian astronomer Āryabhaṭa corrected the Persian theory by "replacing the Persian world-year of 360,000 years by a period twelve times as large" (van der Waerden, 1987, p. 539).

Āryabhaṭa used a *mahāyuga* of 4,320,000 years, and he differed from other Indian astronomers by dividing it into four equal *yugas* (instead of using the 4:3:2:1 division). He was also the sole Indian astronomer to teach that day and night are due to the rotation of the earth on its axis. However, if he thought that the Indian *mahāyuga* used to be much shorter and that his 4.32 million-year cycle was a new invention, he didn't let on. The origin of this period remains a mystery.

8.5 PLANETARY PERIODS AND THE 360-DAY YEAR

Many ancient societies made use of a year of 360 days, and this may seem grossly inaccurate. However, the *Bhāgavatam* shows that certain key astronomical periodicities can be expressed simply in terms of a year of about 360 days. This may account for the widespread use of this period. For example, the *Bhāgavatam* verse 5.22.15 states that Jupiter completes its orbit in 12 years of 360 days, or $4{,}320 = 108 \times 40$ days. Verse 5.22.16 says that Saturn completes its orbit in 30 years or $10{,}800 = 108 \times 100$ days. According to modern data, the correct periods are 4,332.23 days for Jupiter and 10,800.44 days for Saturn (Green, 1985, p. 504). The *Bhāgavatam* approximates these values within 0.3% and 0.004%, respectively.

These simple expressions of 12 and 30 years work, because the *Bhāgavatam* uses a formal year of 360 days, rather than the accurate year of 365 and a fraction days. One way to see this is to note that the modern period of Jupiter is 12 "years" of 361.02 days, and the modern period of Saturn is 30 "years" of 360.015 days.

The shortest period in which both Jupiter and Saturn make a complete orbit is the least common multiple of 12 and 30 years, and this comes to 60 years. Thus the 60-year cycle of Jupiter, which is commonly used in India, may have originally been 60 years of 360 days. This comes to 21,600 days per cycle or 1 day per minute of arc, if we imagine the cycle as a continuous rotation. In the *Sūrya-siddhānta*, this cycle comes to 60.17 360-day years or 59.30 solar years (Burgess, 1860, p. 39).

The orbital period of the moon also simplifies if it is expressed in relation to a solar period of 360 days. The *Bhāgavatam* verse 5.22.8 says that in 2.25 days, the moon travels the distance (in longitude) traveled by the sun in a month. We are dealing with a year of 360 days and a month of 30 days. One way to look at this is to say that the sun covers a full circle of 360° in a 12-month year of 360 days, and the moon covers a full circle in $2.25 \times 12 = 27$ days. These estimates are not very accurate.

But there is another way to interpret these figures. The verse could be taken as saying that the longitude covered by the sun in a 30-day month is not necessarily 30°, but it is the same as the longitude covered by the moon in 2.25 days. Using modern data, at a mean rate of 0.985609°/day, the sun covers 29.56827° in a 30-day month. The moon completes one sidereal orbit (relative to the stars) in 27.32166 days. It therefore moves at a mean rate of $360/27.32166 = 13.17635°$ per day, and in 2.25 days it moves 29.6468°. This is about 0.3% above the sun's monthly movement. Thus the moon does travel in about 2.25 days the distance traveled by the sun in a month.

This interpretation is supported by an old version of the Indian lunar zodiac. In the lunar zodiac, the ecliptic is divided into twenty-seven or twenty-eight intervals, called *nakṣatras*. Like the twelve signs of the zodiac, each *nakṣatra* corresponds both to an interval of the ecliptic and a constellation of stars. Indian astronomy generally assumes twenty-seven *nakṣatras*, which may be equal or unequal in length, depending on the system used.

However, one Indian system uses twenty-eight *nakṣatras*. Here, twenty-seven *nakṣatras* represent the angle covered by the moon in twenty-seven days. This comes to 355.7625°, according to the medieval Indian astronomer Brahmagupta. A twenty-eighth *nakṣatra* called Abhijit is covered by the remainder of the Moon's sidereal period (Dikshit, 1888). Using the modern figure for the sidereal year, we find that the sun covers Brahmagupta's twenty-seven *nakṣatras* in about 361 days. Thus in this system, the 360-day year roughly corresponds to the time for the sun to cross twenty-seven *nakṣatras*.

If the moon covers in twenty-seven days the longitude covered by the sun in 360, we can give the moon a speed of $1/27$ and the sun a speed of $1/360$. This means that the moon overtakes the sun at a speed of $1/27 - 1/360$. The ratio between the moon's speed and its speed of overtaking the sun is the same as the ratio between the synodic month (the time from new moon to new moon) and the sidereal month. If we work this out, we get $1080/999$. Curiously enough, this generates a repeating decimal, 1.08108108 . . .

This estimate differs from the modern ratio by 0.02%. Thus, the average time required for 100 lunar months from new moon to new moon is nearly the same as the time for 108 orbits of the moon relative to the stars, a relationship that could have been important for ancient people using lunar calendars.

It is noteworthy that the *Bhāgavatam's* periods for Jupiter and Saturn, as discussed above, are 108×40 and 108×100. The number 108 is extremely popular in India. For example, it is the number of beads in an Indian rosary, or *japa mālā*. The *guru* is addressed as having 108 glories, and there are said to be 108 (or 1,008) *Upaniṣads*. Perhaps this popularity stems from apparent astronomical coincidences, such as the ones involving Jupiter, Saturn, and the moon.

Subash Kak (1993a) has pointed out yet another relationship involving 108. He notes that this number is roughly the average distance of the sun from the earth in terms of its own diameter, and it is also the average distance of the moon from the earth in terms of the moon's diameter. The true averages according to modern data come to 107.6 and 110.6, respectively. It is due to this coincidence in ratios that the moon has the same apparent size as the sun and can almost exactly cover the disk of the sun during a solar eclipse.

Thus we have found three naturally defined periods of about 360 to 361 days that are connected with the orbital periods of Jupiter,

Saturn, the sun, and the moon. Another such period is defined by the average of the lunar year of twelve lunar months (about 354.367 days) and the sidereal year (of 365.2564 days). These periods may have made it convenient to define a formal year of 360 days, and this period may therefore have never been intended as an actual solar year.

This may shed some light on the curious fact that many nations of antiquity used a year of 360 days. The *Ṛg Saṁhitā* used this figure in a figurative description of the year as a wheel:

> Twelve spoke boards, one wheel, three navels. Who understands these? In these there are 360 Śaṅkus (rods) put in like pegs which do not get loosened (Dikshit, 1969a, p. 18).

The *Bhāgavatam*, as usual, follows ancient standards and says nearly the same thing:

> Your wheel, which has three naves, rotates around the axis of the imperishable Brahman. It has thirteen spokes, 360 joints, six rims and numberless leaves carved upon it (*Bhāgavatam* 3.21.19).

Here the thirteen spokes are the twelve months plus an extra, intercalary month that was periodically added to keep the year in line with the seasons.

The Babylonians used a year of twelve 30-day months, and the archaeoastronomer Otto Neugebauer comments that this was never assumed to be the actual length of the year (Neugebauer, 1945, p. 13). In ancient times, the Chinese had a year of six 60-day periods, which were divided into 10-day 'weeks' (Needham, 1970, p. 397).

The Chinese also divided the circle into 365¼ parts, and this practice may be more recent than that of counting six 60-day periods (Needham, 1970, p. 82). This indicates both a year of 365¼ days and the idea of dividing the circle by an average day's journey of the sun. Of course, when applied to the formal year of 360 days, the same idea gives us the familiar division of the circle into 360 degrees.

The Mayans in Central America had a 260-day sacred year, a 360-day year of eighteen 20-day "months," and a 365-day year that was obtained by adding five unlucky days. In Egypt, the Canopus decree of 238 B.C. ordered that an extra day was to be added every four years to the "360 days and to the five days which it is customary to add to them" (Budge, 1904, p. 63).

Different peoples expressed the same 360-day year in different ways, and this indicates that they were following independent pathways of cultural development. This is especially true of the Mayans, who had a very unique and sophisticated system of astronomy. However, the 360-day figure itself is one of many small pieces of evidence suggesting either common cultural roots or extensive communication between cultures.

9

General Observations

In the nineteenth-century, Jacobi summed up the general understanding of Purāṇic cosmology. He wrote

> Notwithstanding, or rather because of its visionary character, Paurāṇic cosmography became, as it were, an article of faith. The general belief in it was not shaken even by the introduction of scientific astronomy, though the astronomers tried to model the traditional cosmography on the basis of their science (Kay, 1981, p. 15).

For centuries, Purāṇic cosmology has seemed incomprehensible to most observers, and this has encouraged many people either to summarily reject it or to accept it literally with unquestioning faith. This has certainly been true in recent times. If we go back to the medieval period, we likewise find that astronomers such as Bhāskarācārya and Parameśvara dismiss Purāṇic cosmology as imaginary, even though they use Purāṇic ideas and terms in their astronomical writing. At the same time, traditional commentators, such as Śrīdhara Swami, discuss the cosmology of the *Bhāgavatam* from the standpoint of direct literal acceptance.

If we take it literally, the cosmology of the *Bhāgavatam* differs radically from modern astronomy, and it also suffers from internal contradictions and violations of common sense. However, these very contradictions point the way to a different understanding of *Bhāgavata* cosmology in which it emerges as a deep and scientifically sophisticated system of thought.

Study of the contradictions shows that they are caused by overlapping self-consistent interpretations that use the same textual elements to expound different ideas. For example, the *Bhāgavatam* states that the sun god orbits Mount Meru with the mountain to his left and to his right, and this is questioned in the text itself by King Parīkṣit. It turns out, however, that the orbiting with Meru on the right refers to the daily motion of the sun relative to the earth, and it is part of the interpretation of Bhū-maṇḍala as a planisphere map of the earth. The orbiting with Meru on the left refers to the sun's yearly motion relative to the stars, and it is part of the interpretation of Bhū-maṇḍala as a geocentric map of the solar system.

9.1 CONTEXT-SENSITIVE MODELS

Each of these interpretations deserves to be taken seriously because it is supported by many points in the text that are consistent with one another and in agreement with modern astronomy. The contradictions between overlapping interpretations can be understood as the inevitable outcome of a context-sensitive approach to exposition in the *Bhāgavatam*.

In the "contex-sensitive" or "multiple-aspect" approach, different meanings are given to the same subject matter, on the basis of different contexts. The simplest example of this is found in Renaissance paintings, in which several scenes in a story are depicted in one picture. We have given the example of "The Tribute Money" by Masaccio, in which Saint Peter is seen taking a coin from a fish, speaking to Jesus, and paying a tax collector. Each of these phases of the Biblical story makes sense in its own context, but from a literal standpoint it is contradictory to have Saint Peter doing three things at once.

The context-sensitive method maximizes the amount of information that can be stored in a picture or text, and this reduces the work required of the artist or writer. At the same time, it means that the work cannot be taken literally as a one-to-one model of reality, and it requires the viewer or reader to understand the different relevant contexts. This can be difficult when knowledge of context is lost over long periods of time.

In the *Bhāgavatam*, the context-sensitive approach was rendered particularly appropriate by the conviction that reality, in the ultimate issue, is *avāk-manasam* or beyond the reach of the mundane mind or words. This implies that a literal, one-to-one model of reality is unattainable, and so one may as well pack as much meaning as possible into a necessarily incomplete description of the universe.

9.2 REALISTIC ASTRONOMY IN THE BHĀGAVATAM

If we look at the different interpretations that emerge from a study of *Bhāgavata* cosmology, we find that they combine a clear understanding of the earth and the solar system (out to Saturn), with ideas concerning demigods and the soul's travel to higher or lower realms. No explicit information in the *Bhāgavatam* refers to physical objects more than about two billion miles away from the earth. In this sense, the *Bhāgavatam* follows the pattern of medieval European cosmology, which placed the sphere of the fixed stars just outside the orbit of Saturn.

Nevertheless, the idea of large astronomical distances does arise in the traditions surrounding the *Bhāgavatam*. First of all, the *Bhāgavatam* and other *Purāṇas* speak of a multiplicity of universes, or Brahmāṇḍas, each of which is covered by seven-fold layers with an aggregate thickness over ten million times its own diameter. The *Jyotiṣa Śāstras*, *Sūrya-siddhānta,* and *Siddhānta-śiromaṇi*, give the Brahmāṇḍa itself an enlarged radius of about 5,000 light years. Finally, the *Mahābhārata* refers to stars as large, self-luminous objects that seem small because of their great distance, and it remarks that the sun and the moon cannot be seen if one travels to the stars.

But strictly speaking, the *Bhāgavatam* sets the diameter of the Brahmāṇḍa to 500 million *yojanas*, and this equals the diameter of the Bhū-maṇḍala disk, which cuts it in half. At a traditional length of about eight miles per *yojana*, this comes to four billion miles. This is far too small for the universe of stars and galaxies, but it does fall in the right range of size for the solar system. (For example the orbit of Uranus has a radius of about 1.8 billion miles.) This is intriguing, because many points in the *Bhāgavatam* support the identification of Bhū-maṇḍala with the ecliptic plane, which is roughly the plane of the solar system.

Ancient astronomers generally made severe underestimates of the size of the solar system, and the match in size between Bhū-maṇḍala and the solar system may therefore seem like a happy coincidence. However, a remarkable finding emerges if we take this agreement seriously. Bhū-maṇḍala can be interpreted as a map of the geocentric orbits of the sun and the five planets, Mercury through Saturn, and this map becomes highly accurate if we adjust the length of the *yojana* to about 8.5 miles. The rough agreement between Bhū-maṇḍala and the solar system then expands into an accurate agreement between the subdivisions of Bhū-maṇḍala and the orbits of the sun and the five traditional planets.

A nearly identical estimate of about 8.6 miles per *yojana* emerges in an independent, historical study that does not refer to the *Bhāgavatam* or to planets, but does connect the *yojana* with accurate measurements of the earth. This study, in turn, is linked to a general investigation of ancient weights and measures, showing that key units of length were scientifically defined in ancient Egypt and the Near East using geodetic measurements. Going in the opposite direction from India, the *hasta* (or cubit) of the 8.6 mile *yojana* was in use in Indochina in the temple complex of Angkor Wat.

9.3 ADVANCED ASTRONOMY IN ANCIENT TIMES

If an advanced understanding of geodesy existed sometime before the modern era, then it is not so remarkable to suppose that advanced knowledge of spherical astronomy may also have existed. But established reconstructions of history and prehistory do not allow either of these options.

One way to deal with this is to suppose that coincidence has liberally come to the aid of the *Bhāgavatam*, bringing it into harmony with modern astronomy in a number of striking ways. Some points of agreement could be attributed to empirical knowledge coming into India from the Greeks. For example, the use of the planisphere in the *Bhāgavatam* could conceivably be traced back to Ptolemy's *Planisphaerium*. Other, nontraceable points of agreement, such as correlations with modern orbital distances, could be attributed to chance.

From a mystical point of view, chance and intelligent causation can be reconciled by the idea that apparent coincidences may actually be meaningful, since they reflect the workings of an underlying divine intelligence. Thus, we should not be surprised if apparently coincidental patterns in an ancient text prove to harmonize with modern science in unexpected ways. Indeed, we would expect to find such harmony in at least some of the world's inspired texts if the idea of divine inspiration (important to many religions) is actually valid.

Nonetheless, the thoroughly nonmystical character of our data on ancient, scientifically defined measures suggests that many of the correlations with modern astronomy in the *Bhāgavatam* may, indeed, be based on ancient empirical knowledge. We should therefore briefly consider when and where such knowledge might have originated and how it might have been transmitted down to the present.

First, let us consider the question of where. The evidence that we have considered is highly international in character. It does not single out any particular culture or region as the original source of ideas or technical developments. Some of the evidence for advanced astronomy is found in the *Bhāgavatam*, a work from India. Most of the evidence regarding ancient weights and measures relates to Egypt and the Near East, but this may be due to the fact that the studies we have examined deal mainly with these areas.

Seidenberg has argued that geometry and related computational methods may have originated with the tradition of the *Śulvasūtras* in India. However, he remarked that these developments require a date going back at least to 1700 B.C. Since Sanskrit scholars did not give him such a date, he postulated an unknown pre-Old-Babylonian source for *Śulvasūtra* mathematics (Seidenberg, 1978, p. 324).

One objection to the idea of advanced mathematics in ancient times is that surviving mathematical documentation from ancient cultures may indicate a very elementary level of knowledge. For example, the Rhind papyrus and other, similar documents suggest to some scholars that Egyptian mathematics never rose above a very primitive level (Neugebauer, 1945, p. 4). If more advanced knowledge ever existed in Egypt, then where are the records proving this?

One answer is that the high precision and geometrical structure of the great pyramid at Giza indicates that the pyramid builders were not mathematically primitive. This is supported by the studies of Berriman, Stecchini, Schwaller de Lubicz, and others on ancient measures. Could it be that these builders possessed technical knowledge that was later lost? This is quite possible, since advanced technical knowledge tends to be restricted to a small elite and is likely to be ignored or quickly forgotten by the mass of people. Documentary evidence of past scientific achievements tends to be very scanty, and thus we are in the unfortunate position of having to infer past developments from existing fragmentary remains.

Given these reservations, we can postulate an international body of ancient scientists, who were physically based in various parts of the world and who flourished as far back as the Old Kingdom of Egypt. This hypothesis is set within the accepted framework of ancient chronology in Appendix 19.

9.4 THE ROLE OF VEDIC CIVILIZATION

We might ask the relationship between *Bhāgavata* cosmology and the cosmology of the *Vedas* in India. We have not specifically studied the Vedic texts from a cosmological standpoint, but those who have do not report advanced astronomical knowledge in these texts (Dikshit, 1969a and 1969b). The simple astronomy of the *Vedāṅga Jyotiṣa* also suggests that Indian astronomy was poorly developed in the post-Vedic period, when this text was apparently written.

One approach is to suppose that the more advanced knowledge alluded to in the *Bhāgavatam* may have been introduced later on. We have reason to believe that the tropical zodiac, which is mentioned in the *Bhāgavatam*, was of Western origin and is not older than about the second century B.C. The idea of the planisphere could have been introduced from the West along with the tropical zodiac. One could argue, for example, that the planisphere idea allowed for a rational explanation of the pre-scientific Vedic idea that the moon is higher than the sun.

However, it is strange that even though there are many points in the *Bhāgavatam* supporting the planisphere interpretation, we find no evidence indicating that anyone in the medieval tradition of the *Bhāgavatam* specifically knew about it. If it was introduced into India from Hellenistic Greek sources in the early centuries of our era, then it should have been explicitly known in the medieval period along with other material of Greek affinity expounded in *Jyotiṣa Śāstras*.

This suggests that the planisphere idea in the *Bhāgavatam* dates back much further in time, and was forgotten in the medieval period and later. The correlations between Bhū-maṇḍala and modern planetary orbits also suggest that the *Bhāgavatam* contains astronomical material dating back to much earlier times, since realistic knowledge of these orbits is incompatible with the astronomy of classical antiquity.

Since the cosmology of the *Bhāgavatam* is a complex system that differs in many ways from that of the *Jyotiṣa Śāstras*, it stands to reason that it was produced by a different school of thought. We know of many historical contributors to the *Jyotiṣa Śāstras*, such as Āryabhaṭa and Bhāskarācārya, but we know of no one who was involved in developing Purāṇic cosmology. This also suggests that the developmental stage of Purāṇic cosmology took place in an earlier, forgotten era.

De Santillana and von Dechend refer to the idea of a fossilized story, a story which has lost its context and is embedded, like a fossil in a rock, in a foreign cultural matrix. An example is the story of Jack and the beanstalk, which refers to an man-eating giant that lives in the sky. This story has survived out of context as a nursery tale, but it may refer to the near-earth abodes of the Rākṣasas and Bhūtas in the *Bhāgavatam's* hierarchy of worlds.

Technical knowledge may also survive in fossilized form. An example is the verse in the *Sūrya-siddhānta* that encodes accurate values for the diameters of the planets (see Appendix 10). This is lodged out of context in a work where it doesn't belong, and it seems to have no precedent in other Indian astronomical works. But it may be based on a remnant of knowledge that survived from earlier times. The same could be true of the advanced astronomy in the *Bhāgavatam*.

9.5 THE SYMBOLISM OF THE COSMIC AXIS

In the *Bhāgavatam*, sophisticated astronomical information coexists with a philosophical understanding that connects the vertical axis of the universe (the spin-axis defined by Meru and the polestar) with the ascent or descent of the soul in spiritual realization. This understanding is linked in the *Purāṇas* with particular themes—such as the world-mountain and the astral migration of the soul—which can be found in various forms in cultures all over the world. The spread of Buddhism from India partly accounts for the transmission of these ideas, but their presence in Europe, Africa, and North and South America seems to require an earlier society or movement that spread them.

The Vedic texts appear to contain both the spiritual philosophy of the cosmic axis and some of the particular details used to express it in different cultures. Thus they refer a world tree and a primeval, central mountain from which four rivers emerge. A "cosmogonical boar" dug this mountain out of the primordial waters, and the mountain and its surrounding rim of earth still rest upon the waters. The earth divides the cosmos into an upper and lower region, and there is also a "highest heaven" (*parama vyoma* in the *Ṛg Veda*) which is beyond both (Kuiper, 1983).

The treatment of the cosmic axis in the *Bhāgavatam* is closely linked with the *Vedas* through the role of Viṣṇu. In the *Vedas,* Viṣṇu is known for taking three steps. While discussing this, the Indologist F. B. J. Kuiper remarked:

> While Viṣṇu's first two steps express his relationship with the two opposed parts of the cosmos, his third step corresponds to a transcendental world in which the two conflicting parties are united in an all-encompassing totality. In this light we can view the poet's words about '*Asat* and *sat* in the highest heaven.' They point to a world which transcends the cosmic antithesis and in which *sat* and *asat* have been reconciled in the synthesis of an all-embracing unity (Kuiper, 1983, p. 20).

Along the cosmic axis there is a division between lower and upper worlds, with the Asuras representing darkness and chaos (*asat*) in the former and the Devas representing light and divine order (*sat*) in the latter. In the *Bhāgavatam*, Viṣṇu is also situated at both ends of the axis, since He rests on Ananta Śeṣa next to the Garbhodaka Ocean, and He also resides in the polestar, Dhruvaloka. Kuiper argues that in the *Vedas,* Viṣṇu is transcendental to both the Devas and the Asuras, and thus He represents the eternal divine order lying beyond the dualities of the upper and lower worlds. This is also the basic theology of the *Bhāgavatam*.

Since the *Bhāgavatam* is linked to the *Vedas,* the *Vedas* contain rudimentary astronomy, and the *Bhāgavatam* alludes to advanced astronomy, it may seem that we are faced with a contradiction. One resolution may be that the *Vedas,* as purely religious texts, naturally say little about astronomy, while the *Bhāgavatam*, as a *Purāṇa*, contains a section devoted to cosmology. The *Vedāṅga Jyotiṣa*, which does go into detail on astronomy, may be a later work that was appended to the Vedic tradition (see Appendix 19).

In the *Bhāgavatam*, the transcendental position of Viṣṇu is symbolized by the polestar, Dhruvaloka, which is the unmoving center around which all the stars and planets rotate daily on the wheel of time. This understanding appears to have suppressed awareness of the gradual precession of the equinoxes. But if Dhruvaloka refers to an observed star (as opposed to an invisible center of rotation), it may refer back to the period of about 2500 B.C., when the star Thuban was situated close to the north celestial pole.

In greater India, this was the period of the Mature Harappan civilization, characterized by well-planned cities, realistic sculpture, and a tantalizing, undeciphered script. In Egypt, it was the period of the construction of the great pyramid at Giza. Harappan measures of weight apparently survived to recent times in India, and there is a possible connection between the Harappan weight system and the later Roman ounce. There is also evidence of sophisticated geodetic measurements in Egypt at this time (see Appendices 8 and 19).

There were trade links between the Harappan civilization and Mesopotamia, and there were also links between Mesopotamia and Egypt. The period of 2500 B.C. (give or take a few hundred years) may have been the time when both observational astronomy and cosmological philosophy were combined in the kind of synthesis that we find in the *Bhāgavatam*. Of course, to be sure of this, much more research will be required.

Appendices

A1. The 28 Nakṣatras

The *nakṣatras* are twenty-seven or twenty-eight star constellations situated along the ecliptic. They play a role in Indian astronomy similar to that of the twelve constellations of the zodiac in the west. They are particularly connected with the motion of the moon, which completes one sidereal orbit in about 27.3 days. The *nakṣatras* are identified with star constellations, each of which has a principal star or "junction star" (*yoga-tārakā*).

The constellations are irregular in shape, but the *nakṣatras* are also defined to be angular subdivisions of the ecliptic. In one system, there are twenty-seven subdivisions of $13^1/_3$° apiece. In other systems, subdivisions of various lengths are used. The *Sūrya-siddhānta* uses twenty-seven equal divisions, and it places the beginning of its first *nakṣatra*, Aśvinī, 10' west of the principal star of Revatī, thought to be Zeta Piscium (Burgess, 1860, p. 15).

By precession, this star would have been aligned with the vernal equinox in about 570 A.D. In older lists (e.g. in the *Black Yajur Veda* and the *Atharva Veda*), Kṛttikā is listed as the first *nakṣatra* (Burgess, 1860, p. 16). Some have argued that this refers back to a time when Kṛttikā (the Pleiades) was at the vernal equinox, and this would have been in about 2200 B.C.

The names of the twenty-eight *nakṣatras* are listed in Table A1.1, along with modern names of the junction stars thought to correspond to them (as given by Kay, 1981, p. 118). We note that for some junction stars, the corresponding modern star is uncertain. The *nakṣatras* are assigned presiding deities and constellation figures as shown in Table A1.2 (Taluqdar, 1916, p. 169). The *nakṣatras* are divided into groups as shown in Table A1.3, according to Śrīdhara Swami's commentary on the *Bhāgavatam* (Wilson, 1865, pp. 267–68).

TABLE A1.1
Modern Stars Corresponding to the 28 Nakṣatras

#	Sanskrit Name	Modern Name	Latin/Arabic Name
1	Aśvinī	Beta Arietis	Sheratan
2	Bharaṇī	35 Arietis	
3	Kṛttikā	Eta Tauri	Alcyone (Pleiades)
4	Rohiṇī	Alpha Tauri	Aldebaran
5	Mṛgaśīrṣa	Lambda Orionis	Meissa
6	Ārdrā	Alpha Orionis	Betelgeuse
7	Punarvasu	Beta Geminorum	Pollux
8	Puṣyā	Delta Cancri	Asellus Aus.
9	Āśleṣā	Epsilon Hydrae	
10	Maghā	Alpha Leonis	Regulus
11	Pūrvaphalgunī	Delta Leonis	Zosma
12	Uttaraphalgunī	Beta Leonis	Denebola
13	Hasta	Delta Corvi	Algorab
14	Citrā	Alpha Virgini	Spica
15	Svātī	Alpha Bootis	Arcturus
16	Viśākhā	Iota Librae	
17	Anurādhā	Delta Scorpionis	
18	Jyeṣṭhā	Alpha Scorpionis	Antares
19	Mūlā	Lambda Scorpionis	Shaula
20	Pūrvāṣāḍhā	Delta Sagittarii	Kaus Media
21	Uttarāṣāḍhā	Sigma Sagittarii	Nunki
22	Abhijit	Alpha Lyri	Vega
23	Śravaṇ	Alpha Aquilae	Altair
24	Dhaniṣṭhā	Beta Delphini	
25	Śatabhiṣā	Lambda Aquarii	
26	Pūrvabhādrapāda	Alpha Pegasi	Markab
27	Uttarabhādrapāda	Alpha Andromedo	Alpheratz
28	Revatī	Zeta Piscium	

TABLE A1.2
Nakṣatra Deities and Figures

#	Sanskrit Name	Presiding Deity	Figure
1	Aśvinī	Aśvinīs	Horse's head
2	Bharaṇī	Yama	The yoni
3	Kṛttikā	Fire	Razor or knife
4	Rohiṇī	Prajāpati	Wain (or Temple)
5	Mṛgaśirṣa	The Moon	Antelope's head
6	Ārdrā	Rudra	A gem
7	Punarvasu	Aditi	House
8	Puṣyā	Bṛhaspati	Arrow (a crescent)
9	Āśleṣā	The Serpents	Potter's wheel
10	Maghā	The Pitṛs	House
11	Pūrvaphalgunī	Bhaga	Couch or bedstead
12	Uttaraphalgunī	Aryaman	Bed
13	Hasta	Sāvitrī	Hand
14	Citrā	Tvaṣṭri	Pearl (lamp)
15	Svātī	Air	Coral bead (gem, pearl)
16	Viśākhā	Indra & Fire	Festoon
17	Anurādhā	Mitra	Row of oblations
18	Jyeṣṭhā	Indra	Ring (earring)
19	Mūlā	Nirṛti	Lion's tail (couch)
20	Pūrvāṣāḍhā	Water	Couch (elephant's tooth)
21	Uttarāṣāḍhā	Viśvadeva	Elephant's tooth (bed)
22	Abhijit	Brahmā	Triangular nut (triangle)
23	Śravaṇa	Viṣṇu	Three footsteps (trident)
24	Dhaniṣṭhā	The Vasus	Drum or tabor
25	Śatabhiṣā	Varuṇa	Circle
26	Pūrvabhādrapāda	Ajapāt	2-faced figure (couch, bed)
27	Uttarabhādrapāda	Ahibradhna	Couch, bed (2-faced figure)
28	Revatī	Pūṣan	Tabor

TABLE A1.3
Purāṇic Divisions of the Ecliptic

Division	Subdivision	Nakṣatras
Airāvata	Nāgavīthī	1–3
	Gajavīthī	4–6
	Airāvatī	7–9
Jāradgava	Ārṣabhī	10–12
	Govīthī	13–15
	Jāradgavī	16–18
Vaiśvānara	Ajavīthī	19–21
	Mṛgavīthī	23–25 (omitting Abhijit)
	Vaiśvānarī	26–28

A2. Vaṁśīdhara on Priyavrata's Chariot

The commentary by Vaṁśīdhara on *Bhāgavatam* verse 5.1.30 sheds light on how the sun was thought to move in relation to Bhū-maṇḍala. It specifically lends support to the planisphere interpretation of Bhū-maṇḍala. Although Vaṁśīdhara does not specifically mention the planisphere interpretation, he makes a number of points which can be reconciled with astronomy by this interpretation but which do not make sense otherwise.

Verse 5.1.30:

> While Bhagavān Āditya [the sun] illumines the gods' mountain [Meru], continuously going around, he heats only half of the land up to Lokāloka Mountain, and he covers half [with darkness]. Not approving of this, Priyavrata, having accumulated superhuman power by the worship of the Lord, [thought] 'I shall make night into day.' With a chariot built of light of the same speed, he went seven times around, following the movement of the sun like a second sun.

Vaṁśīdhara's commentary is as follows:

The words *tadā hi* means during Priyavrata's government. Not appreciating the situation (that the sun covers half of the earth) with darkness, King Priyavrata followed the sun by rising from the eastern direction when the sun was going to set. He did so not for competing with the sun but for the happiness of his citizens.

Pataṅga means the sun and *paryakrāmat* means surpassed.

During the months of Jyeṣṭhā, etc., the sunlight given by King Priyavrata was cooler than the moonlight and during the months of Mārga-śīrṣa etc., it was hotter than the sun, especially in the morning and evening.

It should be understood that King Priyavrata, by the strength of mystic power could function with his twofold personalities as a king and the sun, like the sages named Saubhari, etc.

The Viśva dictionary refers to the word *pataṅga* as a bird and as the sun, and according to the Amara-kośa, *dyumaṇi, taraṇi,* and *mitra* are synonyms of the sun.

It is to be known that King Priyavrata, after seven circumambulations, was going to continue but was stopped by Lord Brahmā. We have already heard that because of his (Lord Brahmā's) order, Priyavrata was engaged in ruling the kingdom.

It is to be understood that as there are seven oceans in number, so the chariots were also seven which were produced by his mystic power. Those chariots had only one wheel, and they were higher than the chariot of the sun rotating in a circle.

It is also indicated here that because of the larger measurement of the outer circles, the chariots were also understood to be accordingly larger.

Others say, "the King desired, 'May my chariot, though far away, be visible to the eyes of my citizens of Āryāvarta.' Therefore he made each chariot twice as big as the previous one." Because of the larger measurements of the rims, the oceans made by the chariot wheels are also seen to be larger.

The duration of (Priyavrata's) mounting on those seven successively larger chariots is 25 days and 45.5 *ghaṭikās*.

Thus, like the sun, King Priyavrata, from the beginning of *dakṣiṇāyana,* started moving from the northern region to the southern region until the month of Pauṣa, and again from the beginning of *uttarāyaṇa* until the end, by days numbering as many, he moved in the reverse order mounting on those chariots.

Thus, the traveling from the southern region to the northern region lasts up to Āṣāḍha, but turning round even by the left side of Meru, the sun, when he moves by his own rapid speed which is controlled by the *jyotiś-cakra*, makes the days gradually decrease every month during *dakṣiṇāyana.* But in *uttarāyaṇa,* the days gradually increase because of the sun's slower speed.

However, it should be understood that King Priyavrata, keeping Meru on the right, moves by his own will to dissipate the night made by (the absence of) the sun. The days in *uttarāyaṇa* increase even as he willingly moves slowly, and in *dakṣiṇāyana* the days decrease, being under his willful faster speed.

The appearance and disappearance of the chariots should be known to be due to his mystic influence.

It should be known that the chariots were only seven in number as stated before.

It should be explained that after the seven days, it wasn't proper for Priyavrata to stop himself, and it is not even heard that someone else could stop him.

The following points can be made regarding this commentary: First, it seems that Priyavrata's chariot(s) reversed the seasons, being cool and moonlike in summer months and brighter than the sun in winter months. This makes sense if he always stayed 180° from the sun. However, Vaṁśīdhara says that "King Priyavrata, from the beginning of *dakṣiṇāyana,* started moving from the northern region to southern region," and this is inconsistent, since a reversed sun should start from south to north at this time.

Another inconsistency involves the statement in 5.1.30 that Priyavrata goes around seven times (*sapta-kṛtvas taraṇim anuparyakrāmat*). If these are taken as daily circuits, this creates a problem for Vaṁśīdhara's interpretation, which requires Priyavrata to ride for many days. Vaṁśīdhara deals with this by declaring that Brahmā tried to stop Priyavrata after seven days, but later he says that he couldn't be stopped.

The period of 25 days, 45.5 *ghaṭikās,* multiplied by 7, comes to about 180.3 days. This is about the time of *uttarāyaṇa* or *dakṣiṇāyana,* assuming a year of 360 days. So it seems that Priyavrata spent one-seventh of the time on each of seven chariots while going from north to south, and he likewise did the same thing while going from south to north. Since each chariot carved out an ocean, he spent one-seventh of the time orbiting in each ocean basin while going from south to north, and likewise while going from north to south. If he was going around once per day, he must have been going slower while on the inner oceans (of shorter radius) and faster while on the outer oceans.

Since Priyavrata's sun was doing the opposite of the real sun, it follows that the real sun must also spend one-seventh of its time in each ocean and *dvīpa* during an *ayana*. Thus, the sun must spiral gradually in towards the center during *dakṣiṇāyana*, and it must spiral gradually outward during *uttarāyaṇa*. This, of course, is what actually happens in a stereographic projection of the earth and the sun's orbit. But if we take Bhū-maṇḍala as a literal plane, then the sun must greatly change its distance to the center in the course of an *ayana*, and this means that it should greatly change in apparent size—contrary to what anyone can see. Thus, Vaṁśīdhara's description makes sense in light of the planisphere interpretation of the original Purāṇic account, but it does not make sense given a literal plane.

However, note Vaṁśīdhara's comment that (according to some) Priyavrata's chariots were made to double in size as they went out so that people in Āryāvarta could see them. This assumes actual movement out from the center in a literal plane, and it assumes that the resulting reduction in apparent size is offset by the doubling in size of the chariots. Thus Vaṁśīdhara was clearly not thinking of the planisphere interpretation.

Vaṁśīdhara says that the greater length of the day in the summer is caused by the slower speed of the sun during this period. This explanation does not make sense, but we find it in several *Purāṇas*. For example, it is expressed in the *Viṣṇu Purāṇa*, along with the additional confusing idea that in winter the sun travels faster in the day and slower in the night, with the reverse happening in the summer (Wilson, 1980, p. 319). Of course, the *Purāṇas* recognize that day for one person is night for someone else, and so this explanation does not work. We do not find this erroneous explanation in the *Bhāgavatam*.

Thus it appears that the Purāṇic tradition in Vaṁśīdhara's day preserved evidence of a planisphere interpretation of Bhū-maṇḍala, but this interpretation was not understood within the tradition at this time.

The Sanskrit text of 5.1.30 says that the sun illuminates half of the earth's surface (*vasudhā-talam*), while the other half is in darkness. Evidently, Priyavrata illuminated the other half, and thereby created unbroken daylight. This makes sense for a globe or a planisphere, but not for a literal plane, where sunlight should fade out gradually in all directions from the sun, with no sharp demarcation between an illuminated half and a dark half.

The *Siddhānta-śiromaṇi* of Bhāskarācārya maps the seven oceans and *dvīpas* into bands of equal latitude around the earth globe (Wilkinson, 1861, p. 116). The position of the sun, projected onto the earth as the zenith point, does move across these bands, from one to another, during the course of *dakṣiṇāyana* and *uttarāyaṇa*. If the widths of the bands are adjusted properly (which is not done in *Siddhānta-śiromaṇi*), the sun will spend about one-fourteenth of a year in each of seven bands, first going north and then going south. This comes to about 26 days per band. As the sun's zenith point circles in each band, half of the earth's surface, centered on this point, is illuminated, and the other half is in darkness. Thus, the *Siddhānta-śiromaṇi* interpretation of the *dvīpas* reconciles Vaṁśīdhara's understanding with modern science.

It is sometimes argued that the approach taken in *Siddhānta-śiromaṇi* and other *Jyotiṣa Śāstras* was developed after the introduction of Greek astronomy into India as a means of bringing prescientific Purāṇic cosmology into line with newly introduced scientific concepts. However, features of the Purāṇic accounts suggest that they were originally based on a scientific planisphere projection, whether this was inspired by Greek ideas or not. This original understanding seems to have been lost by the time of the known *Bhāgavata* commentators (from roughly the thirteenth century onwards).

A3. Archaic Earth Model

The scholars Giorgio de Santillana of MIT and Hertha von Dechend of Frankfurt University have argued in their book *Hamlet's Mill* that the "flat earth" of all ancient cultures was originally celestial.

Based on their study of many traditions, de Santillana and von Dechend postulated that in ancient times there existed an Archaic Culture. This culture was spread throughout the world, and it flourished before the known civilizations of Greece, Babylon, China, and India. The people of this culture had the following understanding of the earth:

> 1. First, what was the 'earth'? In the most general sense, the 'earth' was the ideal plane laid through the ecliptic. The 'dry earth,' in a more specific sense, was the ideal plane going through the celestial equator.
> 2. The name of 'true earth' (or of the 'inhabited world') did not in any way denote our physical geoid for the archaics. It applies to the band of the zodiac, two dozen degrees right and left of the ecliptic.
> 3. At the 'top,' in the center high above the 'dry' plane of the equator was the Pole star. At the opposite top, or rather in the depths of the waters below, unobserved from our latitudes, was the southern pole, thought to be Canopus" (de Santillana, 1969, pp. 58, 61–63).

If this cosmological scheme is correct, then the Archaic people had a sophisticated idea of the earth, and they knew that the earth in this sense did not correspond directly to what they were standing on. It is therefore noteworthy that prominent Greek thinkers accepted a literal flat earth before the rise of classical Greek astronomy. For example, in the fifth century B.C. the philosopher Thales thought of the earth as a disk floating on water like a log. About a century later, Anaxagoras taught that it is flat like a lid and stays suspended in air. Democratus, in turn, argued that the earth is shaped like a tambourine and is tilted downwards toward the south (Kirk and Raven, 1963, pp. 87, 391, 412).

Although some say that Pythagoras, in the sixth century B.C., was the first to view the earth as a sphere, this idea apparently did not catch on quickly among the Greeks, and the first attempt to measure the earth's diameter is generally attributed to Eratosthenes in the second century B.C.

If de Santillana and von Dechend are correct, then there must have been a loss of astronomical understanding between the Archaic period and the time of the pre-Socratic Greek philosophers. After this, Greek astronomical knowledge underwent a resurgence with the development of mathematical planetary models—a process beginning with Plato's contemporary, Eudoxus, and culminating with Ptolemy's Almagest in the second century A.D.

A4. Background on Modeling The Solar System

In modern times, the dimensions of the solar system have been learned only recently. Now the sun is known to be about 93 million miles from the earth, but a few centuries ago, it was widely believed to be much closer.

The first accurate measurement of the earth-sun distance was made in 1671, and the result was 87 million miles. This measurement required high-precision telescopes. Observers stationed in Paris and in the city of Cayenne in French Guiana used telescopes to measure the direction of Mars. This enabled them to triangulate the distance to Mars, and the earth-sun distance was computed from this information. This method requires very accurate measurements, because Paris is very close to Cayenne, compared with the closest distance from the earth to Mars.

The most accurate nontelescopic astronomer is said to be Tycho Brahe, who lived in the late sixteenth century. Using Brahe's naked-eye observations, the famous astronomer Johannes Kepler concluded that the earth-sun distance is at least thirteen and a half million miles.

Kepler and his contemporary, Galileo, accepted the heliocentric, or sun-centered, model of the universe introduced by Nicholas Copernicus in the sixteenth century. Before this time, Western astronomers followed the geocentric system expounded by Claudius Ptolemy in the days of the Roman Empire.

Ptolemy estimated that the distance from the earth to the sun is about five million miles. This is only one-nineteenth of the modern value and is typical of estimates made by pretelescopic astronomers.

Ptolemy is often criticized for giving the erroneous geocentric model, rather than the correct heliocentric one. But geocentric or heliocentric motion can be seen as a matter of relative point of view. Newtonian dynamics require the planets to orbit the sun, but one can still represent planetary motions relative to the earth. In fact, this is necessary in practice for astronomical observations made from the earth, and there was a tendency in ancient times for astronomers to convert heliocentric systems into geocentric ones (van der Waerden, 1987).

Tycho Brahe accepted that the planets other than the earth orbit the sun, but he kept the earth in the center by having the sun orbit the earth. Thus his system preserved all relative planetary motions by combining heliocentric planetary motion with geocentric solar motion.

Seen from the viewpoint of the earth, a planet traces out a looping path. This path can be approximated with a simple mechanical model (Figure A4.1). Here, the short arm represents the sun orbiting around the earth, which is at the center. The long arm represents the motion of the planet Mars around the sun. In combination, they trace out the orbit of Mars around the earth. (This simple model omits elliptical motion, of course.)

Medieval and Renaissance diagrams typically show Ptolemy's orbits as simple circles. But Ptolemy actually gave each planet a realistic, geocentric orbit (Figure A4.2). He erred by making the orbits too small, and by stacking them up, one inside the other, as we see in the figure. Indeed, the Ptolemaic orbits out to Saturn are so small that they would fit within the earth's orbit, as given in modern astronomy (Figure A4.3).

For comparison, the actual geocentric orbits of the planets are as shown in Figure A4.4, according to modern astronomy. Notice that the curling orbital paths follow off-centered ovals caused by the planets' elliptical orbits around the sun. A realistic geocentric model like this one implies an accurate knowledge of relative planetary motion, and

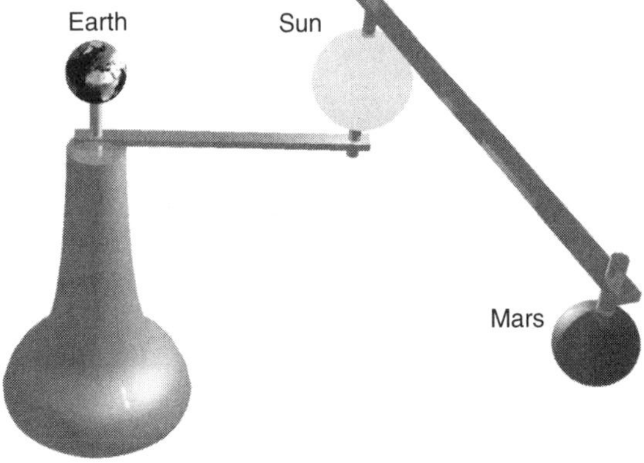

Figure A4.1 In this mechanical model of geocentric motion, the sun (middle) revolves around the earth (left), as Mars (right) in turn revolves around the sun.

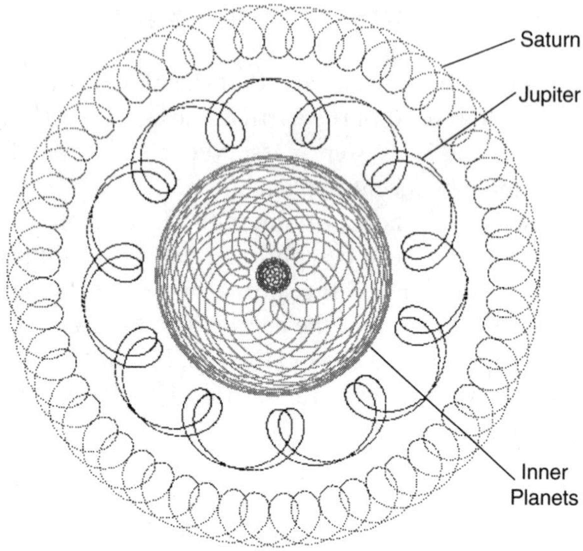

Figure A4.2 The actual sizes and shapes of Ptolemy's planetary orbits are shown here. These are (from the center to the outside): Mercury, Venus, the sun, Mars, Jupiter, and Saturn.

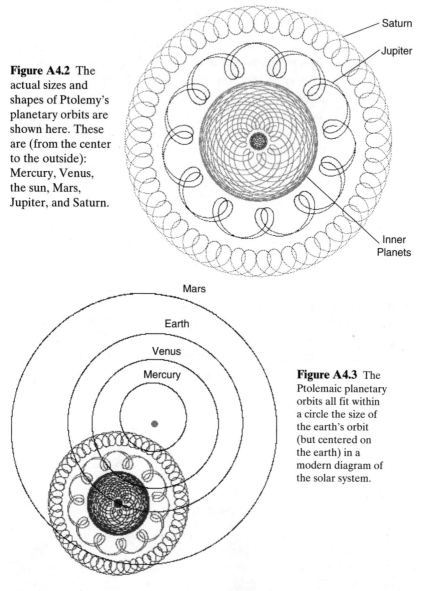

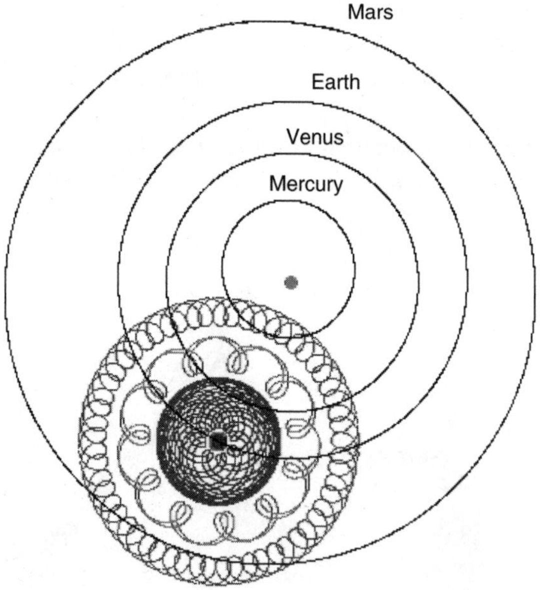

Figure A4.3 The Ptolemaic planetary orbits all fit within a circle the size of the earth's orbit (but centered on the earth) in a modern diagram of the solar system.

therefore it probably will be accompanied by at least a theoretical awareness that the planets orbit the sun. This happened in the case of Brahe, who knew about the heliocentric model, but preferred to represent planetary motions geocentrically.

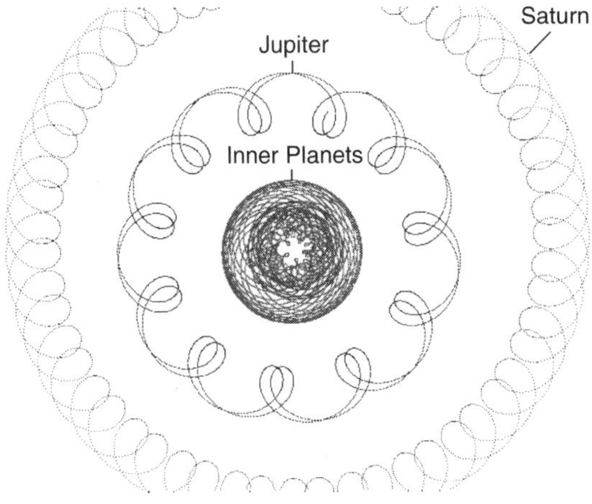

Figure A4.4
The actual geocentric orbits of the planets are shown here. The orbits of the inner planets and the sun over-lap one another, whereas in Ptolemy's system they are kept separate.

B. L. van der Waerden argued that the heliocentric theory may have a more extensive historical background than we commonly suspect. The general story of the heliocentric theory is that it was invented by Aristarchus of Samos and then taken up centuries later by Copernicus. However, van der Waerden argued that the system of the Indian astronomer Āryabhaṭa (fifth–sixth century A.D.) could be traced to a heliocentric theory cultivated in Persia or Near Eastern countries (van der Waerden, 1987). One may thus raise the question of whether or not Purāṇic astronomy may have been influenced by the heliocentric theory.

A5. Goodness of Fit

For a *yojana* length y, the goodness of fit, G(y), is defined as follows. The terms used in this definition are given in Figure 4.9 (p. 96).

Each boundary curve has two extreme points where it becomes tangent to a circle centered on the earth. For the outer boundary curve, these are the apogee of the planet, and the point designated apogee-, where this boundary curve approaches closest to the earth. For the inner boundary curve they are the perigee of the planet and the point, perigee+, where the curve is furthest from the earth. These four points are called orbital turning points.

By observation, we arrived at the hypothesis that each orbit has at least one turning point that matches the radius of a circular feature of Bhū-maṇḍala. Thus a measure of goodness of fit should be based on the minimal distance between turning points and circular features for each planet. Assuming y miles per *yojana*, we can formally define this as follows:

For each planet, Mercury through Saturn, find the minimum difference between a Bhū-maṇḍala feature radius and an orbital turning point converted into *yojanas* using y. The difference is expressed as a percentage of the width of the Bhū-maṇḍala ring in which the turning point falls. Take this minimum over the set of all Bhū-maṇḍala circles (listed in Table 2.1, p. 22) and over the set of four orbital turning points of the planet. Take the root mean square of these minimal percentage differences for the five planets. The reciprocal of this is called G(y). It is large if the orbits line up well with the circular features, and it is small if they do not line up well.

A6. Criteria for Orbital Alignment

It is possible to define several simple criteria that evaluate how well the planetary orbits line up with the circular features of Bhū-maṇḍala. These are based on the observation that if the alignments between orbits and features are not coincidental, we would expect them to follow an orderly pattern, in which all Bhū-maṇḍala features play a role. In this appendix, we develop this idea.

In Table 4.2 (p. 98), N lists the number of the Bhū-maṇḍala feature that comes closest to the indicated orbital turning point. We will say that this feature is *used* or occupied by that turning point. The feature numbers, N, are used by the planets as indicated in Table A6.

We would expect a random series of alignments to use some features and omit others in an irregular fashion. So it is noteworthy that all of the features from 8 to 17 are used in the pattern in this table. We also see that the small, solid planets (Mercury, Venus, and Mars),follow a symmetric pattern in the table, centered on the sun. This pattern is (11,12), (10,13), (8,14), (9,15), with only 8 and 9 switched out of order. A different pattern is followed by the large, gaseous planets, Jupiter and Saturn.

TABLE A6
Occupation Table

Body	Feature Number	
	Perigee	Apogee
Sun	11	12
Mercury	10	13
Venus	8	14
Mars	9	15
Jupiter	16	16
Saturn	17	17

The numbers in this table reflect the heliocentric arrangement of the solar system, and they also reflect the fact that Mercury, Venus, and Mars (but not Jupiter and Saturn) can come closer to the earth than the sun. But an arbitrary arrangement of rings would not be expected to do this in such a regular and symmetric way.

The information in Tables 4.2 and A6 can be evaluated using several criteria which assess the strengths and weaknesses of the orbit correlations. These are as follows:

1. First, the following two points are based on the text of the *Bhāgavatam*:
   1a. Features beyond the circular Lokāloka Mountain (feature 17) should not be used in the alignment, since it is said in text 5.20.37 that no luminaries (planets) pass beyond Lokāloka Mountain.
   1b. The sun should be somewhere between the center (earth) and the circular Mānasottara Mountain (feature 13), since the sun's chariot axle extends from Meru to Mānasottara (see 5.21.13).

   We call these criteria 1a and 1b, respectively, and we assign them 1 or 0 for true or false. Both are satisfied by Table 4.2.
2. In the ideal pattern, each perigee and apogee of a planet (or the sun) should come close to a Bhū-maṇḍala ring. To show how well this is satisfied, let n be the number of perigees or apogees within P percent of their closest feature radius. Using $P = 6\%$, the pattern in Table 4.2

is assigned 5, but the highest possible value would be 11 (2 for each planet and at most 1 for the sun).

3. It would be ideal if each feature corresponded to exactly one perigee or apogee. So let r be the ratio of the number of features with this property to the total number of features used. The pattern in Tables 4.2 and A6 is assigned r = 8/10 by this criterion, since features 8–15 each correspond to one perigee or apogee. In contrast, feature 16 serves for both the apogee and the perigee of Jupiter, since the apogee lacks a ring of its own. The situation is similar for feature 17 and Saturn.

   Ideally, all circular Bhū-maṇḍala features should be used in the alignment, since unused features would be superfluous in a planetary map. Criteria 4–6 address this idea:

4. Let n be minus the number of unused features from Jambūdvīpa up to the first feature used in the alignment. The minus sign means that the pattern gets a lower evaluation as n increases. Here the pattern in Table 4.2 gets a low score of -7, since the used features begin with number 8.
5. Let m be minus the number of unused features between Lokāloka Mountain and the outermost used feature. In this case, the pattern in Table 4.2 is assigned the highest score of 0.
6. Finally, let k be minus the number of blocks of contiguous unused features in the whole pattern. This measures how much the pattern is broken up by unused circles. By this measure, the pattern in Table 4.2 is assigned -1.

Criteria 2 through 6 are intended to express what we would expect to find in a solar system map in which perigees and apogees of geocentric planetary orbits are represented by a series of concentric circles. They also express criticisms that can be lodged against the particular map given in the Table 4.2. To sum up, in such a map, each perigee or apogee should correspond to a circle, and each circle should correspond to a perigee or apogee. Criteria 1a and 1b express the special roles of Lokāloka Mountain and Mānasottara Mountain.

Our first observation is that the six criteria can be used to define the optimal *yojana* length, without making any reference to the goodness of fit function, G(y) (see Appendix 5). Consider the range of possible *yojana* lengths from 1 to 16 miles. For a given *yojana* length, add criteria 1a, 1b, and 2–6 together, using weights designed so that each criterion varies over the same range on the interval of possible *yojana* lengths. This is done to give the criteria equal weight. The resulting curve C(y) is plotted in Figure 4.10 (p. 97), along with G(y). (We added 10 to the curve to make it positive.) This curve has a pronounced maximum at 8.489 miles, close to the maximum of G(y).

A7. Critical Analysis Of the Orbital Study

It is clear that Bhū-maṇḍala, as described in the *Bhāgavatam*, can be interpreted as a geocentric map of the solar system out to Saturn. But an obvious and important question is: Did some real knowledge of planetary distances enter into the construction of the Bhū-maṇḍala system, or are the correlations between Bhū-maṇḍala features and planetary orbits simply coincidental?

One problem with interpretations in general is that they pick out certain features from a body of material, while neglecting others. This choice may be dictated by the pattern that is being seen, and thus this pattern may be imposed by the viewer on the evidence, rather than being inherent in the evidence itself.

In this case, the decision to give an astronomical interpretation to an ostensibly geographical description is supported by substantial material in the text of the *Bhāgavatam* connecting Bhū-maṇḍala and the adjoining region of Antarikṣa with the ecliptic (sun's orbit) and the planetary orbits. The circular features of Bhū-maṇḍala stand out as likely candidates for an astronomical interpretation, due to their shape and due to the fact that they have roughly the right size for planetary orbits. Also, since they are given dimensions in the text, they can be examined quantitatively.

Given this starting point, we can carry out a statistical analysis by defining a null hypothesis as follows: The medieval author of the *Bhāgavatam* had no access to correct knowledge of planetary distances, and therefore all correlations between Bhū-maṇḍala features and planetary distances are due to chance.

If such a null hypothesis involves a known statistical distribution, such as a normal distribution, then there are standard statistical methods for evaluating whether or not the observed data satisfy this hypothesis. The basic method would be to ask how probable the correlations in question are, given a statistical distribution of possible Bhū-maṇḍala features. The problem is that we do not know this statistical distribution.

Nonetheless, by looking at the *Bhāgavatam's* discussion of distances in Bhū-maṇḍala, we can make some general observations about how these distances were expressed numerically. For example, from Table 2.1 (p. 22), we see that large powers of 10 were used. Throughout Purāṇic literature, numbers such as *sahasra* (1,000), *lakṣa* (100,000), and *koṭi* (10,000,000) are common. Fractions of these numbers, such as 1/2, 1/4, and 1/8 are also common, and we see such fractions in the table. The table also shows the procedure of doubling a previous distance. In other parts of the *Bhāgavatam*, we encounter multiples of a previous distance by ten (i.e. the shells of the Brahmāṇḍa).

Table 2.1 presents a combination of regular rules and seemingly arbitrary decisions, such as the decision to set thickness 16 equal to radius 13 instead of doubling thickness 15. We took the null hypothesis to mean that such decisions were made by complex cultural causes that would be effectively random relative to the unknown dimensions of the solar system. Thus, we interpret the table as a combination of regularity and effectively random choice.

Based on such observations, we wrote an algorithm to generate sets of artificial Bhū-maṇḍala feature radii. This algorithm applies rules generalized from Table 2.1, and it applies these rules in a random fashion. We are prepared to make the C code for this algorithm available for examination. Although the algorithm is in many ways arbitrary, it generates sets of radii similar to those in the table, and one particular set of random choices generates the table itself. (In line with the table, the algorithm also designates one ring as Mānasottara Mountain and another as Lokāloka Mountain.)

We used this algorithm to determine how common are patterns which satisfy the criteria we have discussed in Appendix 6. The specific method is as follows: We say that a randomly generated set of radii and a particular *yojana* length *satisfies* a criterion if it does as well or better by this criterion than the actual set of radii defined in the Table 2.1, using 8.489 miles/*yojana*. Let x and y be two sets of rings and *yojana* lengths. If C(x) represents a criterion for x, then x does as well or better than y on C if C(x)≥C(y).

The purpose of the "as well or better" rule is to avoid the following problem: If we observe that one thing matches another, we may be misled by adopting loose criteria for a match, so that a match by our criteria may be quite probable by chance. But if the formal analysis considers matches that are as loose as those we observe, then it should reveal whether such loose matches are probable or not.

We combined criteria 1a and 1b into a single criterion, (simply called 1), and we included the goodness of fit function G(y) as a seventh criterion.

For each nonempty subset of these seven criteria (127 subsets in all), we calculated the probability that a randomly generated set of radii satisfied all the criteria in the subset for some *yojana* length between 1 and 16 miles. This was done by using a computer to generate 20,000 random sets of rings, and checking each set for the full range of *yojana* lengths. (We used an increment of .00375 miles in *yojana* length).

TABLE A7
Probability of Combined Criteria

Individual Criteria	Percentage	Combined Criteria	Percentage
1	45.695	1	45.695
2	43.405	1–2	29.680
3	24.705	1–3	6.390
4	59.780	1–4	6.035
5	64.300	1–5	0.785
6	74.410	1–6	0.000
7	27.135	1–7	0.000

The probability that criterion k is satisfied is fairly large for each k=1, . . . ,7, considered separately. These percentages are listed in columns 1 and 2 of the above table. But if we combine several criteria, the percentage goes down rapidly. This is illustrated in columns 3 and 4. For example, 0.785% of the trials satisfied all of the criteria from 1 through 5, and none of the trials satisfied criteria 1 through 6 or 1 through 7.

Note that the addition of criterion 4 reduced the percentage only slightly, from 6.39% to 6.035%. This is due to the fact that the original pattern in Table 4.2 does not score very well on criterion 4, and therefore many randomly generated patterns do as well or better on this criterion. However, the addition of criterion 6 reduces the percentage from 0.785% to 0%. This is because the original pattern is not broken up by unused circles, even though this is likely to happen by chance.

If we combine criterion 6 with criteria 1, 2, and 3 directly, we find that the four criteria, 1, 2, 3, and 6, are satisfied by only 0.04% of the trials. Leaving aside 1, we find that 0.105% of the trials satisfy the three criteria, 2, 3, and 6. These are among the strongest criteria, in the sense that no more than about one set of artificial radii in a thousand do better than Table 4.2 on these three criteria combined, for some *yojana* length between 1 and 16 miles.

Criterion 7, the goodness of fit function G(y), also has a strong effect, especially in combination with 6. Thus the combination 2, 6, and 7 is satisfied for 0.23% of the trials and 3, 6, and 7 is satisfied for 0.03%. The combination 2, 3, 6, and 7 was satisfied for only 1 of the 20,000 trials (0.005%).

One might ask: Why look at combinations of criteria that yield a low probability? Why not look at single criteria, or at combinations yielding a high probability, and conclude that the observed orbit correlations are quite probable? The answer is that *all* of our criteria are reasonable features of an orbital map and thus all should be considered in a statistical assessment. This yields a probability of less than 1 in 20,000 trials. (The addition of further criteria, which we have overlooked, would simply decrease this probability further.) It is interesting to see, however, which criteria contribute most strongly to the low probability, and we therefore examined different combinations.

Criteria 2 through 6 are general in nature, and they are designed to penalize irregularities in the correlation between Bhū-maṇḍala features and perigees and apogees of planets. Ring patterns satisfying criteria 2, 3, and 6 for some *yojana* length have a probability of about 0.1%, and this probability goes down sharply as more criteria are added. It can be concluded that patterns of rings satisfying such combinations of criteria are quite rare in the output of our pattern-generation algorithm, which was intended to create sets of rings similar to those of Bhū-maṇḍala in the *Bhāgavatam*. This goes against the null hypothesis, which says that any correlation between Bhū-maṇḍala features and planetary orbits must be coincidental. The alternative to the null hypothesis is that some real knowledge of planetary distances may have entered into the construction of the Bhū-maṇḍala system in the *Bhāgavatam*.

A8. Ancient Metrology

The mathematician R. A. Schwaller de Lubicz remarked that units were sometimes used with variable lengths in ancient Egypt. He gave the following example of the use of the Egyptian fathom in the temple of Luxor:

> The strange rhomboidal distortion of the plans of the west pylon prompted us to measure them carefully several times, rectifying the gaps between the stones (which are sound in this location)—gaps caused by settling or other accidental causes.
>
> The length of the pylon under the cornice, between tori, gives, from the north side (along 12 fathoms), the meridian fathom at 90 degrees (North Pole), and from the south side the meridian fathom at 0 degrees (Equator); that is, respectively 1.86166 m and 1.8429 m (difference along 12 fathoms = 22.5 cm).
>
> This could be coincidence, but these measurements recur at several important points; let us therefore concede a repeating coincidence . . . (Schwaller de Lubicz, 1977, p. 66).

By "meridian fathom" at a given latitude, Schwaller de Lubicz means a unit of measurement that is roughly the span of a man's outstretched arms, but which is precisely defined to be one-thousandth the length of the minute of latitude. This unit varies when defined for different latitudes because the length of a minute of latitude varies as one goes from south to north. This is caused by the fact that the earth globe is slightly oblate.

One may speculate that units representing different latitudes were used in temple construction to symbolize the earth as a whole. But to say that the Egyptians consciously used such scientifically defined units is an extraordinary claim, since they supposedly thought the earth was flat and knew nothing about the oblateness of the earth globe. Therefore Schwaller de Lubicz spoke of coincidences.

However, such coincidences turn out to be widespread and systematic. The scholar Livio Stecchini maintained that "The Egyptians had measured the circumference of the earth and had realized that degrees of the meridian become longer as one moves to the north. They established a geodetic system with benchmarks for the purpose of showing that the main physical features of Egypt fit the patterns of meridians and parallels" (Stecchini, 1961, p. 19). He claimed that this accomplishment was part of a widespread system of scientifically defined weights and measures developed in the earliest phases of known civilization. According to Stecchini,

> The scholars to whom we are most indebted for the decipherment of the Sumerian language, Julius Oppert and Carl Friedrich Lehmann-Haupt, proved that by the time the Sumerians wrote their first texts at the beginning of the third millennium B.C., they were in possession of a highly scientific system of measures, linking length, volume, and weight with the highest precision. All the measures used in the Old World, up to the adoption of the French metric system, are related to this system (Stecchini, 1966, p. 163).

Not surprisingly, many notable scholars reject such claims. Thus the historian of science Otto Neugebauer deplored "Fantastic ideas about the level and importance of astronomy in the earliest periods of Babylonian history," which "led to theories which brought measures of time and space in close relationship with alleged astronomical discoveries" (Neugebauer, 1945, p. 27). But the coincidences that lead to such ideas are there, and the question is, are they mere products of chance, or are they traces of a forgotten empirical science?

A thorough survey of the field of ancient metrology—the study of ancient weights and measures—is a monumental task that lies far beyond the scope of this work. However, in this section we will briefly examine a few topics in this field for the purpose of acquainting the reader with the nature of metrological evidence. We will note some of the claims made by Stecchini and others and present the results of our own research.

A8.1 TRACKING THE ARTABA AND THE ROMAN POUND

We begin with units of weight. Stecchini defines the *artaba*, A, as 90 Roman pounds or *librae*, where each *libra* is 12 Roman ounces, or *uncia*, of 27 gm (Stecchini, 1971, p. 312). The *libra* is therefore 324 gm, and the *artaba* is 29,160 gm. Stecchini also defines a "geometric *libra*" of $^{81}/_{80}$ *librae*, or 328.05 gm. He explains that the ratio of $^{81}/_{80}$ comes up frequently in the study of ancient weights.

For comparison, the famous Egyptologist Flinders Petrie pointed out that many types of Roman *libra* were created by Romans, Greeks, and others under the influence of unification with other standards of weight (Flinders Petrie, 1929, p. 145). He lists three specifically Roman variants of the *uncia* as 26.7 gm (Roman trade), 27.02 gm (Roman solidi), and 27.28 (Roman aurei). These figures agree moderately well with Stecchini's *libra* and geometric *libra*, since the geometric *uncia* comes to 27.34 gm.

We can find a closer confirmation of Stecchini's units by examining medieval and modern English weights, which are known to be rooted in classical antiquity. These include the Troy and Avoirdupois pounds, which are still used today, and the Tower pound, which was used in the mint at the Tower of London during the Middle Ages.

The Tower pound was abolished by Henry VIII in 1527. The relevant Exchequer minute illustrates how historical documentation can define relationships between units:

> Now it is determined by the King's Highness and the said councelle, that the foresaid pounde Tower shall be no more used and occupied, but al ma`ner of golde and sylver shall be wayed by the pounde Troye, which maketh XII oz Troye, which exceedeth the pounde Tower in weight iii quarters of the oz (Berriman, 1953, p. 152).

This means that a Tower pound is 11.25 Troy ounces, and the mass ratio of (Tower lb)/(Troy lb) is therefore 11.25/12 or 15/16.

The Tower pound was divided into 12 Tower ounces, and 16 Tower ounces defined the widely used Mercantile pound (*libra mercatoria*). It turns out that the Tower ounce is fundamental to Stecchini's system. He sets the *artaba* equal to 1000 Tower ounces, and we have the following equations:

100 Tower ounce = 108 *uncia*
1,000 Tower ounce = 1,080 *uncia* = *artaba* = A
16 Tower ounce = 15 Troy ounce = Mercantile lb
70 Tower ounce = 72 Avoirdupois ounce

Using the modern value for the Troy ounce, the value of A is almost exactly 29,160 gm, as given by Stecchini. The question is, how accurately is this modern value reproduced by ancient data?

The engineer A. E. Berriman (1953, p. 136) pointed out that the *livre poid de marc* used in France before the metric system is 3/2 *libra* (to which he gave a slightly different value than Stecchini). The history of this unit gives some insight into how ratios such as 3/2 come about.

In the ninth century, the Caliph Al Ma'mun (786–833) is reputed to have sent the *yusdruma*, or later Arab pound, to Charlemagne, who adopted it as the *livre esterlin* (Hallock and Wade, 1906, pp. 38–39). Between 1076 and 1093, Philip I defined the *marc* to be 2/3 of this unit. Then King John the Good doubled it, producing the *livre poid de marc*. From the *yusdruma* to the prerevolutionary *livre*, the ratio to the *libra* went from 9/8 to 3/4 to 3/2, and in earlier times it may have gone through other, similar transformations.

When the metric system was adopted, the *livre* was defined as 489.506 gm. This gives us a *libra* about .25 gm less than Stecchini's 324 gm figure.

The important point here, is that royal edicts generally change units by rational numbers such as 9/8 or 16/15. If one can track these numbers historically, then one can be sure of the theoretical value of a sequence of related units over the centuries. One can then compute what ancient units should have been by using modern values for related units. The results can be checked by measuring ancient weights or other measures found in archeological sites. Here, of course, we must recognize that weights and measuring rods used by ancient merchants may not have agreed closely with the standards accepted at that time. Taking this into account, our study suggests that ancient units have, in fact, been transmitted down to modern times with impressive accuracy.

The Romans had a measure of volume, called the *amphora* or *quadrantal*, that contained 80 *librae* of water. Stecchini points out that there was also an enlarged *quadrantal* that contains 81 *librae*, or equivalently 80 geometric *librae*. The enlarged *quadrantal* is 0.02% larger than the modern Russian *chetverik* of 26,238.75 cc, that was still in use up to the time of the Bolshevik revolution. (Stecchini points out that *chetverik* means *quadrantal* in Russian.) Here we assume that 1 cc of water weighs 1 gm.

Direct assessment of the volume of Roman vessels gives a less accurate confirmation. Thus Flinders Petrie lists 25,807 to 26,300 cc for 80 *librae* of water, while Stecchini's two *quadrantals* are 25,920 and 26,244 cc (Flinders Petrie, 1929, p. 144). These estimates are consistent with the *libra*, but the measured values for a variety of Roman containers are all considerably larger.

Here is an example of this discrepancy. Wilfred Airy measured a first century bronze congius of six Roman *sextarii,* which was labeled P. X., meaning 10 pounds. This is the appropriate weight, since there are 6×8 *sextarii* to the *amphora* of 80 *librae* of water. But the vessel turned out to actually contain 10.1 Roman pounds of distilled water (Airy, 1908–9, p. 167).

Weights closer to the *artaba* are reported from Knossos in Crete. Sir Arthur Evans reported that in the archeological excavations of the palace of Minos at Knossos, a standard talent weight was found in the form of a purple gypsum block covered with a bas-relief carving of an octopus. This weight scales at exactly 29,000 gm—about 0.6% lower than the *artaba*.

In addition, nineteen copper ingots were found walled up in the basement of the palace of Hagia Triada. Evans reported that "The average weight of these ingots—which themselves do not vary greatly in weight—is 29,131.6 grammes, and two of them weigh exactly 29 kilogrammes" (Evans, 1935, p. 652). The ingots are about 0.1% lighter than the *artaba*, on the average. It seems apparent that Stecchini's *artaba* did exist, with connections through related units all the way to the Tower of London. Evans remarks that the octopus weight is a "light talent of a peculiarly Egyptian type," and this jibes with Stecchini's contention that the *artaba* originated in Egypt.

Hallock and Wade state that the original Greek standard of weight was the heavier Babylonian talent, which was used in the Greek island of Aegina and spread from there to Sparta and Corinth. In about 592 B.C., the Athenian ruler Solon decreed a smaller talent, equal to 3/5 of the Babylonian talent, in order to release the people from usurers (Hallock and Wade, 1906, p. 27). Solon divided this Attic talent into 60 *minas*, and "the same weight of water contained in the *amphora* was divided into 80 pounds, thus making 3 attic *minas* equal to 4 Roman pounds" (Hallock and Wade, 1906, p. 28).

This might be taken to imply that the Roman *libra* was defined after Solon's decree. However, Hallock and Wade also say that the Roman pound was originally established as 9/10 of the Aeginetan half *mina*, which is 1/2 of 1/60 of the Babylonian talent. This gives the same value for the Roman pound.

A8.2 THE HARAPPAN UNCIA

There is evidence suggesting that the Roman *libra* has a history going back long before the beginning of the Roman Empire. The excavation of Mohenjo-daro and Harappa revealed a large number of small, rectangular stone blocks, made mostly of chert and of other hard rocks, such as gneiss. It turned out that these were weights belonging to a graded system.

Table A8.1 lists the results of weighing 331 of these weights, as described by A. S. Hemmy in the report of the excavations of Mohenjo-daro between 1927 and 1931 (Hemmy, 1938). The third column, under Ratio, indicates the ideal ratio between each successive weight and the smallest weight. With one exception, the smaller weights increase by powers of two, and thus they could easily be used to weigh objects in a balance by a binary system.

Note that the most common weight is 27.405 gm, which is close to the Roman *uncia*. (This was first observed by Berriman, 1953, p. 34.) This weight was calculated by averaging 94 weights that fell between 26.312 and 29.225 gm. We can also get an average based on all 331 weights by dividing each weight by its ratio in column 3, to get the corresponding unit weight, near .87 gm. These unit weights can be averaged, using the numbers of specimens of each weight as weighting factors. This, multiplied by 32, gives an average of 27.438 gm for the most common weight. For comparison, the geometric *uncia* is 27.34 gm.

John Mitchiner (1978) published evidence showing that the Indus Valley weights survived as contemporary or near contemporary Indian weights. His data are in Table A8.2. Note that the equivalent of the *uncia* comes to 27.28 gm in this report.

The culture of Mohenjo-daro and Harappa is provisionally dated from about 2600–2500 B.C. to 1900 B.C., using C-14 dating (Lal, 1998, p. 114). If the weight of about 27.438 gm survived historically to become the Roman *uncia* (and as a recent Indian weight), then wemight wonder how this could be possible, given the range of variation in these weights. One would think that variation over the

TABLE A8.1
Weights from Mohenjo-daro and Harappa

Number of Specimens	Mean Weight in Grams	Ratio
5	0.871	1
13	1.770	2
2	2.285	8/3
31	3.434	4
45	6.829	8
91	13.731	16
94	27.405	32
23	54.359	64
11	136.02	160
1	174.50	200
4	271.33	320
1	546.70	640
3	1417.5	1600
3	2701.4	3200
1	5556	6400
1	6903	8000
2	10865	12800

TABLE A8.2
Survival of the Indus Weights

Indus Weights							
Unit	1	2	4	8	16	32	64
grams	.8525	1.705	3.41	6.82	13.64	27.28	54.56
Later Indian Weights							
Rattis	8	16	32	64	128	256	512
Karṣas			1	2	4	8	16
grams	.8375	1.675	3.35	6.70	13.40	26.80	53.60

centuries would greatly alter the weight standard, even if it remained in continuous use through a succession of cultures.

The answer is that empirical measurements of artifacts found in archeological sites can only tell us about weights and measures in common use in the marketplace. They do not tell us about carefully conserved standard units which would be kept in small numbers in the royal palace or in suitable government buildings. These standards would have been kept with great care, and they would have been gradually passed from one society to another, as we saw in the post-Roman history of the French *livre*. Certainly, if the Roman *uncia* could survive the Middle Ages and reach modern times, then under other names it could have descended from the time of the Indus Valley civilization. A similar story could apply to the history of this weight in India.

Hemmy computed the degree of scatter in the weights in each of the categories in Table A8.1. For the *uncia* weight, the ratio of scatter to weight was 1.34%, and these ratios were somewhat higher for the other weights. He commented for all of the weights that "this ratio is much lower than is found in other countries at about the same period; it appears to point to a stricter regulation of commerce" (Hemmy, 1938, p. 603).

The weight system of the Harappan culture cannot be directly derived from the contemporary systems of weights and measures in the

Near East, although there is an indirect relationship. Table A8.3 lists measured values of weights belonging to the "light Babylonian system" of ancient Iraq, as given by Sir John Marshall in his report on the Mohenjo-daro excavations. (Marshall, 1973, p. 592). Stecchini defines the Sumerian *sila* as *artaba*/60 and the *shekel* as *sila*/60 (Stecchini 1971, p. 312). In this table the *mina* corresponds to the *sila*.

The weights in this table show a great deal of variation, and this tends to be most extreme for the smallest weights. The third column gives the ideal ratio between the talent and the given weight. The fourth column gives the implied talent obtained by multiplying the given weight by this ratio. These can be compared with the *artaba* enlarged by 81/80, or 29524.5 gm. The rightmost column gives a running average of the percentage difference between the implied talent and this enlarged *artaba*. This is under 1% for all but the smallest weights.

TABLE A8.3
The Light Babylonian System of Weights

Name	Number of Specimens	Mean Weight (in grams)	Ratio	Implied Talent	Percentage Difference
Talent	1	29680	1	29680	.53
30 Minas	1	14975	2	29950	.98
	2	2466	12	29592	.73
	1	1492	20	29840	.82
	4	970	30	29100	.37
Mina	3	486	60	29160	.10
	6	246	120	29520	.08
	5	170	180	30600	.53
	6	82.8	360	29808	.58
	7	41.8	720	30096	.71
	4	16.91	1800	30438	.93
Shekel	11	8.31	3600	29916	.96
	16	4.37	7200	31464	1.39
	5	2.15	14400	30960	1.64
1/8 Shekel	4	.96	28800	27648	1.11

Thus the Babylonian weights seem to be based on subdivisions of a large weight, which is close to the enlarged *artaba*. In contrast, the Indus Valley weights seem to be multiples and fractions of a small weight corresponding to the enlarged or "geometric" *uncia*.

A8.3 ANCIENT FEET

In his empirical study of ancient units of length, Flinders Petrie included the versions of the "foot" listed in Table A8.4.

Each of these units was used in Greece, and for each one we list in column two the average of the empirically measured values reported by Flinders Petrie. Each unit turns out to be almost exactly 1.02 times the one before it in the list, and this suggests that they are all related.

TABLE A8.4
Ancient Units that Approximate the Foot

Unit	Measured	Calculated
Roman foot	29.585 cm	29.595 cm
Hasta/1.5	30.175 cm	30.238 cm
Olympic foot	30.903 cm	30.907 cm
Babylonian foot	31.555 cm	31.579 cm

The Babylonian foot can be derived from the enlarged *artaba*, namely 81A/80. Simply define a palm to be the cube root of the *mina* defined as 1/60 of the enlarged *artaba*. The Babylonian foot is four of these palms. These steps reduce down to the cube root of 1.08A, and they generate the computed value listed in column 3. If the Babylonian foot is truly Babylonian in origin, it confirms the identity of the light Babylonian talent as the enlarged *artaba*.

The Olympic foot is the cube root of the enlarged *artaba*. The Roman foot is the cube root of the *quadrantal*, or *amphora*, which is 8A/9. Their computed values are also listed in column 3. The Greek stadium was defined to be 600 Olympic, or Greek, feet. Since Pliny stated that the stadium contains 625 Roman feet (Berriman, 1953,

p. 116), it follows that the ratio of Greek to Roman feet should be 25/24. In fact, 25/24 is close to the ratio of the computed values given in the table.

Hasta is the Sanskrit term for the cubit, or distance from the elbow to the end of the hand. The unit listed above as *hasta* was so-called by Flinders Petrie because it was found in measurements of rock-cut temples at Elora in India (Flinders Petrie, 1877, pp. 126–27). We have divided his average value by 1.5 to convert it from a cubit to a foot for comparison with the three other feet. Since this unit was also used in Greece, we can infer a connection between Western and Indian units. Just as there were several different units of length used in the ancient Western world, we might also expect to find several different lengths of the *hasta*, some of which were related to Western measures.

The ratio of 1.08A to 81A/80 is 16/15, and the ratio of 1.08A to 8A/9 is very close to 16/15 cubed. By analogy, each term in the series in Table A8.4 should be the cube root of 8A/9 times a power of 16/15. This gives us an estimate of *hasta* as the cube root of 16A/5, and this (over 1.5) is also listed in column 3.

We noted above that the heavier Babylonian talent was the original Greek standard of weight, according to Hallock and Wade. Based on their figures, the *quadrantal* of 80 *librae* must equal 3/5 of the Babylonian talent, so that the latter is 40/27 of the *artaba*. The heavier Babylonian talent is therefore 43,200 gm. Hallock and Wade point out that the cube root of this weight, considered as a cube filled with water, is a unit of length, which they misidentify as the Olympic cubit or 1.5 Olympic feet (Hallock and Wade, 1906, p. 27). Actually, this unit turns out to be the foot defined as 2/3 of the Egyptian royal cubit. By this calculation, the royal cubit comes to 52.632 cm, a figure given by (Stecchini, 1971, p. 320). If we simplify the calculation, we find that the royal cubit is the cube root of five times the *artaba*, and this formula is also given by Stecchini.

A8.4 METRIC CUBITS

Both Stecchini and Schwaller de Lubicz argue that the royal cubit was defined in several different ways, resulting in different lengths that were used for different applications. In one, the average degree of latitude for Egypt (about 27°) was divided into 210,000 cubits of about

52.7 cm. This cubit was used in the nilometer of Elephantine, and the stadium defined as 300 of these cubits was used by Eratosthenes in his measurement of the size of the earth (Schwaller de Lubicz, 1998, p. 299).

A widely used form of the cubit was defined as one sixth of the circumference of a circle of one meter in diameter (Schwaller de Lubicz, 1998, p. 289). This comes to $\pi/6$ m or 52.36 cm. Here the use of the meter may seem anachronistic, since this unit was originally defined in 1791 as one ten-millionth of the meridian quadrant from the equator to the north pole (Berriman, 1953, p. 142).

However, Schwaller de Lubicz maintains that the meter was used in Egyptian monuments, and he gives many examples (e.g. Schwaller de Lubicz, 1998, pp. 932–33). He says that the meter was also defined by the Egyptians to be one ten-millionth of the meridian quadrant. This, of course, assumes that the Egyptians not only knew that the earth is a globe but were able to accurately measure it.

The fathom was also defined in terms of geodetic measurements. This unit is roughly the length of a man's outstretched arms, but it is defined exactly as one thousandth of a minute of latitude. Since the minute of latitude varies as one goes from north to south, this unit could take on different values ranging from 1.843 m for the equator to 1.861 m for the north pole. According to Schwaller de Lubicz, these values were used systematically in Egyptian monuments (Schwaller de Lubicz, 1998, p. 299).

He argues that the mean fathom was used to define the Egyptian meter (e-meter for short). There are $60\times90\times1000$ mean fathoms in the meridian quadrant, and this means that 100 e-meters equal 54 mean fathoms. Curiously, if we take the fathom defined for 45° of latitude (i.e. 1.852189 m) as the mean fathom, then the e-meter comes to 1.000182 m. The meter is presently defined so that the meridian quadrant is equal to 10,001,970 m, and therefore it is 10,000,150 e-meters—very close to 10 million.

We can check these units by consulting the scientific survey of the great pyramid conducted by the engineer J.H. Cole in 1925. Using modern surveying techniques, Cole found that the lengths of the sides of the great pyramid are 230.357 m, 230.253 m, 230.391 m, and 230.454 m for the west, north, east, and south sides, respectively (Stecchini, 1971, p. 364). There are said to be 440 royal cubits in each side of the great pyramid (Berriman, 1953, p. 78). Using the Cole's average for the length of a side, this gives us a royal cubit of 52.355 cm, close to the value obtained from $\pi/6$.

We get an even closer agreement by observing that there are 500 fathoms in the perimeter of the great pyramid. This gives a fathom of 1.84291 m, which corresponds to a latitude of 0° (the equator). In Section 4.5.3, we noted that the *hasta* of the short *yojana* goes almost exactly 2000 times into the perimeter of the great pyramid. Indeed, this *hasta* is equivalent to the cubit of the Egyptian fathom defined at the equator.

A8.5 LATITUDES IN ANCIENT EGYPT

Stecchini makes many points in support of the controversial claim that the ancient Egyptians made accurate measurements of latitude and longitude and were aware that the length of a degree of latitude changes as one moves north or south. Unfortunately, it is difficult to check many of his assertions, because he said he could not present the textual evidence that backs them up due to lack of space (Stecchini, 1971, p. 332). However, some of his statements can be checked, and we will give one example.

He refers to three Egyptian measuring rules found at the Temple of Amon in Thebes. In 1921, the famous Egyptologist Ludwig Borchardt published a report on these rules, in which he pointed out that they contain an inscription referring to distances in Egypt. The inscription states that the distance from Syene to Pi-Hapy is 86 *atur*, the distance from Pi-Hapy to Behdet is 20 *atur*, and the distance from Syene to Behdet is 106 *atur*.

Stecchini argues that the latitude of Syene can be taken as 24° N, a traditional ancient value for the latitude of the Tropic of Cancer. He says that Behdet was a predynastic center on the Mediterranean coast at the northernmost point of the Nile delta, and he gives it a latitude of 31.5° N (Stecchini, 1971, pp. 293–94). Using modern geodetic calculations, this gives a distance along the meridian of 831.122 km from Syene to Behdet.

Borchardt observed that the length of an *atur* in royal cubits must be expressed by numbers such as 5,000 or 10,000. By assuming that the distance from Syene to Behdet was measured along the winding course of the Nile, he concluded that it should be around 20,000 cubits. Stecchini disagrees, saying that if we take 15,000 royal cubits per *atur*, we find that the north-south distance in latitude from Syene to Behdet is very close to 106 *atur*. In fact, using the royal cubit of 52.36 cm, and assuming 106 *atur* in the 831.122 km from Syene to Behdet, we find that the length of an *atur* comes to 14,974.739 royal cubits. This is certainly close to 15,000 cubits.

Given that Pi-Hapy is 20 *atur* from Behdet at 31.5° N and 86 *atur* from Syene at 24° N, we can compute what the latitude of Pi-Hapy should be to give these proportional distances. This comes to 30° 5.135' N, taking into account the variation in the degree as we go from south to north. Stecchini argues that Pi-Hapy, called Nilopolis by the Greeks, was on the right bank of the Nile, facing the southern tip of the island al-Warraq (Stecchini, 1971, p. 335). This latitude gives a good match for its position. I note that if the distances of 20 and 86 *atur* had indicated distances along the winding course of the Nile, then we would not expect this geodetic calculation to work out so well.

Using the royal cubit of 52.36 cm, we find that 12×106×15,000 royal cubits equals 9,990,288 m, which is close to the meridian quadrant. (The error is -0.11%.) Thus the meridian quadrant is very close to twelve times the traditional length of Egypt, as Stecchini points out.

Stecchini argues that the traditional length of Egypt was divided into 1,800,000 geographic cubits (Stecchini, 1971, p. 317). This, he says, is the origin of the *artaba*, which is the cube of the geographic foot (2/3 of a geographic cubit), and which shows up in so many measurement systems. From this, we can use our length of 831.122 km to calculate that the *artaba* should be 29,167.76 gm, and this can be compared with Stecchini's figure of 29,160 gm.

Six feet or four cubits should equal one fathom. Using the geographic foot just calculated, the fathom should be 1.8469 m, corresponding to a latitude in the middle of Egypt, between 27° and 28°. This links Stecchini's geographic foot with one of the fathom lengths discussed by Schwaller de Lubicz.

A8.6 CONCLUSIONS

In this section we have seen a hint of the many relationships that run through ancient weights and measures. Although some of these relationships may be coincidental, there seems to be good evidence that many units have been accurately transmitted from one culture to another over the centuries. More controversial is the claim that ancient units were based on sound knowledge of the shape and size of the earth. Here too, there may be coincidences. Nonetheless, the many correspondences between units and geodetic quantities strongly suggest that advanced knowledge of the size and shape of the earth did exist in early civilizations.

This implies a loss of scientific knowledge at some point in ancient times. Eratosthenes is famous for having carried out a pioneering measurement of the size of the earth during the Hellenistic period in Egypt. In his day, advanced geographic knowledge evidently did not exist among the Greeks and the Egyptians, and so a decline in knowledge must have taken place. Indeed, Pierre-Simon de Laplace (1884) was convinced that Eratosthenes based his work on fragments of earlier advanced knowledge. The implied breakdown in knowledge is not surprising, since we know that an even greater decline in scientific knowledge occurred in Europe after the fall of the Western Roman Empire.

A9. Origins of Mathematics

Evidence for advanced mathematical ability in ancient times is given by the formula 1;24,51,10 for the square root of two, found inscribed on Old Babylonian cuneiform tablets (Neugebauer and Sachs, 1945, p. 43). This formula is written in sexagesimal notation, where successive numbers are divided by ascending powers of 60 (starting with $60^0 = 1$) and then summed. If we square this, the result differs from two by less than 1.7 millionths.

It is interesting to consider how this value of $\sqrt{2}$ was computed. Unfortunately, this is not specified in the texts. However, Neugebauer and Sachs argue that a method of successive approximations was used. If a is an estimate of $\sqrt{2}$, then 2/a is an estimate on the other side of $\sqrt{2}$, and (a+2/a)/2 should be an even closer estimate. If we start with a=1 and apply this method three times, we get the estimate 1;24,51,10 by truncating higher-order sexagesimal terms.

This suggests that the Old Babylonians (dating back to about 1700 B.C.) had the idea of computing successive approximations using an algorithm. This is a very powerful idea that could have been used in many other applications.

Turning to India, A. Seidenberg gives the following expression for $\sqrt{2}$ from the *Śulvasūtra* of Āpastamba (Seidenberg, 1978, p. 327):

$$1 + 1/3 + 1/(3\times4) - 1/(3\times4\times34)$$

This is $577/(17\times24)$, and it is the exact result of applying the above method of successive approximations three times, starting with a=1. (This is slightly less accurate than the Babylonian result, since sexagesimal rounding happened to produce an improvement.) It would seem that this method or something equivalent to it became widely known in ancient times.

The *Śulvasūtras* are a group of texts that explain how to use geometry to construct altars for fire sacrifices. The *Śulvasūtra* of Āpastamba has been dated to the third century B.C., or somewhat earlier, but it may preserve a much older tradition. Seidenberg cites passages from the *Śatapatha Brāhmaṇa* referring to altar constructions of the kind given in the *Śulvasūtras*. Although the *Śatapatha Brāhmaṇa* is not a mathematical text, Seidenberg infers that the mathematics of altar construction given in the *Śulvasūtras* must have been in use at the time the *Śatapatha Brāhmaṇa* was written.

Since this goes back to before the sixth century B.C., before the time of Classical Greece, it follows that the *Śulvasūtras* could not have borrowed from classical Greek geometry (Seidenberg, 1978, p. 323). Seidenberg concludes that since Greek geometry resembles *Śulvasūtra* geometry both in principles and details, it must be that Greek geometry either originated from Indian geometry or both descended from a common source.

The Pythagorean theorem is present in the *Śulvasūtras*, in Babylonian mathematics, and, of course, in Greek geometry. In *Śulvasūtras* it is applied in altar construction, where there is a need to construct a square with an area equal to the sum of the areas of two other squares. Seidenberg suggests that this is the setting in which the theorem first arose.

Seidenberg argues that the *Śulvasūtras* contain a geometric tradition that goes back before Old Babylonian times. He points out that the *Śulvasūtras* present geometric constructions, and they contain what he calls geometric algebra, or algebraic calculations expressed through geometric constructions. In contrast, even though Babylonian mathematics contains similar material, it is expressed in a purely computational form.

Otto Neugebauer had concluded in the 1930s that "What is called Pythagorean in the Greek tradition had better be called Babylonian" (Seidenberg, 1978, p. 307). B. L. van der Waerden argued that the Greek emphasis on geometric constructions rather than computations can then be explained as a response to the Pythagorean discovery of irrational quantities (such as $\sqrt{2}$). Some of these quantities can be exactly constructed geometrically, but they cannot be exactly calculated. However, the existence of *Śulvasūtra* geometry before the days of Pythagoras throws a monkey wrench into this theory.

Seidenberg argues that the Indians are not likely to have geometrized Babylonian computational procedures. Since *Śulvasūtra* geometry is entirely bound up with ritualistic procedures involved with building altars for fire sacrifices, he also considers it unlikely that it could have been derived from Greek geometry—even if the dates would have allowed this. Vedic priests were not likely to incorporate foreign abstract mathematics into their rituals, but they may have incorporated geometric methods developed in their own culture or handed down from an ancestral culture. If Greeks borrowed sacred geometry, they might have secularized it—and there is at least one Greek reference to doubling the size of an altar (Seidenberg, 1962, pp. 493–94). Babylonians might likewise have dropped geometric constructions and emphasized pure computation (as we tend to do today with analytic geometry).

Seidenberg proposes that *Śulvasūtra* geometry is the source of both Old Babylonian mathematics and Greek geometry. But since Indologists do not allow a date for Vedic culture in India as far back as the Old Babylonian period (c. 1700 B.C.), he therefore postulates an unknown source of this geometric tradition.

This confronts us with the mysterious chronology of Babylon. Babylonian mathematics is said to have flourished in 1700 B.C. Then there is a gap of 1300 years with no Babylonian mathematical texts. Historians have no idea what was going on mathematically in this period. But in the Seleucid period about 300 B.C., Babylonian mathematics picks up again in nearly the same form in which it had existed before the gap (Seidenberg, 1978, p. 310). At the very least, this shows that our knowledge of the past is extremely fragmentary.

Seidenberg tends to stress the ideas that great discoveries are made only once and that the appearance of similar ideas in widely separated cultures implies cultural diffusion. It may well be that many important ideas were transmitted in this way. Arbitrary details, which could easily have been expressed differently, may be a particularly reliable sign of cultural diffusion. Thus there may be many ways of approximating $\sqrt{2}$, but when the same method appears in two different places, cultural diffusion can be reasonably inferred.

At the same time, there is evidence indicating that independent invention may have played an important role in past scientific developments. For example, the story of the mathematician Mādhava, who lived in India in the fourteenth century, provides an illustration of repeated scientific achievement. We normally associate the use of power series to compute trigonometric functions with the development of calculus in Europe, starting with Newton and Leibniz. However, Mādhava is credited with inventing the power series expansion for the arc tangent function, which was independently discovered in Europe by James Gregory in 1671 (Amma, 1979, pp. 182–83). Since Mādhava lived in a traditional Indian cultural milieu, such mathematical creativity could, in principle, have arisen in India at any time over a period of thousands of years.

We should also note that the Indian mathematician Śrīnivāsa Rāmānujan had a very poor education in mathematics. But entirely on his own, he made mathematical discoveries that astonished the best mathematicians of Europe. Such a person could easily have lived many centuries ago in India or in other civilized societies. His work might well have been used in pioneering scientific studies that did not find their way into standard texts intended for students or ritualistic priests.

Thus it is possible that an advanced science of mathematics existed somewhere in the world prior to 1700 B.C. This may have involved sophisticated applications that went far beyond elementary texts, such as *Śulvasūtras*, intended for simple applications. There is no need here to postulate "secret knowledge." Advanced knowledge, by its very nature, would have been known only to a small elite, and it could easily have become lost in the course of time.

If advanced mathematics existed, it would have provided the basis for advanced quantitative science. This ties in consistently with the evidence for sophisticated astronomy and earth measurement that we have discussed in this study.

A10. Planetary Diameters In the Sūrya-siddhānta

The Indian astronomical text *Sūrya-siddhānta* gives a rule for computing the angular diameters of the planets. By combining these angular diameters with the circumferences of the planetary orbits listed in this text, it is possible to compute the diameters of the planets (Thompson, 1997). When these computations are carried out, the results agree surprisingly well with modern astronomical data. In this appendix, we discuss several possible explanations for this and hypothesize that the angular diameter rule in the *Sūrya-siddhānta* may be based on advanced astronomical knowledge that was developed in ancient times but has now been largely forgotten.

A10.1 ANGULAR DIAMETERS OF PLANETS

In chapter 7 of the *Sūrya-siddhānta* (Burgess, 1860), the thirteenth verse gives the following rule for calculating the apparent diameters of the planets Mars, Saturn, Mercury, Jupiter, and Venus:

> 7.13. The diameters upon the moon's orbit of Mars, Saturn, Mercury, and Jupiter, are declared to be thirty, increased successively by half the half; that of Venus is sixty.

The meaning is as follows: The diameters are measured in a unit of distance called the *yojana*, which in the *Sūrya-siddhānta* is about five miles. The phrase "upon the moon's orbit" means that the planets look from our vantage point as though they were globes of the indicated diameters situated at the distance of the moon. (Our vantage point is ideally the center of the earth.) Half the half of thirty is 7.5. Thus the verse says that the diameters "upon the moon's orbit" of the indicated planets are given by 30, 37.5, 45, 52.5, and 60 *yojanas*, respectively.

The next verse uses this information to compute the angular diameters of the planets. This computation takes into account the variable distance of the planets from the earth, but for the purposes of this discussion it is enough to consider the angular diameters at mean planetary distances. The *Sūrya-siddhānta* lists mean planetary distances from the earth, and the diameters upon the moon's orbit were given for the planets at these distances.

The *Sūrya-siddhānta* says that there are fifteen *yojanas* per minute of arc at the distance of the moon (giving 324,000 *yojanas* as the circumference of the moon's orbit). Thus the mean angular diameters of the planets in minutes can be computed by dividing the diameters upon the moon's orbit by fifteen. These figures are listed in the following table, and three other estimates of planetary angular diameters are included for comparison.

TABLE A10.1
Angular Diameters of Planets

Planet	*Sūrya-siddhānta*	Tycho Brahe	Ptolemy	Āryabhaṭa	Modern Minimum	Modern Maximum
Mars	2.0	1.67	1.57	1.260	0.058	0.392
Saturn	2.5	1.83	1.74	1.575	0.249	0.344
Mercury	3.0	2.17	2.09	2.100	0.076	0.166
Jupiter	3.5	2.75	2.61	3.150	0.507	0.827
Venus	4.0	3.25	3.13	6.300	0.159	1.050

These are the angular diameters measured by the Danish astronomer Tycho Brahe, those reported by the second-century Alexandrian astronomer Claudius Ptolemy in his book *Planetary Hypotheses*, those given by the Indian astronomer Āryabhaṭa in his *Āryabhaṭīya*, and those measured recently by modern astronomers. The modern minimum and maximum angular diameters correspond to the greatest and least distances of the planets from the earth.

The *Sūrya-siddhānta* angular diameters are roughly the same size as those reported by Claudius Ptolemy. Ptolemy attributed his angular diameters to the Greek astronomer Hipparchus, but he did not say how they were measured. According to the historian of astronomy Noel Swerdlow, no earlier reports of planetary angular diameters are known, and Ptolemy's angular diameters were reproduced without change by later Greco-Roman, Islamic, and European astronomers up until the rise of modern astronomy in the days of Galileo, Kepler, and Tycho Brahe (Swerdlow, 1968).

Brahe's figures were obtained by sighting through calibrated pinholes by the naked eye. They are very similar to Ptolemy's, and they are clearly much larger than the angular diameters measured in more recent times by means of telescopes. It is well known that a small, distant light source looks larger to the naked eye than it really is. This phenomenon makes it likely that angular diameters of planets would inevitably have been overestimated by astronomers before the age of the telescope.

It is noteworthy that Brahe's angular diameters are the closest to modern values, and they are high by 298% to 2750%. It is evident that naked eye measurements do not disclose the actual angular sizes of planets, even roughly. They simply measure a blob of planetary light generated by the poor optics of the human eye.

It has been argued that Indian astronomy was heavily influenced by Hellenistic astronomy between the second and fifth centuries A.D. (Pingree, 1976). This suggests that the angular diameters given in the *Sūrya-siddhānta* may have been based on Ptolemy's angular diameters. Indeed, Ptolemy's figures are very close to $94/(60 - 7.5i)$, where $i+1$ is the line number in Table A10.1. The corresponding *Sūrya-siddhānta* figures are given by $(30 + 7.5i)/15$, and Āryabhaṭa's are given by $6.3/(6 - i)$ (Clark, 1930, pp. 13–15).

Whether or not this indicates an Indian adaptation of Greek material, the angular diameters from *Sūrya-siddhānta* have an important property that the Ptolemaic angular diameters lack. To see this, it is first necessary to examine the sizes of the mean planetary orbits, as given in *Sūrya-siddhānta*.

A10.2 PLANETARY ORBITS IN SŪRYA-SIDDHĀNTA

Verses 12.85–90 of *Sūrya-siddhānta* give the circumferences of the planetary orbits in *yojanas*. These figures are reproduced in Table A10.2, accompanied by orbital radii computed using five miles/*yojana*.

TABLE A10.2
Planetary Orbits in Sūrya-siddhānta

Planet	*Sūrya-siddhānta* orbital circumference (*yojanas*)	*Sūrya-siddhānta* orbital radius (miles)
Moon	324,000	258,000
Mercury	4,332,000	3,447,000
Venus	4,332,000	3,447,000
Sun	4,332,000	3,447,000
Mars	8,147,000	6,483,000
Jupiter	51,376,000	40,884,000
Saturn	127,668,000	101,595,000

The circumferences of the *Sūrya-siddhānta* orbits are proportional to the mean orbital periods of the planets. For Mercury and Venus, the mean planetary position is the same as the position of the sun, and thus the orbital circumferences in the table are the same for Mercury, Venus, and the sun. For Mars, Jupiter, and Saturn, the mean position corresponds to the average motion of the planet in its heliocentric orbit.

Verse 1.59 of the *Sūrya-siddhānta* gives the diameter of the earth as 1,600 *yojanas*. Several scholars have argued that the *yojana* in the *Sūrya-siddhānta* is about 5 miles, thereby bringing the earth's diameter to the realistic value of 5×1,600 = 8,000 miles. Examples are Sarma (1956), Burgess (1860), and Dikshit (1969b).

Different standards were adopted for the *yojana* by different medieval Indian astronomers. This was noted by the astronomer Parameśvara (A.D. 1380–1450), who said that "What is given by Āryabhaṭa as the measure of the earth and the distances [of the Planets from it], etc., is given as more than one and a half times by other [astronomers]; this is due to the difference in the measure of the *yojana* [adopted by them]" (Sarma, 1956, p. 83).

We discuss different *yojana* lengths in Section 4.5. These include a short *yojana* for which the diameter of the earth comes to 1,728 = 16×108 *yojanas*—a number related to the Kṛta-yuga length of 1,728,000 years. Since there are 1,600 *Sūrya-siddhānta yojanas* in the diameter of the earth, the *Sūrya-siddhānta yojana* must be longer by a factor of exactly 1.08.

Verse 4.1 of the *Sūrya-siddhānta* gives the diameters of the sun and moon as 6,500 and 480 *yojanas*, respectively. Given 5 miles per *yojana*, the resulting lunar diameter of 5×480 = 2,400 miles is about 11% higher than the modern value. The corresponding earth-moon distance of about 258,000 miles is high by 8.3%. However, the sun's diameter comes to 5×6,500 = 32,500 miles, which is far too small.

It is easy to see why the diameter of the moon should be reasonably accurate. The dimensions of the moon and its orbit were well known in ancient times. For example, the lunar diameter given by Ptolemy in his *Planetary Hypotheses* falls within about 7% of the modern value, if we convert his earth-diameters into miles using the modern diameter of the earth (Swerdlow, 1968).

It is also easy to see why the diameter for the sun is too small. Ancient astronomers tended to greatly underestimate the earth-sun distance, and the table shows that this also happened in the *Sūrya-siddhānta*. The angular diameter of the sun is easily seen to be about the same as that of the moon—about ½ degree. This angular diameter, combined with a small earth-sun distance, leads inevitably to a small estimate for the diameter of the sun. Ptolemy's solar diameter figure is similar to the *Sūrya-siddhānta's*.

A10.3 DIAMETERS OF THE PLANETS

What about the planets? Ptolemy listed wildly inaccurate diameters for Mercury, Venus, Mars, Jupiter, and Saturn in his *Planetary Hypotheses*. To see what the *Sūrya-siddhānta* says about the diameters of these planets, we should multiply the *Sūrya-siddhānta* orbital radii by the *Sūrya-siddhānta* angular diameters (converted to radians). The results are listed in miles in the Table A10.3. The error percentages compare the *Sūrya-siddhānta* diameters with the corresponding modern planetary diameters.

Note that even though the angular diameters are too large, and the orbital radii are too small, the calculated diameters are close to modern values for Mercury, Mars, and Saturn.

TABLE A10.3
Diameters of Planets According to Sūrya-siddhānta

Planet	Modern Diameter	*Sūrya-siddhānta* Diameter	% Error
Mercury	3,032	3,008	-1
Venus	7,523	4,011	-47
Mars	4,218	3,772	-11
Jupiter	88,748	41,624	-53
Saturn	74,580	73,882	-1

For Venus and Jupiter, they are too small by about 50%. One explanation is that radii were given for Venus and Jupiter, rather than diameters. On this hypothesis, Venus and Jupiter also agree well with modern data. If we multiply these *Sūrya-siddhānta* diameters by two, we get 83,248 miles for Jupiter and 8,022 miles for Venus. These figures differ from the corresponding modern values by -6% and 7%. Given this correction, all five planets have an error of 11% or less. (The root-mean-square error comes to 6.3%.)

It is striking that the error percentages in the table are either small or close to 50%, but it may seem gratuitous to suppose that radii are involved in the latter case. In order to get more insight into this, we calculated the root-mean-square percentage of error between the *Sūrya-siddhānta* diameters and the planetary diameters given by modern astronomy. We also did the same calculations using the angular diameter data of Ptolemy, Tycho Brahe, and the Indian astronomer Āryabhaṭa. The results are listed in Table A10.4.

The percent error under "Diameter" was computed on the assumption that a computed planetary size was a diameter. The percent error under "Radius or Diameter" was computed on the assumption that a radius or a diameter was assumed, with the one that fits best being chosen. In this case, the choice for radius was made for Venus and Jupiter in the *Sūrya-siddhānta* data.

We see that the error percentage goes down as expected when we switch from the "diameter" hypothesis to the hypothesis of "radius or diameter." For *Sūrya-siddhānta* it went down by a factor of 5 to 6.3%,

TABLE A10.4
Percent Errors in Planetary Diameters Estimates

Data Source	Diameter	Radius or Diameter
Sūrya-siddhānta	32.0	6.3
Ptolemy	45.7	28.2
Tycho Brahe	43.4	24.8
Āryabhaṭa	39.6	21.0

but the decrease was much less in the other cases. The question is, is this unusual, or is it what we might expect by statistical fluctuation? To check this, we introduce a statistical hypothesis as follows:

Since Tycho Brahe is known as an excellent naked-eye observer, let us suppose that naked-eye angular diameter observations will exhibit statistical scatter around mean values agreeing with Brahe. The idea here is that someone making naked-eye observations of planets would be likely to come close to Brahe's values, but not likely to hit them exactly. Given some random error centered on Brahe's values, how likely is it that the observations, combined with *Sūrya-siddhānta* orbital data, will come close to the right planetary diameters?

For simplicity, we will assume that the naked-eye observations will be uniformly distributed between Brahe minus a percentage of spread and Brahe plus that percentage. Given this hypothesis, we compute the probability that naked-eye angular diameter measurements, combined with *Sūrya-siddhānta* orbital data, give results better than those obtained from the actual *Sūrya-siddhānta* angular diameters.

We say that the calculated diameters based on simulated naked-eye measurements are "better" if the root mean square of the error percentages of calculated vs. real diameters is lower than the corresponding root mean square based on *Sūrya-siddhānta* verse 7.13. The probability of doing better is computed by running 20,000 random trials, picking angular diameters at random within that percentage of spread. These probabilities are listed in Table A10.5.

Given our "diameter" hypothesis, the probability of doing better than the *Sūrya-siddhānta* reaches 2% to 3%, assuming a large spread in the naked-eye measurements. Given the "radius or diameter" hypothesis, the probability of doing better never rises above 0.4%, no matter what spread we assume. Our conclusion is that the correlations between *Sūrya-siddhānta* calculations and modern planetary diameters might have come about by chance, but the chances are very small.

TABLE A10.5
Probability of Bettering Sūrya-siddhānta Diameters Using Naked-Eye Measurements (in Percent)

Percent Spread Around Brahe	Diameter	Radius or Diameter
10	0.0000	0.0000
20	0.0000	0.0000
30	0.0000	0.0001
40	0.0039	0.0036
50	0.0098	0.0034
60	0.0181	0.0015
70	0.0230	0.0008
80	0.0258	0.0005
90	0.0251	0.0002
100	0.0285	0.0001

For comparison, we can likewise compute the probability of doing better than Āryabhaṭa's planetary diameters. But in this case, we get percentages as high as 14.2% under "Diameter" and 44.2% under "Radius or Diameter."

If the observed correlations did not arise by chance, then perhaps they are due to design. One hypothesis is that at some time in the past, ancient astronomers possessed realistic values for the diameters of the planets. They might have acquired this knowledge during a forgotten period in which astronomy reached a high level of sophistication. Later on, much of this knowledge was lost, but fragmentary remnants were preserved and eventually incorporated into texts such as the *Sūrya-siddhānta*. In particular, the real diameters of the planets were later combined with erroneous orbital circumferences to compute the diameters "upon the moon" given in verse 7.13. These figures were then accepted because they gave realistic values for the angular diameters of the planets as seen by the naked eye.

With this hypothesis, we can go back to consider the fact that the *Sūrya-siddhānta* diameters of Jupiter and Venus are almost exactly half of the corresponding modern diameters. One can argue that the *Sūrya-siddhānta* diameters for Jupiter and Venus were actually the radii for these planets that were accepted as diameters by mistake. Or radii might have been deliberately used instead of diameters in order to allow for the simple rule of 30+7.5i used in verse 7.13. This is consistent with the fact that such verses were intended as memory aids and brevity was considered to be a virtue.

A10.4 ALTERNATIVE EXPLANATIONS

Let us review the steps taken thus far. Angular diameters for the five planets, Mercury through Saturn, are given in the *Sūrya-siddhānta*. The *Sūrya-siddhānta* orbital radii were computed from orbital circumferences listed in the text using the conversion factor of five miles per *yojana*. This factor is based on the *Sūrya-siddhānta's* diameter for the earth, and it is corroborated by the *Sūrya-siddhānta* figures for the moon's diameter and the earth-moon distance. There is no scope for juggling numbers here.

The only proposed adjustment of the numbers is the doubling of the *Sūrya-siddhānta* diameters of Jupiter and Venus. Since the *Sūrya-siddhānta* numbers can be so easily brought into line with modern data, it may be that they have a genuine relationship with this data.

One possible explanation is that verse 7.13 may have been written recently, using modern planetary data, and falsely interpolated into the text. But this is ruled out by the fact that there is a manuscript of the *Sūrya-siddhānta* that scholars date to the year 1431 A.D. (Shukla, 1957). This manuscript includes a commentary by Parameśvara, who died in 1450 A.D., and thus it definitely dates back to the fifteenth century. Verse 7.13 is present in this manuscript, and it agrees with the Burgess translation quoted above. The commentary explains the verse point by point, and thus it confirms that the verse was present in the manuscript in the same form in which it appears today.

In fifteenth-century Europe, the prevailing ideas concerning the sizes of the planets came from medieval Islamic astronomers who were following the teachings of Ptolemy. The first telescopic observations of planets were made by Galileo in 1609–10 (Drake, 1976). As late as 1631, Pierre Gassendi of Paris was shocked when his telescopic observation of a transit of Mercury across the sun revealed that its angular diameter was much smaller than he had believed possible (Van Helden, 1976). It is clear that the information on planetary diameters in the *Sūrya-siddhānta* antedates the development of modern knowledge of these diameters.

It is also clear that Hellenistic astronomers did not have accurate diameters for the planets. Ptolemy computed planetary diameters from his angular diameters and his estimates of planetary distances, and these were reproduced without significant change by European and Islamic astronomers for centuries (Swerdlow, 1968). However, his figures disagree strongly both with modern data and with the diameters computed from *Sūrya-siddhānta.*

A10.5 CONCLUSION

In summary, verses 7.13 and 12.85–90 of the *Sūrya-siddhānta* contain information regarding the true diameters of the five planets Mercury, Venus, Mars, Jupiter, and Saturn. This information enables us to compute the diameters of three of these planets with errors of 11% or less. If the computed figures for Jupiter and Venus are interpreted as their radii rather than their diameters, then these radii are in error by about -6% and 7%, respectively. This may not be due to mere coincidence. Rather, it may indicate that accurate knowledge of planetary diameters was possessed by ancient astronomers and used in the composition either of the *Sūrya-siddhānta* or of some earlier astronomical text on which it was based. It is not apparent how such knowledge may have been obtained, but we should be on the alert for other possible examples.

A11. The Cave Heavens

There is a book entitled *The Report Concerning the Cave Heavens and Lands of Happiness in Famous Mountains,* by Tu Kuang-t'ing, who lived from A.D. 850 to 933. This book lists ten "cave heavens" and thirty-six "small cave heavens" that were supposed to exist within mountains in China. Here are the reported experiences of a man who entered a passageway leading to one of these cave heavens:

> After walking ten miles, he suddenly found himself in a beautiful land with a clear blue sky, shining pinkish clouds, fragrant flowers, densely growing willows, towers the color of cinnabar, pavilions of red jade, and far flung palaces. He was met by a group of lovely, seductive women, who brought him to a house of jasper and played him beautiful music while he drank a ruby-red drink and a jade-colored juice. Just as he felt the urge to let himself be seduced, he remembered his family and returned to the passageway. Led by a strange light that danced before him, he walked back through the cave to the outer world; but when he reached his home village, he did not recognize anyone he saw, and when he arrived at his house, he met his own descendants of nine generations hence. They told him that one of their ancestors had disappeared into a cavern three hundred years before and had never been seen again (Kafton-Minkel, 1989, p. 191).

The time dilation effect in this story suggests that we are dealing with a parallel reality rather than an ordinary three-dimensional cave. In European stories of the Fairy Folk, a standard theme is that if someone returns to this world after living in the world of the Fairies for a short time, then he will find that many years have passed.

The same theme occurs in Sanskrit literature. For example, the *Bhāgavatam* recounts the story of King Kakudmī and his daughter Revatī, who visited Brahmā in Satyaloka. Even though they were there for only an hour or so, when they returned they found that millions of years had passed (*Bhāgavatam* 9.3.28–32).

In the *Bhāgavatam*, there is a description of a region called Bila-svarga, or the subterranean heaven, which is clearly related to the Chinese story of the cave heavens. Bila-svarga is described as a very beautiful place, with brilliantly decorated cities, lakes of clear water, and extensive parks and gardens. At the same time, the sun and the moon cannot be seen there, and the inhabitants have no sense of the passing of time.

One of the seven levels of Bila-svarga is Atala, which is said to be inhabited by three groups of women, called *svairiṇī, kāmiṇī,* and *puṁścalī.* If a man manages to visit this region,

> these women immediately capture him and induce him to drink an intoxicating beverage made with a drug known as *hāṭaka.* This intoxicant endows the man with great sexual prowess, of which the women take advantage for enjoyment. A woman will enchant him with attractive glances, intimate words, smiles of love and then embraces. In this way she induces him to enjoy sex with her to her full satisfaction. Because of his increased sexual power, the man thinks himself stronger than ten thousand elephants and considers himself most perfect. Indeed, illusioned and intoxicated by false pride, he thinks himself God, ignoring impending death (*Bhāgavatam* 5.24.16).

A12. Spirit Paths in the Sky

The *Bhagavad-gītā* (8.26) states that "there are two ways of passing from this world—one in light and one in darkness. When one passes in light, he does not come back; but when one passes in darkness, he returns."

The path of darkness is called the *pitṛ-yāna*, or path of the *pitṛs* (the ancestral spirits). According to the *Viṣṇu Purāṇa*, on the north of the star Agastya, and south of Ajavīthī (the three *nakṣatras* Mūlā, Pūrvāṣāḍhā, and Uttarāṣāḍhā), outside of the Vaiśvānara path, lies the road of the *pitṛs* (Wilson, 1980, p. 327).

The *nakṣatras* Mūlā, Pūrvāṣāḍhā, and Uttarāṣāḍhā correspond to parts of the constellations Scorpio and Sagittarius, and it is thought that Agastya corresponds to the southern hemisphere star called Canopus. According to Śrīdhara Swami's commentary on the *Bhāgavatam*, the path of Vaiśvānara corresponds to the nine *nakṣatras* from Mūlā to Revatī. (The last three are specifically called Vaiśvānarī.) (Wilson, 1865, p. 268).

This puts Pitṛloka, or the path to it, south of the ecliptic, starting with the region of Scorpio and Sagittarius. From the latitude of India in the northern hemisphere, the stars on the path of the *pitṛs* tend to rise only briefly above the horizon, and thus they were associated with darkness and the underworld.

According to the *Viṣṇu Purāṇa*, in this region

> There dwell the great Ṛṣis, the offerers of oblations with fire, reverencing the Vedas, after whose injunctions creation commenced . . . for as the worlds are destroyed and renewed, they institute new rules of conduct, and reestablish the interrupted ritual of the Vedas.
>
> Mutually descending from one another, progenitor springing from descendant, and descendant from progenitor, in the alternating succession of births, they repeatedly appear in different houses and races . . . residing to the south of the solar orb as long as the moon and stars endure (Wilson, 1980, p. 328).

These Ṛṣis are connected with the family, the ancestors, and the return of the soul to a new family situation in the cycle of birth and death. But on the northern path, the path of light, the soul is said to attain an eternal destination and does not return.

A12.1 THE PATH OF LIGHT

The path of light is followed by perfected yogis and mystics, and it is also known as *deva-yāna*, the path of the demigods. The *Viṣṇu Purāṇa* states that the path of the demigods lies to the north of the orbit of the sun (the ecliptic), north of Nāgavīthī (the *nakṣatras* Aśvinī, Bharaṇī, and Kṛttikā), and south of the stars of the seven *ṛṣis*.

The three *nakṣatras*, Aśvinī, Bharaṇī, and Kṛttikā, which define the southern border of the path of the demigods, are located in parts of the constellations Aries and Taurus. The seven *ṛṣis* correspond to the constellation Ursa Major, commonly known as the Big Dipper, which is situated in the northern celestial hemisphere.

After reaching the seven *ṛṣis,* the soul enters the path of Viṣṇu, called Viṣṇupāda. This extends north from the seven *ṛṣis* to the polestar, called Dhruvaloka.

In many ancient cultures, the stars which rise and set are associated with the temporary things of this world, which repeat in cycles. In contrast, the stars that endlessly circle the polestar and do not set symbolize eternity. This is also true in Indian cosmology. There the region of the circumpolar stars is regarded as Viṣṇu Paramam Padam—the feet of the Supreme Being, Viṣṇu, who controls time while remaining outside of time.

> This is that excellent place of Vishṇu to which those repair in whom all sources of pain are extinct in consequence of the cessation of . . . piety or iniquity, and where they never sorrow more. There abide Dharma, Dhruva and other spectators of the world, radiant with the superhuman faculties of Vishṇu, acquired through yoga; and there, fastened and inwoven, too, are all that is and all that shall ever be, animate or inanimate (Wilson, 1865, pp. 270–71).

It is noteworthy that at the latitude of New Delhi, all but one of the stars of the Big Dipper now set beneath the horizon in the course of a day and night. However, in about 2500 B.C., when Thuban was the polestar, the seven stars of the Big Dipper never set. Before Polaris reached the pole within the last thousand years, the last good polestar was Thuban, about 2000 to 3000 B.C. So it may be that the traditions about the paths of the Devas and of Viṣṇu date back to this period.

A12.2 CELESTIAL PATHS IN MANY CULTURES

The Milky Way plays a role in both the *pitṛ-yāna* and *deva-yāna* paths. It is seen in the sky as a somewhat irregular band of light and concentrated stars extending in a great circle that tends to run north and south, cutting the celestial equator at an angle of roughly 62°. A very bright region of the Milky Way intersects the ecliptic in the constellation Sagittarius near the *nakṣatras* Mūlā and Pūrvāṣāḍhā. This is the beginning of the path of the *pitṛs*. At the diametrically opposite point, the Milky Way intersects the ecliptic at the boundary of the constellations Taurus and Gemini, near the beginning of the path of the Devas.

Once we are able to locate the *pitṛ-yāna* and *deva-yāna* paths on the celestial sphere, we can ask whether or not similar accounts of the celestial travels of the soul might be present in other cultural traditions. It turns out that many cultures around the world regard the ecliptic and the Milky Way as pathways for transmigrating souls. Here are some examples:

1. In China there are traditional stories about a monkey named Sun who gets involved in various remarkable adventures. In one story, two "harpooners of death" capture him, claiming he has reached the limit of his destiny on the earth, and is due to be taken to the underworld. The story's translator notes that according to the Chinese, it is the constellation Nan Teou, the Southern Dipper, that decides everybody's death, and the orders are executed by these "harpooners of death" (Wou, 1957, p. iii, and Schlegel, 1875, pp. 172ff).

   The Chinese Southern Dipper consists of six stars in the constellation Sagittarius (Mu, Lambda, Phi, Sigma, Tau, and Zeta Sagittarii) (Wou, 1957). It is interesting to note that this constellation shares stars with Pūrvāṣāḍhā and Uttarāṣāḍhā, two of the *nakṣatras* marking the beginning of the path of the *pitṛs,* according to the *Viṣṇu Purāṇa*. Thus the beginning to the route to the headquarters of Yamarāja corresponds in this Chinese tradition to the place in the heavens where the fate of the dead is decided. In addition, the Chinese tradition has messengers of death that are similar to the Yamadūtas, the messengers of Yamarāja.
2. The German scholar Franz Boll has analyzed ancient Greek traditions regarding Hades, the river Styx, and the ferryman of the underworld. We tend to think of Hades as lying beneath our feet, within the earth. However, Boll cites texts placing this region in the heavens around the southern crossroads of the Milky Way and the ecliptic, between Scorpius and Sagittarius (Boll, 1903, pp. 246–51).
3. Boll points out a close relationship between Greek and Babylonian traditions. According to his analysis, the Babylonian god Dikud, the judge of Hades, may correspond to the star, Theta Ophiuchi. This star lies just to the north of the *nakṣatra* Mūlā in the constellation Scorpius, and thus it is close to the beginning of the *pitṛ-yāna* path. A text cited by Boll refers to this star as "the beginning of the road of the lower heavenly vault" (Boll, 1903).
4. In North America the Pawnee and Cherokees say that "the souls of the dead are received by a star at the northern end of the Milky Way, where it bifurcates. He [God] directs the warriors on the dim and difficult arm, and women and those who die of old age upon the brighter and easier path. The souls journey southwards; at the end of the celestial path they are received by the Spirit Star" (Hagar,

1906, p. 363, and Alexander, 1916, p. 117). The anthropologist S. Hagar thinks the Spirit Star is Antares. Antares is Alpha Scorpionis in the constellation Scorpius, and it corresponds to the *nakṣatra* Jyeṣṭhā. Jyeṣṭhā is next to Mūlā, at the beginning of the path of the *pitṛs*.

5. The Roman writer, Macrobius, in his *Commentary on the Dream of Scipio* 1.12.1–8, says that souls of the dead ascend by way of Capricorn, and to be reborn, descend again through the gate of Cancer. He has shifted everything by one sign of the zodiac; Capricorn is next to Sagittarius, and Cancer is next to Gemini. In fact, he says in 1.12.5 of his *Commentary* that the gate of Cancer is at the intersection of the zodiac and the Milky Way (Stahl, 1952).
6. In Honduras and Nicaragua the Sumo say that their "Mother Scorpion . . . is regarded as dwelling at the end of the Milky Way, where she receives the souls of the dead, and from her, represented as a mother with many breasts, at which children take suck, come the souls of the new-born" (Alexander, 1920, p. 185). Here the "Mother Scorpion" is reminiscent of the constellation Scorpius. We note that the tail of the constellation Scorpius corresponds to the *nakṣatra* Mūlā.
7. In general, Polynesians have traditionally believed in reincarnation, and they have maintained that the Milky Way is the pathway of transmigrating souls. The Mangaians of the Austral Islands in Polynesia claim, in particular, that souls can enter heaven only on evenings of solstices (north islanders at one solstice and south islanders at the other) (Gill, 1876, pp. 156ff, 185ff). The important point here is that the solstices occur when the sun is in the constellations Sagittarius or Gemini, near the intersection between the Milky Way and the ecliptic. At sunset during a solstice these constellations would therefore be at the islanders' horizon.

The specific details that repeatedly appear in these stories suggest the existence of a common cultural tradition. The differences between the stories, and the lack of clear historical records of their origin, suggest that this common cultural source dates from the remote past (see Section 5.2).

A13. Arjuna and Ulūpī

The theme of mystical travel into a parallel world is illustrated by a story in the *Mahābhārata* involving the Pāṇḍava hero Arjuna. The story began when Arjuna was exiled for twelve months because of having intruded accidentally on his brother Yudhiṣṭhira and their common wife, Draupadī. Arjuna, known also as the son of Kuntī, went to visit Haridvāra along the Ganges River in the Himalayas. There he began to participate in sacrificial rites with a number of sages.

> While the son of Kuntī resided there among the *brāhmaṇas*, O Bhārata, the sages brought to fruition many *agni-hotras*, the offering to the sacred fire. As the fires on both banks of the river were roused and brought to blaze, the offerings poured, and flowers offered in worship by learned, self-controlled sages, duly consecrated and fixed as great souls on the spiritual path, then, O king, the gateway of the Ganges shone with exceeding splendor.
>
> When his residence was thus crowded with divinity, the darling son of Pāṇḍu and Kuntī then went down into the Ganges water, to be consecrated for holy rite. Taking his ritual bath and worshiping his forefathers, Arjuna, happy to take his part in the rite of fire, was rising out of the water, O king, when he was pulled back in by Ulūpī, the virgin daughter of the serpent king, who could travel about at her will and was now within those waters. Holding onto him, she pulled him down into the land of the Nāgas, into her father's house.

Ulūpī then proposed to Arjuna, arguing that she felt extreme desire for him and therefore he should be merciful and satisfy her. Arjuna did this in accordance with the code of the *kṣatriyas*, the Vedic warrior class. Thus, "The fiery hero Arjuna spent the night in the palace of the Nāga king, and when the sun rose he too rose up from Kauravya's abode."

Kauravya is the name of the Nāga king. Note that when Ulūpī pulled Arjuna down, instead of finding himself on a rocky or sandy river bottom, he found himself in the Nāga kingdom. This is an example of mystic travel, and in this case the travelers entered into a parallel or higher-dimensional world. The Nāgas are a race of intelligent beings that are said to live either in the subterranean worlds called Bila-svarga, or in parallel domains on the surface of the earth.

A14. Madhvācārya's Visit to Vyāsadeva

Madhvācārya (1238–1317) was a major Indian religious reformer and the founder of an important school of Vaiṣṇavism. He introduced the philosophy of Dvaita, which maintains that there is an absolute distinction between the individual soul and God, and he stressed the worship of Kṛṣṇa as the Supreme God.

It is said that Madhvācārya directly met Vedavyāsa, the compiler of the *Vedas.* The story of this meeting is pertinent to this cosmological study, because Vedavyāsa is said to be living in a place called Uttarā-badarikāśrama, which is not accessible to ordinary human beings. Badarikāśrama in the Himalayas is a famous place of pilgrimage visited by thousands of people every year. But Uttarā (or "northern") Badarikāśrama illustrates how higher, parallel realities enter into traditional geographic thinking in India.

The story is recorded in Nārāyaṇa Paṇḍitācārya's *Sumadhva Vijaya,* a biography of Madhvācārya dating to the fourteenth century. Madhvācārya was visiting Badarikāśrama with his disciples, and he decided to depart alone for Uttarā-badarikāśrama. One of the disciples, named Satyatīrtha, tried to follow him:

> The monk Satyatīrtha . . . followed him not being able to bear the separation from Madhvācārya.
>
> Satyatīrtha could not reach Madhvācārya when the sun was becoming red (sunset) by running behind him, as the latter had got onto the path difficult to be crossed by others. Madhvācārya was jumping easily in speed over the distant stones having no resting place between one another (Rau, 1983, p. 74).

Madhvācārya was apparently flying over the Himalayan peaks in the manner of Hanumān's famous flight to Lanka. In fact, Madhvācārya is compared with Hanumān (Anjaneya), and like Hanumān, he is regarded as an incarnation of Vāyu, the god of wind:

> This famous Madhvācārya, who is going on the peak of the Himalayas (the best of mountains) and who has a name that destroys sins (of the

devotees) shone like Anjaneya (the best of apes) who has speed like the wind and like Bhīmasena who causes fear to the demons (Rau, 1983, p. 74).

One way to look at this is that Madhvācārya was simply jumping over a mountain into an inaccessible valley. However, the description of northern Badarikāśrama suggests that it is more than simply a remote valley that could be reached by mountaineers:

> Madhvācārya saw that Badarikāśrama which is like Vaikuṇṭha. It is filled with groups of flowers and sages. It fulfills the desires of the minds of the virtuous who are devoted to the (supreme) independent Lord. It is inaccessible to those devoid of knowledge and devotion. It contains people having no hatred for one another. It is the abode of Lord Vedavyāsa (Rau, 1983, p. 78).
>
> This Vedavyāsa, having sweet speech, wandered long in this world for the protection of knowledge, of those possessing knowledge, and of the things that are the subject of knowledge.
>
> The respectable Vedavyāsa now living in this Badarikāśrama gave up the sight of the people for the working of the Kali age like the sun giving up the sky for the working of the night (Rau, 1983, pp. 81–82).

In short, Uttarā-badarikāśrama is actually part of a higher world, even though it is ostensibly part of this world. This is the way the *Bhāgavatam* describes Jambūdvīpa: Jambūdvīpa represents this world, but at the same time it represents a heavenly realm with divinely qualified inhabitants who are not of this world.

A15. The Story of Duḥkhī Kṛṣṇa Dāsa

There are many stories in Vaiṣṇava literature which involve communication between this world and a higher, parallel realm. In this example, a sixteenth-century Vaiṣṇava saint named Duḥkhī Kṛṣṇadāsa was performing the daily service of sweeping the sacred area of Sevā-kuñja in Vṛndāvana, a famous pilgrimage place in India (Rosen, 1991).

Figure A15.1 Duḥkhī Kṛṣṇadāsa finding the golden anklet, meeting the old lady who requested its return, and seeing the old lady in her original form as Lalitā-sundarī. Painting by Julia Wilson.

While doing this one day, he found a golden anklet that seemed to emanate a remarkable aura. Impressed by the influence that it had on his consciousness, he considered it to be very important, and he buried it in a secret place.

Shortly thereafter an old lady came to him, asking for the anklet and saying that it belonged to her daughter-in-law. Because of its spiritual influence, Duḥkhī Kṛṣṇadāsa was convinced that the anklet must really belong to Rādhārāṇī, the eternal consort of Kṛṣṇa. After a long discussion, the old lady finally admitted that this was so, and revealed that her true identity was Lalitā-sundarī, one of Rādhārāṇī's servants.

At this point, Duḥkhī Kṛṣṇadāsa wanted to see his visitor in her true form, but she said he would be unable to bear such a revelation. After being convinced of his sincere desire, however, she finally acquiesced to his request and revealed her true, incomparable beauty. After giving him several benedictions and receiving the anklet from him, she disappeared, and he was unable to find where she had gone.

One of the benedictions given to Duḥkhī Kṛṣṇadāsa was a special *tilaka* mark on his forehead, and a new name, Śyāmānanda. Since Lalitā had sworn him to secrecy about their meeting, it was difficult for Śyāmānanda to explain the *tilaka* and new name to his *guru,* who thought that he had simply concocted them. In the course of dealing with this difficult situation, Śyāmānanda again met Lalitā-sundarī. This time, however, he met her by entering into her transcendental realm in a state of meditation.

This story illustrates the idea of an inhabited parallel reality which is not normally visible or accessible to ordinary people. It is interesting that one can enter this reality by a process of meditation, so that it seems to be related to the mind or consciousness. At the same time, objects and people can pass in solid form from that reality into this one.

A16. History of Precession

Precession of the equinoxes is said to have been discovered by the Greek astronomer Hipparchus in the second century B.C. He gave it a value of 1° per century of Egyptian, 365-day years. According to Otto Neugebauer, this was an upper estimate, his real estimate being 1° in 77 Egyptian years (Neugebauer, 1975, p. 298).

Theon, writing in the second century A.D., held that the equinox "trepidates" back and forth in a zigzag at a rate of 1° in 80 years. In contrast, modern astronomy teaches that precession proceeds uniformly through a complete 360° cycle.

The medieval Indian astronomy text *Sūrya-siddhānta* maintains that the equinoxes trepidate back and forth 600 times in a *divya-yuga* of 4,320,000 years. This yields a period of 7,200 years per cycle (Burgess, 1860, p. 114). The complete cycle covers 108° in four equal legs going east, west, west, east by 27°. The rate of precession in the *Sūrya-siddhānta* comes to 54 arcseconds/year (which equals 108/2) or 66.67 years per degree. These numbers clearly seem to be adjusted to the ideal number 108.

Most medieval Indian astronomers either ignored precession or accepted a theory of trepidation. However, Munjal is cited by Bhāskarācārya as saying that there are 199,669 revolutions of the equinoxes in a *kalpa* of 4,320,000,000 years (Dikshit, 1969b, p. 211). This gives a precessional rate of about 60 years per degree or 1 year per arcminute, and a full cycle is close to 21,600 years.

According to modern astronomy, the rate of precession of the equinoxes in A.D. 2000 is 50.3878 arcseconds/year (Green, 1985, p. 211). At this rate, a full cycle comes to 25,720.5 years at 71.4459 years per degree. However, the rate of precession is known to change slowly with the passage of time.

A popular definition of precession allots 2,160 years for the equinoxes to pass through one sign of the zodiac, so that one cycle of precession comes to 25,920 years. This approximation assumes 72 years per degree. The Egyptologist Jane Sellers has argued that the precessional cycle of 25,920 years was known in the ancient Near East (Sellers, 1992). This suggests that the "years" of the cycle may be of 360 days, so that it requires 70.96 sidereal years per degree. In either case, this estimate of the rate of precession is much more accurate than any of the other premodern rates mentioned above.

A16.1 NOTE ON ĀRYABHAṬA

According to the *Sūrya-siddhānta's* theory of trepidation, the cycle of precession was at its center point (neither east nor west) at the beginning of Kali-yuga. According to many *Jyotiṣa Śāstras*, Kali-yuga began in 3102 B.C. The trepidation returns to its center point after 3600 years, which comes to A.D. 499. So the *Sūrya-siddhānta* is saying that the position of the equinoxes was the same in 3102 B.C. and in A.D. 499.

The latter date falls in the life of Āryabhaṭa, who is the first of the known authors of Jyotiṣa texts. Āryabhaṭa wrote that he was 23 years old when sixty 60-year cycles had elapsed in Kali-yuga (Dikshit, 1969b, p. 55), and this was in A.D. 499. It would be interesting to know why the *Sūrya-siddhānta's* theory of precession happens to make the sky look the same in Āryabhaṭa's lifetime as it was at the accepted beginning of Kali-yuga.

A17. Van der Waerden's Argument

As evidence that 3102 B.C. was calculated using Jupiter-Saturn conjunctions, B. L. van der Waerden noted that, according to Alberuni, certain Chaldeans and inhabitants of Babel assigned the deluge to 3351 B.C. (van der Waerden, 1980, p. 124). Alberuni also said that "astrologers" specified that a conjunction had occurred 229 years and 108 days before the deluge.

By adding 229 years to 3351 B.C., we can estimate that 478 years separated the astrologers' conjunction from 3102 B.C. This is almost exactly 24 small conjunctions or two middle conjunctions. This suggests that these astrologers were working with planetary parameters indicating a Jupiter-Saturn conjunction in 3102 B.C. But evidently they didn't think the deluge occurred at this time.

We can imagine that, later on, astrologers jumped forward two middle conjunctions to 3102 B.C. When they realized that other planetary conjunctions occurred at this date, they decided that this was when the deluge really happened. This is van der Waerden's idea. But one could just as well argue that Alberuni's astrologers already knew about 3102 B.C. but rejected it. Their 3351 B.C. flood date shows that they didn't think the deluge should fall on a Jupiter-Saturn conjunction.

There were evidently differences in opinion among the astrologers. The Islamic writer Mashallah put the deluge in 3301 B.C. (van der Waerden, 1980, p. 124). This is ten small conjunctions before 3102 B.C. But Mashallah, writing in the ninth century or later, probably knew about 3102 B.C. and rejected it for some reason.

According to van der Waerden, Alberuni's Chaldean and Babylonian astrologers were living in the Hellenistic period. But all we really know about them is that they came before Alberuni, who wrote in the tenth century. For all we know, their knowledge of the 3102 B.C. date may have come from India, and it may even have come from Āryabhaṭa, who was active around A.D. 500.

A18. The Yuga System in America

According to the *Purāṇas,* the bull of Dharma, or religious principles, begins with four legs in Kṛta-yuga. (See the *Bhāgavatam* verses 1.17.24–25.) In each successive *yuga* the bull loses one leg and virtue decreases, until finally it totters on one leg in Kali-yuga and corruption becomes rampant.

A striking parallel to this story is told by the Sioux Indians of North America, who also have a cyclic chronology of four ages. The anthropologist Joseph Epes Brown writes,

> According to Siouan mythology, it is believed that at the beginning of the cycle a buffalo was placed at the west in order to hold back the waters. Every year this buffalo loses one hair, and every age he loses one leg. When all his hair and all four legs are gone, then the waters rush in once again, and the cycle comes to an end. . . .
>
> It is believed by both the American Indian and the Hindu that at the present time the buffalo or bull is on his last leg, and he is very nearly bald. Corresponding beliefs could be cited from many other traditions (Epes Brown, 1971, p. 9).

An interesting feature of these parallel accounts is that both apply the sequence 4:3:2:1 to the four ages (by counting legs).

A19. On the History of Astronomy

In the course of this study we have repeatedly encountered evidence suggesting that the history of science has not been one of linear progress. In this appendix we will briefly outline some evidence indicating a decline in astronomical knowledge between roughly 2500 B.C. and the rise of scientific Babylonian astronomy late in the first millennium B.C.

We begin by considering the great pyramid. This remarkable structure was built around 2500 B.C. out of some 2.5 million limestone blocks, weighing an average of 2.6 tons apiece. Many fantastic things have been written about the great pyramid, but the sober facts are even more remarkable in their implications.

The perimeter of the great pyramid was accurately measured at 921.455 meters by the engineer J. H. Cole, using modern surveying methods (Stecchini, 1971, p. 364), and its height is about 146.73 meters (Krupp, 1983, p. 101). If we divide the perimeter by the height, the ratio is about 2 times 3.14. Thus the angular pyramid imitates a sphere, where the circumference divided by the radius is 2 times π.

If we divide the surface area of the pyramid (assuming it to be a regular geometric figure) by the area of its base, we get 1.6195, which is close to the golden mean (1.618), a famous ratio in the history of art and architecture. This relationship was known to the Greek historian Herodotus (485–425 B.C.), who commented that the surface area of one face of the great pyramid equals its height squared (Stecchini, 1971, p. 370). This is mathematically equivalent to saying that the ratio of surface area to base area is the golden mean.

By a kind of mathematical coincidence, the π relationship and the golden mean relationship cannot both be exactly true, but if one is nearly true, the other will also be nearly true. Could either one have been built into the great pyramid intentionally? Quite possibly both were intended, but this would imply a knowledge of π and the golden mean in 2500 B.C.

To add to the mystery, John Legon observed that the three Giza pyramids fit precisely in a rectangle, aligned to the cardinal directions, with an east-west side of 1414 cubits and a north-south side of 1732 cubits (Bauval, 1994, p. 54). These lengths come to a thousand times the square roots of two and three, respectively. The hypotenuse of this rectangle is a thousand times the square root of five, which is related to the golden mean. If this is not coincidental, it implies both an interest in mathematics and a unified plan for the construction of all three pyramids.

The eminent historian of science Otto Neugebauer commented, on the basis of surviving texts, that Egyptian mathematics "never rose above a very primitive level" (Neugebauer, 1945, p. 4). This may be a proper conclusion from texts such as the Rhind papyrus, dating to Egypt's sixteenth dynasty. But it is not borne out by the Giza pyramids of the fourth dynasty.

Actually, even the surviving texts give hints of sophisticated knowledge. B. L. van der Waerden has pointed out that the Moscow papyrus (c. 2050–1800 B.C.) gives the correct formula for the volume of a truncated pyramid—which hardly seems primitive. (Homework problem: Derive this formula using primitive methods, and don't look up the answer in advance.) He noted that the ancient Chinese also have this formula, but the ancient Babylonian texts do not mention it. So he assumed a pre-Babylonian common source (van der Waerden, 1983, p. 44).

A19.1 EGYPTIAN ASTRONOMY

Neugebauer declared that, "It is a serious mistake to try to invest Egyptian mathematical or astronomical documents with the false glory of scientific achievements or to assume a still unknown science, secret or lost, not found in extant texts" (Neugebauer, 1945, p. 8). Nonetheless, the layout of the great pyramid betrays a level of astronomical achievement not reflected in extant texts.

In his scientific survey of the great pyramid, J. H. Cole found that the average length of the four sides of the pyramid was 230.364 meters. The four sides (W, N, E, and S) deviate from this average by only -0.7, -11.1, 2.7, and 9 centimeters, respectively (Stecchini, 1971, p. 366). The four sides were accurately aligned with the cardinal directions with an average discrepancy of about three minutes of arc in any direction (Bauval and Gilbert, 1994, p. 38).

The alignment with the cardinal directions implies that astronomical sighting was used to determine true north. In Appendix 10, we note that the angular diameters of the planets, as measured by Tycho Brahe using refined naked-eye techniques, range from 1.57 to 3.13 arcminutes. These values represent blurring in the human eye and are much larger than the true angular diameters of the planets. This indicates that the position of a star or planet probably cannot be measured with an average error less than about 1.5 minutes. To appreciate this, try looking at a quarter at a distance of 200 feet. At this distance, it has an angular diameter of 1.43 minutes.

At least two star measurements are needed to determine true north, resulting in a composite error of about 1.4 times the error in one measurement. After this, many additional error-prone steps are needed to construct a six-million-ton pyramid.

The archaeoastronomer E. C. Krupp commented on the Egyptian achievement as follows: "Accuracy of this sort is possible, even with very simple techniques, provided that care is taken in setting out the lines. Preserving this accuracy on the monumental scale of the Great Pyramid, however, means not 'twisting' the sides at higher levels, and the Egyptian's success is impressive" (Krupp, 1983, p. 102). Indeed, an accuracy of 3 arcminutes must lie at the very limit of what can be achieved by simple techniques—if it does not exceed that limit.

The latitude of the great pyramid is noteworthy. This is 29° 58' 51", very close to 30°. A former Astronomer Royal of Scotland observed that if the designers of the great pyramid intended the north pole to appear to be at an elevation of 30° at the pyramid's site, then due to atmospheric refraction, they should have placed it at a latitude of 29° 58' 22" (Hancock, 1996, p. 40). This off by only 29 arcseconds. (For additional evidence of ancient, accurate latitude measurements, see Section 4.5 and Appendix 8).

Within the great pyramid there are four famous shafts that extend north and south through the mass of the building, starting from the "King's" chamber and the "Queen's" chamber. It has been shown that in the period of about 2500 B.C., these four shafts were aimed at four prominent stars at their points of culmination (the highest point reached by a star during the day). This is summed up in the following table (Hancock, 1996, p. 65):

TABLE A19
Star Alignments in the Great Pyramid

Chamber	Shaft	Angle	Star
Queen's	northern	39°	Kochab (Beta Ursa Minor)
Queen's	southern	39° 30'	Sirius (Alpha Canis Major)
King's	northern	32° 28'	Thuban (polestar)
King's	southern	45° 14'	Al Nitak (lowest in Orion's belt)

Here "angle" is the angle of elevation of the shaft from horizontal. According to the SkyGlobe astronomy program, the declination of Thuban in 2500 B.C. was 88° 13'. This means that the star would have culminated at 31° 47', quite close to the angle of the northern King's chamber shaft. Similar statements can be made about the other stars. We note that, even if the angle to a star at culmination was measured quite accurately, to accurately build a shaft for many meters through the pyramid at this angle would have been a very difficult task.

A19.2 BABYLONIAN ASTRONOMY

Now let us turn to the history of Babylonian astronomy. In about the seventh century B.C., the Babylonian scribes of Enūma Anu Enlil began a program of systematic astronomical observation, aimed at predicting astronomical phenomena (such as heliacal risings of planets) for purposes of divination and magic (Swerdlow, 1998). By the third to first centuries B.C., they developed sophisticated computational procedures that were used to generate ephemeris tables, listing predicted dates of phenomena.

The archaeoastronomer N. M. Swerdlow argues that "The Scribes great science of the heavens is as close to the origin of science, and of the methods and practices of science, as we shall ever come" (Swerdlow, 1998, p. 33). Based on his extensive analysis of Babylonian astronomical tablets, he is convinced that the scientific method of collecting observational data and fitting mathematical rules to it was created by the Babylonian priest-astronomers.

Swerdlow emphasizes that the strong point of Babylonian astronomy was its prediction of phenomena in time. He points out, however, that the Babylonians were very limited in their ability to mathematically denote positions of celestial bodies in space and to observe or predict such positions. They also did not use geometric models in the manner of the Greek astronomers. Indeed, their approach was arithmetical, rather than geometrical, and Swerdlow is convinced that even the division of a circle into 360° was "a Greek geometrical adaptation of a Babylonian arithmetical convention" (Swerdlow, 1998, p. 35).

Positions of planets in the sky were defined, at best, in terms of the twelve signs of the zodiac. Thus, the Babylonian astronomers "had no reliable method of finding longitude more precisely than by zodiacal sign, or by beginning and end of zodiacal sign, as reported in the Diaries, meaning in both cases nothing more precise than location in the vicinity of particular stars of irregular zodiacal constellations" (Swerdlow, 1998, p. 72).

From Swerdlow's analysis, we can be reasonably sure that astronomy of the Babylonian type (along with nascent Greek efforts) represents the high point of Western astronomical knowledge in the period from the seventh to the first centuries B.C. But is it correct to assume that this marked the beginning of scientific astronomy? If we assume a linear model of scientific progress, then this must be so. But the evidence we have been considering indicates that progress may have its ups and downs.

Consider the evidence of accurate astronomical measurements

built into the structure of the great pyramid. The measurements involved are orders of magnitude better than crude estimates in terms of roughly defined zodiacal signs. The pyramid builders must have made use of some kind of numerical notation for angles, since to build a shaft at a prescribed angle, it is necessary to record the angle and then reproduce it later on with some kind of instrument. After all, the measurement of a star's culmination could be made only at certain times at night, while construction activity presumably went on during the day. (Note that the angle and time of culmination define a coordinate system for star positions.)

It follows that there must have been a decline in standards of astronomical position measurement between 2500 B.C. in Egypt and 700 B.C. in Mesopotamia. This is not to say that the Babylonians of the first millennium B.C. did not create an ingenious system of empirical astronomy. But others came before them and surpassed them, at least in the matter of position measurements.

Swerdlow comments that, "interestingly, the observations from the third to second centuries are not more accurate than those from the seventh century" (Swerdlow, 1998, p. 81). Possibly, the Babylonians saw their low standard of position measurement as adequate for purposes of divination, and therefore they made no real effort to find improved techniques of measurement.

A19.3 LOST KNOWLEDGE?

Lack of documentation for ancient advanced science cannot be used to conclude that such science never existed. Swerdlow points out that in Babylon, "the astronomical texts were restricted to, indeed, intelligible to, a very small circle of scholars and were in no sense 'published' works" (Swerdlow, 1998, p. 28). The Babylonian astronomical tablets are evidently survivals from the workshop of a small group of researchers. It is surprising that they survived, and it would not be at all surprising if they had been lost.

An example of the nonsurvival of ancient technical documentation is provided by the story of the Antikythera computer. An advanced astronomical computer, based on an intricate system of gear wheels, was discovered in a shipwreck off the coast of the Greek island of Antikythera. The ship was loaded with statues and other objects of art, and it sank in about 65 B.C. The computer was first recovered from the wreck as a shapeless lump that split open to reveal a set of brass plates. Careful study revealed a mechanism made of at least twenty gear wheels, including differential gears and a crown wheel. It appears to have been a computing machine that could exhibit on a series of dials the motions of the sun, moon, and planets.

The principles behind the computer's design remain unknown. No surviving literature refers to such machines, but surely this example could not have been unique. It must correspond to a well-developed system of astronomy and a well-developed technology for producing geared machines. Both seem to have disappeared without a trace, and the Antikythera find itself was purely accidental. If it were not for this chance discovery, we would remain completely ignorant of the existence of such machines.

A19.4 DARK AGES

In the case of the Antikythera computer, the great decline in knowledge that occurred with the fall of the Roman Empire may have been more than sufficient to wipe out nearly all traces of the science behind its construction. Of course, we can easily imagine knowledge being lost even without a period of social disruption. But it is nonetheless interesting that a "dark age" apparently prevailed well after the time of the great pyramid and just before the rise of Babylonian astronomy.

Peter James has assembled evidence for coordinated dark ages in Mediterranean and Near Eastern civilizations in roughly the first quarter of the first millennium B.C. (James, 1991). His thesis is that this period represents a gap in chronology that should be filled in by reducing the age of everything before 1000 B.C.

The more general view of his data is that the gap is a real period, in which civilized life was greatly disrupted. In Greece, the gap is the famous Greek Dark Age, spanning roughly 1200 to 700 B.C. (James, 1991, pp. 68–94). Vincent Desborough, an expert on this period, wrote that when it began,

> The craftsmen and artists seem to vanish almost without a trace: there is very little new stone construction of any sort, far less any massive

> edifices; the metal-worker's technique reverts to the primitive and the potter, except in the early stages, loses his purpose and inspiration; and the art of writing is forgotten. But the outstanding feature is that by the end of the twelfth century the population appears to have dwindled to about one-tenth of what it had been little over a century before (James, 1991, p. 72).

The corresponding dark age in the Near East appears to have been particularly severe. Thus no Babylonian buildings date with certainty between 1046–722 B.C. (James, 1991, p. 280). Fewer than sixty texts from Babylon date to 1000–750 B.C., even though there were some 12,000 from the previous 500-year Kassite period. According to John Brinkman, a leading authority on the post-Kassite period, "Babylonian history during the first quarter of the first millennium B.C. may be characterized as a period of obscurity or 'dark age', with the land frequently overrun by foreign invaders and with the central government often unable to assert its jurisdiction in many areas" (James, 1991, p. 279).

A strange feature of Babylonian prehistory is that there are records of quite sophisticated Babylonian mathematics dating to about 1700 B.C. Records of similar mathematics appear in roughly 300 B.C., but in the intervening period of some 1300 years there are no mathematical texts from Babylonia (Seidenberg, 1978, p. 310). Since the mathematical tradition was somehow kept alive, this simply shows how easy it is for records of scientific knowledge to disappear.

The record suggests that the Babylonians began their program of systematic astronomical research shortly after the end of their dark age. One may ask: Did this represent a fresh start in a new era of optimism, after a period of cultural decline? Whether this is so or not, the rise of Greek and Babylonian astronomy set the standard of ancient science until the time of the Renaissance at the end of the post-Roman dark age.

A19.5 PARALLELS IN INDIA

In India there is a parallel to the dark age of the first millennium B.C., but in this case the period of apparent cultural decline seems to have been much longer. Based on radiocarbon dating, the mature phase of the Harappan, or Indus Valley, civilization extended from about 2600 to 1900 B.C., and the late phase persisted for a couple hundred years after 1900 B.C. (Lal, 1998, p. 114). This is called the first South Asian urbanization.

According to anthropologist Jim Shaffer, many scholars accept that the period between 1900 and 700 B.C. was marked by the disappearance of cultural traits such as "large-scale public architecture, writing, a system of weights, and the many other material artifacts that are used to characterize the Indus Valley civilization" (Shaffer, 1993, pp. 53–54). This was followed by a second urbanization that took place in the Ganges Valley beginning about 700 B.C. and continues to the present. Some authorities have argued that a clean cultural break separates the two urban periods. However, Shaffer emphasizes that there is substantial evidence for continuity of a single Indo-Gangetic cultural tradition bridging the gap.

Indus Valley sites such as Harappa and Mohenjo-daro are famous for advanced city planning and for realistic sculpture reminiscent of the classical Greeks. Stone weights have been recovered from Mohenjo-daro, and archeologist A. S. Hemmy remarked that their low ratio of scatter to mean weight may indicate a stricter regulation of commerce than in other countries of that era (Hemmy, 1938, p. 603).

Harappan society seems to have been advanced and well-organized. But, unfortunately, the Harappan script has not been successfully deciphered, and we do not even know what language the people spoke. We have very little knowledge of their intellectual life.

In the period of the second urbanization, astronomical developments in India appear to have paralleled those of Babylon and Greece, either through direct cultural borrowing or through parallel creation inspired by the diffusion of ideas. The early phase of communication with Mesopotamia may be represented by the *Jyotiṣavedāṅga*, which is dated by David Pingree to the fourth or fifth century B.C., mainly on linguistic grounds (Pingree, 1973, pp. 3–4). The later *Jyotiṣa Śāstras* may represent a phase in which indigenous developments were influenced by ideas introduced from Greek as well as from Babylonian astronomy.

In Indian astronomy and in Indian culture in general, the idea is always prominent that knowledge dates back to a very remote era. Thus the sixth-century astronomer Āryabhaṭa wrote, "This work,

Āryabhaṭīya by name, is the same as the ancient *Svāyambhūva* (which was revealed by Svayambhū) and as such it is true for all time" (Kak, 1987, p. 216). At the same time, he said that "By the grace of Brahmā the precious sunken jewel of true knowledge has been brought up by me from the ocean of true and false knowledge by means of the boat of my own intellect" (van der Waerden 1983, p. 213). Taken together, these statements suggest that Āryabhaṭa saw himself as reconstructing ancient truth from fragments of knowledge that were available to him.

We have seen that Indian astronomical and cosmological works may contain precessional references pointing back to periods much earlier than those accepted for the texts in question (see Sections 3.2 and 8.2). We have also seen evidence of advanced astronomical knowledge in the *Sūrya-siddhānta* and in the *Bhāgavatam* (see Appendix 10 and Section 4.4). A hypothesis to explain this is that advanced astronomical knowledge may have existed in India in the period of the first Indian urbanization. At this time, as in later eras, there was diffusion of knowledge and inspiration along trade routes linking East and West. Thus there may have existed an international scientific elite pursuing similar ideas in countries ranging from India to Egypt during this period. Subsequently, knowledge declined throughout this area in a period of darkness, only to increase again after about 700 B.C. At present, of course, this hypothesis is very tentative and much additional research is needed to give it a solid foundation.

Bibliography

Agrawal, D. P. and Kusumgar, Sheela, 1947. *Prehistoric Chronology and Radiocarbon Dating in India,* Delhi: Munshiram Manoharlal Publishers Pvt. Ltd.

Airy, Wilfred, 1908–9. "On the Origin of the British Measures of Capacity, Weight and Length," *Proceedings of the Institute of Civil Engineers*, vol. clxxvii, part 3.

Alexander, Hartley B., 1916. *North American Mythology*, in *Mythology of All Races*, Vol. 10, L. H. Grey, ed., Boston: Marshall Jones Co.

Alexander, H. B., 1920. *Latin American Mythology*, in *Mythology of All Races*, Vol. 11, New York: Cooper Square Publishers.

Ali, S. M., 1966. *On the Geography of the Puranas,* New Delhi: People's Publishing House.

Allen, Richard Hinckley, 1963. *Star Names, Their Lore and Meaning*, New York: Dover.

Amma, T. A. Sarasvatī, 1979. *Geometry in Ancient and Medieval India*, Delhi: Motilal Banarsidass.

Apocrypha, 1970. *The New English Bible with the Apocrypha*, Oxford and Cambridge: Oxford and Cambridge University Presses.

Baker, D., 1981. *The History of Manned Space Flight*, New York: Crown.

Bauval, Robert and Gilbert, Adrian, 1994. *The Orion Mystery*, New York: Crown Trade Paperbacks.

Berriman, A. E., 1953. *Historical Metrology*, London: J. M. Dent & Sons Ltd., New York: E. P. Dutton & Co., Inc.

Bhagavad-gītā: Bhaktivedanta Swami Prabhupāda, A. C., 1983. *Bhagavad-gītā As It Is*, Los Angeles: Bhaktivedanta Book Trust.

Bhaktivedanta, 1982: Bhaktivedanta Swami Prabhupāda, A. C., 1982. *Śrīmad Bhāgavatam*, Los Angeles: Bhaktivedanta Book Trust.

Bhaktivinode, Srila Thakur and Saraswati Thakur, Bhakti Siddhanta, 1968. *Vaishnavism and Nam-bhajan*, Madras: Sri Gaudiya Math.

Bhattacharya, S. A. (trans.), 1981. *The Varāha-Purāṇa with English Translation*, A. S. Gupta, ed., Varanasi: All-India Kashiraj Trust.

Boll, F., 1903. *Sphaera: Neue Griechische Texte und Untersuchungen zur Geschichte der Sternbilder*, Leipzig.

Budge, E.A. Wallis, 1904. *The Decree of Canopus*, Vol. 3, London: Kegan Paul, Trench, Trubner and Co. Ltd.

Burgess, Ebenezer, trans., 1860. *The Sūrya Siddhānta*, Ganguli, P., ed., Delhi: Motilal Banarsidass (reprinted in 1989).

Caitanya-caritāmṛta: Bhaktivedanta Swami Prabhupāda, A. C., 1974. *Śrī Caitanya- caritāmṛta*, Los Angeles: Bhaktivedanta Book Trust.

Campbell, Tony, 1981. *Early Maps*, New York: Abbeville Press.

Chambers, R., 1967. *The Book of Days*, Detroit: Gale Research Co.

Clark, Walter E., 1930. *The Āryabhaṭīya of Āryabhaṭa*, Chicago: Univ. of Chicago Press.

Clifford, Richard J., 1972. *The Cosmic Mountain in Canaan and the Old Testament*, Cambridge: Harvard University. Press.

Corliss, W., Nov.–Dec. 1991. *Science Frontiers Book Supplement*, No. 78, Glen Arm, MD: Sourcebook Project.

Cunningham, Alexander, 1871. *The Ancient Geography of India*, Delhi: Low Price Publications, reprinted in 1990.

de Santillana, Giorgio and von Dechend, Hertha, 1969. *Hamlet's Mill,* Boston: Gambit.

Deshpande, N. A., 1988. *The Padma-Purāṇa*, Delhi: Motilal Banarsidass.

Dikshit, 1969a: Dikshit, S. B., 1969. *English Translation of Bharatiya Jyotish Sastra, Part I*, R. V. Vaidya, trans., Delhi: Manager of Publications, Civil Lines.

Dikshit, 1969b: Dikshit, S. B., 1969. *English Translation of Bharatiya Jyotish Sastra, Part II*, R. V. Vaidya, trans., Delhi: Manager of Publications, Civil Lines.

Dikshit, S. B., 1888. "The Twelve-Year Cycle of Jupiter," *The Indian Antiquary,* vol. XVII, pp. 1–317.

Drake, Stillman, 1976. "Galileo's First Telescopic Observations," *Journal for the History of Astronomy*, Vol. vii, pp. 153–168.

Dubreuil-Jouveau, G. 1937. *Iconography of Southern India*, A. C. Martin, trans., Paris: Librairie Orientaliste Paul Geuthner.

Duffett-Smith, Peter, 1985, *Astronomy with Your Personal Computer*, Cambridge: Cambridge University Press.

Eggeling, J. (trans.), 1882–1900. *The Śatapatha Brāhmaṇa*, i–v, Oxford: The Clarendon Press.

Eliade, Mircea, 1959. *Cosmos and History*, W. R. Trask, trans., New York: Harper & Row.

Eliade, Mircea, 1964. *Shamanism*, Bollingen Series LXXVI, Princeton: Princeton University Press.

Epes Brown, 1971: Epes Brown, Joseph, ed., 1971. *The Sacred Pipe*, Baltimore: Penguin Books.

Evans, Sir Arthur, 1935. *The Palace of Minos*, London: Macmillan and Co.

Evans-Wentz, W.Y., 1981. *Cuchama and Sacred Mountains*, Frank Waters and Charles L. Adams, eds., Chicago: Swallow Press.

Flammarion, Camille, 1964. *The Flammarion Book of Astronomy,* New York: Simon and Schuster.

Flinders Petrie, William M., 1877. *Inductive Metrology*, London: Hargrove Saunders.

Flinders Petrie, William M., 1929. "Measures cand Weights, Ancient," *The Encyclopedia Britannica*, 14th ed., vol. 15, London: The Encyclopedia Britannica Co., Ltd.

Ganguli, K. M., trans., 1970. *The Mahabharata of Krishna-Dwaipayana Vyasa*, vols. I–XII, Delhi: Munshiram Manoharlal Publishers Pvt. Ltd.

Gill, W.W., 1876. *Myths and Songs from the South Pacific*, London: H. S. King and Co.

Gole, Susan, 1989. *Indian Maps and Plans,* New Delhi: Manohar Pub.

Gonzalez-Reimann, Luis, 1988. *Tiempo Ciclico y Eras del Mundo en la India*, Mexico City: El Colegio de Mexico.

Gonzalez-Reimann, Luis, 1989. "The Ancient Vedic Dice Game and the Names of the Four World Ages in Hinduism," in *World Archeoastronomy*, Anthony Aveni, ed., Cambridge: Cambridge Univ. Press.

Goswāmi, 1975. Srila Sanātana Goswāmi, 1975. *Sri Brihat Bhāgavatāmritam*, Madras: Sree Gaudiya Math.

Green, Robin, 1985. *Spherical Astronomy*, Cambridge: Cambridge University Press.

Hagar, S., 1906. "Cherokee Star-Lore," in *Festschrift Boas*.

Hallock, William and Wade, Herbert, 1906. *The Evolution of Weights and Measures and the Metric System*, New York: The Macmillan Company.

Hancock, Graham, 1995. *Fingerprints of the Gods,* New York: Crown Trade Paperbacks.

Hancock, Graham and Bauval, Robert, 1996. *The Message of the Sphinx*, New York: Crown Publishers.

Hardy, Friedhelm, 1983. *Viraha-Bhakti: The Early History of Kṛṣṇa Devotion in South India*, Delhi: Oxford University Press.

Hartner, W., 1938. "The Pseudoplanetary Nodes of the Moon's Orbit in Hindu and Islamic Iconographies," *Ars Islamica*, vol. 5, pp. 112–54.

Hartner, Willy, Jan.–April 1965. "The Earliest History of the Constellations in the Near East and the Motif of the Lion-Bull Combat," *Journal of Near Eastern Studies*, vol. XXIV, no. 1 & 2.

Heinberg, Richard, 1989. *Memories and Visions of Paradise*, Los Angeles: Tarcher, Inc.

Hemmy, A. S., 1938. "Chap. XVII. System of Weights," in *Further Excavations at Mohenjo-Daro*, by E. J. H. Mackay, vol. 1, Delhi: Manager of Publications.

Heninger, Jr., S. K., 1977. *The Cosmographical Glass: Renaissance Diagrams of the Universe,* San Marino, Calif.: Huntington Library.

Holmberg, Uno, 1964. *The Mythology of All Races: Finno-Ugric, Siberian*, Vol. IV, John MacCulloch, ed., New York: Cooper Square Publishers, Inc.

Hooper: Hooper, Greg (Gokula dāsa), "Universal Features of Pre-Industrial Culture," private communication.

Hudson, Dennis, 1995. "The *Śrīmad Bhāgavata Purāṇa* in Stone: The Text as an Eighth-Century Temple and its Implications," *Jour. of Vaiṣṇava Studies, Vol. 3, No. 3,* Summer 1995.

Hues, Robert, 1638. *A Learned Treatise of Globes, Both Coelestiall and Terrestrial: with their several uses*, John Chilmead, trans., London.

James, Peter, 1991. *Centuries of Darkness*, London: Jonathan Cape.

Jena, Siddheswar, 1987. *The Narasiṁha Purāṇam*, Delhi: Nag Publishers.

Jones, Sir William, 1801. *Asiatic Studies*, vol. 2.

Kafton-Minkel, Walter, 1989. *Subterranean Worlds,* Fort Townsend, Washington: Loompanics Unlimited.

Kak, Subash, 1987. "On Astronomy in Ancient India," *Indian Jour. of the History of Science,* 22(3): 205–221.

Kak, 1993a: Kak, Subash, 1993. "The Structure of the *Ṛgveda,*" *Indian Jour. of the History of Science,* 28(2): 71–79.

Kak, 1993b: Kak, Subash, 1993. "Astronomy of the Vedic Altars," *Vistas in Astronomy*, vol. 36, pp. 117–140.

Kay, G. R., 1981. *Hindu Astronomy*, New Delhi: Cosmo Publications.

Kirk, G. S. and Raven, J. E., 1963. *The Presocratic Philosophers*, Cambridge: Cambridge University Press.

Kloetzli, W. Randolph, Nov. 1985. "Maps of Time—Mythologies of Descent: Scientific Instruments and the Purāṇic Cosmograph," *History of Religion*, vol. 25, No. 2.

Kramrisch, Stella, 1946. *The Hindu Temple*, Calcutta: University of Calcutta.

Krupp, E. C., 1983. *Echoes of the Ancient Skies,* Oxford: Oxford University Press.

Kuiper F. B. J., 1983. *Ancient Indian Cosmogeny*, New Delhi: Vikas Publishing House Pvt. Ltd.

Lal, B. B., 1998. *India: 1947–1997: New Light on the Indus Civilization*, New Delhi: Aryan Books International.

Laplace, Pierre-Simon de, 1884. *Exposition du Systeme du moude,* vol. 6, *Oeuvres complètes,* Paris. Leon-Portilla, Miguel, ed., 1980, *Native Mesoamerican Spirituality*, New York: Paulist Press.

Lost Books, 1963. *The Lost Books of the Bible and the Forgotten Books of Eden*, Cleveland and New York: World Publishing Co.

Macaulay, Thomas Babington, 1952. *Macaulay: Prose and Poetry,* Cambridge: Harvard Univ. Press.

Majumdar, R. C., 1960. *The Classical Accounts of India*, Calcutta: Firma K. L. Mukhopadhyay.

Marshall, Sir John, ed., 1973. *Mohenjo-Daro and the Indus Civilization*, Delhi: Indological Book House.

McCrindle, J., trans., 1926. *Ancient India as Described by Megasthenes and Arrian*, Calcutta: Chuckervertty Chatterjee.

Microsoft Encarta 98 Encyclopedia, 1997. Redmond, Wash.: Microsoft.

Mitchiner, John, E., 1978. *Studies in the Indus Valley Inscriptions*, Delhi: Oxford & IBH.

Mohammed: Mohammed, Delail-i Hatrat Ierhi: *The Evidence of the Auspicious Explanations*, a book of Hadis (teachings of Mohammed other than the Koran), translation from Turkish manuscript.

Mukhopadhyaya, S. M., *et al.*, trans., 1968. *The Vāmana Purāṇa with English Translation*, A. S. Gupta, ed., Varanasi: All-India Kashiraj Trust.

Needham, Joseph, 1970. *Science and Civilization in China*, vol. 3, Cambridge: Cambridge University Press.

Needham, Joseph, 1959. *Science and Civilization in China*, vol. 3, Cambridge: Cambridge University Press.

Neugebauer, O., Jan. 1945. "The History of Ancient Astronomy: Problems and Methods," *Jour. of Near Eastern Studies*, vol. 4, no. 1, pp. 1–38.

Neugebauer, O. and Sachs, A., eds., 1945. *Mathematical Cuneiform Texts*, New Haven: American Oriental Society and American Schools of Oriental Research.

Neugebauer, O., 1975. *A History of Ancient Mathematical Astronomy*, New York: Springer-Verlag.

North, J. D., 1977. "Chronology and the Age of the World," *Cosmology, History, and Theology*, Yourgrau, W. and Breck, A. D., eds., New York: Plenum Press.

O'Flaherty, Wendy Doniger, 1975. *Hindu Myths*, Baltimore: Penguin Books.

Pargiter, F. Eden, trans., 1981. *The Mārkaṇḍeya Purāṇa*, Varanasi: Indological Book House.

Pingree, David, 1973. "The Mesopotamian Origin of Early Indian Mathematical Astronomy," *Journal for the History of Astronomy*, Vol. iv, pp. 1–12.

Pingree, David, 1976. "The Recovery of Early Greek Astronomy from India," *Journal for the History of Astronomy*, Vol. vii, pp. 109–123.

Pingree, David, 1981. "Jyotiḥśāstra, Astral and Mathematical Literature," *A History of Indian Literature*, vol. VI, Fasc. 4, Jan Gonda, ed., Weisbaden: Otto Harrassowitz, pp. 3–18.

Rall, Gloria, Sept. 1998. "The Native American Bear in the Sky," *Planetarian*, Vol. 27, No. 3.

Rau, D. R. Vasudeva, trans., 1983. *Nārāyaṇa Paṇḍitācārya's Sumadhva Vijaya,* Viśākhapatnam: Śrimadānanda Tirtha Publications.

Resnick, Howard, 1999. Excerpt from the *Mahābhāratatātparyanirṇaya* of Madhvācārya, personal communication.

Rocher, Ludo, 1986. *The Purāṇas*, Weisbaden: Otto Harrassowitz.

Roe, Peter, 1982. *The Cosmic Zygote*, New Brunswick, NJ: Rutgers University Press.

Rosen, Steven, 1991. *The Lives of the Vaishnava Saints: Shrinivas Acharya, Narottam das Thakur, Shyamananda Pandit,* New York: Folk Books.

Rydberg, Viktor, 1907. *Teutonic Mythology*, London: Norroena Society.

Sachau, Edward, 1910. *Alberuni's India*, Delhi: Low Price Publications, reprinted in 1993.

Sagan, Carl, 1980. *Cosmos*, New York: Random House.

Sanders, N. K., 1972. *The Epic of Gilgamesh*, London: Penguin Books.

Sarma, K.V., trans., 1956. *The Goladīpikā by Parameśvara*, Madras: The Adyar Library and Research Center.

Sāstri, Bāpū Deva, trans. 1860. *Sūrya-siddhānta* (Calcutta: Baptist Mission Press, reprinted in *Bibliotheca Indica*, New Series No. 1, Hindu Astronomy I).

Schlegel, G., 1875. *L'Uranigraphie Chinoise*, Leiden.

Schwaller de Lubicz, R. A., 1977. *The Temple in Man*, Brookline, Mass.: Autumn Press.

Schwaller de Lubicz, R. A., 1998. *The Temple of Man,* Rochester, Vermont: Inner Traditions.

Schwartzberg, Joseph, 1987. "Introduction to South Asian Cartography," in Harley, J. B. and Woodward, David, eds., *Cartography in the Traditional Islamic and South Asian Societies*, Chicago: University of Chicago Press.

Seidenberg, A., 1960–62. "The Ritual Origin of Geometry," *Archive for History of Exact Sciences*, vol. 1, Berlin: Springer-Verlag.

Seidenberg, A., 1978. "The Origin of Mathematics," *Archive for History of Exact Sciences*, vol. 18, Berlin: Springer-Verlag.

Sellers, Jane B., 1992. *The Death of Gods in Ancient Egypt,* London: Penguin.

Sen, Rajendra Nath, 1922. *Brahma-vaivarta Puranam*, vol. XXIV of *The Sacred Books of the Hindus*, Part 2, Allahabad: Sudhindra Nath Vasu, The Panini Office, Bhuvaneshwari Ashram.

Sewell, Robert and Dikshit, S. B., 1896. *The Indian Calendar*, London: Swan Sonnenschein & Co.

Shaffer, Jim G., 1984. "Bronze Age Iron in Afghanistan: Its Implications for South Asian Protohistory," in *Studies in the Archeology and Paleoanthropology of South Asia*, Kennedy, K. A. R. and Possehl, G. L., eds., New Delhi: Oxford & IBH Publishing Co.

Shastri, Hari Prasad, 1976. *The Ramayana of Valmiki*, Vol. II, London: Shanti Sadan.

Shukla, K. S., 1957. *The Sūrya-siddhānta with the Commentary of Parameśvara,* Dept. of Mathematics and Astronomy, Lucknow: Lucknow University.

Sircar, D. C., 1960. *Studies in the Geography of Ancient and Medieval India*, Delhi: Motilal Banarsidass.

Śiva, 1990. *The Śiva Purāṇa*, 1990. trans. by a board of scholars, Delhi: Motilal Banarsidass.

Sivananda, Swami, 1985. *The Brihadaranyaka Upanishad*, Shivananda-nagar, India: The Divine Life Society.

Skelton, R. A., Marston, T. E., and Painter, G. D., 1965. *The Vinland Map and the Tartar Relation*, New Haven: Yale University Press.

Snodgrass, Adrian, 1985. *The Symbolism of the Stupa*, Southeast Asia Program, Ithaca, New York: Cornell University.

Snodgrass, Adrian, 1990. *Architecture, Time and Eternity*, vol. 1, New Delhi: Aditya Prakashan.

Spirit, 1992. *The Spirit World*, by the editors of Time-Life Books, Alexandria, Virginia: Time-Life Books.

Stahl, W. H., trans., 1952. *Macrobius: Commentary on the Dream of Scipio*, New York: Columbia University Press. Records of Civilization, Sources and Studies, vol. 48.

Stecchini, Livio Catullo, March 1961. "A History of Measures," *The American Behavioral Scientist*, vol. 4, no. 7.

Stecchini, Livio Catullo, 1966. "Astronomical Theory and Historical Data," *The Velikovsky Affair*, Alfred de Grazia, Ralph Juergens, and Livio C. Stecchini, eds., New York: University Books.

Stecchini, Livio Catullo, 1971. "Notes on the Relation of Ancient Measures to the Great Pyramid," in Tompkins, Peter, *Secrets of the Great Pyramid*, New York: Harper and Row.

Sthapati, Ganapati, V., 1997. *Some Glimpses of Science and Technology of Vāstu Shāstra*, part 2, Madras: Vaastu Vedic Research Foundation.

Sturluson, Snorri, 1929. *The Prose Edda*, Arthur Broduer, trans., New York: The American-Scandinavian Foundation.

Swerdlow, Noel Mark, 1968. *Ptolemy's Theory of the Distances and Sizes of the Planets: A Study of the Scientific Foundations of Medieval Cosmology*, Yale Univ. Ph.D. thesis.

Swerdlow, Noel, Mark, 1998. *The Babylonian Theory of the Planets*, Princeton: Princeton University Press.

Tagare, G. V., 1980. *The Nārada-Purāṇa*, Delhi: Motilal Banarsidass.

Tagare, G. V., 1981. *The Kūrma-Purāṇa*, Delhi: Motilal Banarsidass.

Tagare, G. V., 1987. *The Vāyu Purāṇa*, Delhi: Motilal Banarsidass.

Taluqdar of Oudh, A., trans., 1916. *The Matsya Purāṇam*, Allahabad: Sudhīndra Nātha Vasu, Pāṇini Office, Bhuvaneśvarī Āśrama.

Tarkhedkar, A. R., 1995. *Vastushastra, The Edifice Science*, vol. 1, Dhulia: Cosmo Publishing House.

Thibaut, G., trans., 1968. *The Pañchasiddhāntikā*, Varanasi: The Chowkhamba Sanskrit Series Office.

Thompson, Richard, 1997. "Planetary Diameters in the Surya-Siddhanta," *Jour. of Scientific Exploration*, vol. 11, no. 2, pp. 193–200.

Tokunaga, Muneo, 1996. *The Machine-readable Text of the Mahābhārata, Based on the Poona Critical Edition*, Kyoto, Japan, Upgrade version(1_1): October 1, 1996.

Tripathi, M. P., 1969. *Development of Geographic Knowledge in Ancient India*, Varanasi: Bharatiya Vidya Prakashan.

van Buitenen, J. A. B., trans., 1973. *The Mahābhārata*, Book 1, Chicago: University of Chicago Press.

van Buitenen, J. A. B., trans., 1975, *The Mahābhārata*, Books 2 and 3, Chicago: Univ. of Chicago Press.

van der Waerden, B. L., 1953. "History of the Zodiac," *Archiv für Orientforschung*, vol. 16.

van der Waerden, B. L., 1980. "The Conjunction of 3102 B.C.," *Centaurus*, vol. 24.

van der Waerden, B. L., 1983. *Geometry and Algebra in Ancient Civilizations*, Berlin: Springer-Verlag.

van der Waerden, B. L., 1987. "The Heliocentric System in Greek, Persian and Hindu Astronomy," *Annals of the New York Academy of Sciences*, vol. 500.

Van Helden, Albert, 1976. "The Importance of the Transit of Mercury of 1631," *Jour. for the History of Astronomy*, Vol. vii, pp. 110.

Villa Rojas, Alfonso, 1988. "The Concepts of Space and Time among the Contemporary Maya," in Leon-Portilla, Miguel, *Time and Reality in the Thought of the Maya*, Norman: Univ. of Oklahoma Press.

Wilford, Francis, 1799. "On the Chronology of the Hindus," *Asiatic Researches*, vol. 5, London.

Wilford, Francis, 1805. *Asiatick Researches*, vol. 8, Calcutta, 245–376.

Wilkinson, L., trans., 1861. *Siddhānta-śiromaṇi of Bhāskarācārya,* rev. by B. D. Sāstri (Calcutta: Baptist Mission Press, reprinted in *Bibliotheca Indica*, New Series No. 1, Hindu Astronomy I).

Wilson, H. H., 1865. *The Vishṇu Purāṇa* (with extensive notes), Vol. II, London: Trübner & Co.

Wilson, H. H., trans., 1980. *The Viṣṇu Purāṇa*, Delhi: Nag Publishers.

Wou Tch'eng Ngen, 1957. *Si Yeou ki, ou le Voyage en Occident*, L. Avenol, trans., Paris: Vol. 1.

Wright, Thomas, 1750. *An Original Theory of the Universe*, New York: Neale Watson Academic Publications, 1971 (original printing 1750).

Tables

Glossary

Angular diameter—the angle subtended by a planet's disk, as seen by an observer on the earth. The angular diameter in radians times the planet's distance gives the planet's diameter.

Antarikṣa—the narrow space between the upper and lower hemispheres of the Brahmāṇḍa, literally "inner space."

Āryabhaṭa—famous Indian astronomer who was born in A.D. 476 and whose *Āryabhaṭīya* described the earth as rotating on its axis.

Astrolabe—an astronomical instrument with the stereographic projections of the earth, some stars, and the ecliptic on a series of metal plates.

Astronomical unit—the mean distance from the earth to the sun, about 93 million miles. Distances in the solar system are often expressed as multiples of this unit.

Bhāskarācārya—medieval Indian astronomer who wrote the *Jyotiṣa Śāstra* known as *Siddhānta-śiromaṇi.*

Bhāgavata Purāṇa—one of the most famous and popular of the *Purāṇas,* especially among the Vaiṣṇavas, and one which contains an extensive section on cosmology. It is also known as *Śrīmad Bhāgavatam,* or simply *Bhāgavatam.*

Bhāgavatam—same as *Bhāgavata Purāṇa.*

Brahe, Tycho (1546–1601)—Danish astronomer known for his accurate naked-eye observations and planetary measurements. He considered that the sun revolved about the earth while the other planets revolved about the sun.

Brahmāṇḍa—literally Brahmā egg, one of the innumerable universes, described in the *Purāṇas*. It consists of a spherical shell bisected by an earth-disk, Bhū-maṇḍala, of the same radius, with a region of space above and a watery region below.

Bhārata-varṣa—southernmost of the nine subdivisions (*varṣas*) of Jambū-dvīpa, said to refer either to India or to the earth as a whole.

Bhū-maṇḍala—the earth-disk bisecting the sphere of the Brahmāṇḍa, the Purāṇic universe. Its central region consists of seven alternating ring-shaped oceans and islands (*dvīpas*), known as Sapta-dvīpa.

Bode-Titius law—a simple rule giving the distances of the planets from the sun. It was first written down by Titius of Wittenburg, and it was discovered independently by Bode in 1772. It is expressed by the formula $D(n) = .4 + .3 \times 2^n$ where D(n) is the distance of planet n in astronomical units and n = -infinity for Mercury, 0 for Venus, 1 for earth, 2 for Mars, 3 for the asteroids, 4 for Jupiter, 5 for Saturn, etc.

Brahmā, Lord—the creator in the Hindu trinity of Brahmā, Viṣṇu, and Śiva, traditionally seen as the original disseminator of the *Vedas* in human society, after his enlightenment by Viṣṇu from within.

Cakras—seven centers of psychic energy arrayed along the spine that are awakened in the practice of yoga. These can be seen as analogous to the seven worlds (*lokas*) from Bhū-maṇḍala (base of spine) to Satyaloka (crown of head).

Canopus—a star in the southern celestial hemisphere that is sometimes identified as the southern polestar (although it is not very close to the southern pole). In Purāṇic texts it is called Agastya.

Celestial equator—the projection of the earth's equator onto the celestial sphere. It is perpendicular to the earth's spin axis, which passes through the center of the earth and the north and south poles.

Celestial north—If the earth's grid of latitude and longitude is projected onto the celestial sphere, it defines a direction of north on the sphere. The northernmost point is the north celestial pole, corresponding to the earth's north pole.

Celestial south—If the earth's grid of latitude and longitude is projected onto the celestial sphere, it defines a direction of south on the sphere. The southernmost point is the south celestial pole, corresponding to the earth's south pole.

Celestial sphere—an imaginary sphere much larger in diameter than the earth and centered on the earth's center. The stars and planets can be thought of as points projected onto the surface of this sphere. Positions on the celestial sphere are measured by celestial longitude, called right ascension, and celestial latitude, called declination. See diagram on right.

Copernicus, Nicolaus (1473–1543)—the Polish astronomer famous for introducing the heliocentric (sun-centered) theory of planetary motion.

Dhruvaloka—the spiritual abode of King Dhruva which is said to situated at the north celestial pole.

Dvīpa—island.

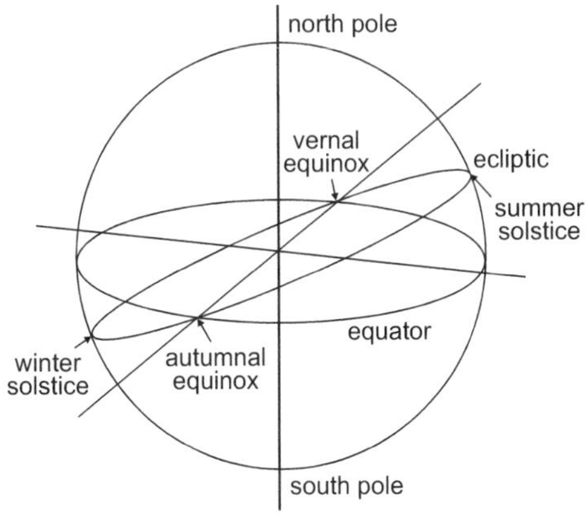

Ecliptic—the geocentric orbit of the sun projected onto the celestial sphere as a great circle. This great circle is tilted at an angle of about 23.5° to the celestial equator. It intersects the celestial equator at two points, known as the vernal and autumnal equinoxes, as shown on right.

Ephemeris—a table of planetary positions at successive times.

Equinox—one of the two points on the celestial sphere where the ecliptic intersects the equator, known as vernal and autumnal equinoxes. In one year, the sun travels around the ecliptic, traveling counterclockwise as seen looking down from the north. At the vernal equinox the sun cuts the celestial equator going from south to north, and at the autumnal equinox it cuts the celestial equator going from north to south, as shown above. The length of the day equals the length of the night at the equinoxes.

Galileo Galilei (1564–1642)—Italian astronomer who accepted the heliocentric model and first used the telescope for astronomical observations.

Geocentric orbit of a planet—From the viewpoint of a person standing on the earth, the sun moves around the earth and a planet orbits the sun. This is shown for Mercury in Figure 4.9 (p. 96). The combination of the sun's motion around the earth and the planet's motion around the sun forms the apparent orbit of the planet around the earth. This is called the planet's geocentric orbit. It lies between two curves: the inner boundary curve (A) and the outer boundary curve (B).

Geographical north—north as defined by the grid of latitude and longitude on the earth globe. Note that the *Bhāgavatam* uses a completely different system of cardinal directions (north, south, east, and west) in Bhū-maṇḍala, centered on Mount Meru.

Geographical south—south as defined by the grid of latitude and longitude on the earth globe.

Great circle—any circle on the surface of a sphere that is centered on the sphere's center. All other circles on a sphere are smaller than a great circle.

Hasta—Indian cubit. Key *hasta* lengths discussed in this study are 432 mm and 460.7 mm.

Hipparchus—a Greek astronomer who lived about 150 B.C. and who is commonly thought to have discovered precession of the equinoxes.

Indra—the ruler of the heavenly region in Hinduism.

Jambūdvīpa—central island (*dvīpa*) of Bhū-maṇḍala having a central mountain (Meru) and nine subdivisions (*varṣas*).

Jyotiṣa Śāstras—medieval Indian astronomy texts which contain instructions for calculating planetary motions and solar and lunar eclipses. *Sūrya-siddhānta* is a text of this type.

Kali-yuga—the age of quarrel and degradation in the Purāṇic system of cyclic time. There are four cyclically repeating *yugas,* Satyā (Kṛta), Tretā, Dvāpara, and Kali, with lengths proportional to 4:3:2:1. Kali-yuga is said to last 1,200 divine years, which comes to 432,000 solar years. The major *Jyotiṣa Śāstras* all assume that Kali-yuga began on February 18, 3102 B.C., as measured by the Julian calendar. They assume a mean alignment of the planets on this date (see pp. 212–223).

Kepler, Johannes (1571–1630)—an astronomer famous for acceptance of the heliocentric (sun-centered) model of the solar system and for his laws of planetary motion.

Ketu—an invisible planet positioned at the descending node of the moon.

Krośa—an Indian unit of length, one quarter the length of a *yojana.*

Kṛṣṇa, Lord—the original transcendental Supreme Lord, as described in the *Bhāgavata Purāṇa* and *Bhagavad-gītā.*

Lokāloka Mountain—circular mountain dividing the inner, illuminated region of Bhū-maṇḍala from the dark, uninhabited, outer region, called Aloka-varṣa, which extends from Lokāloka to the shell of the Brahmāṇḍa.

Lunar nodes—the point where the orbit of the moon on the celestial sphere crosses the sun's orbit going north is called the ascending node, and the opposite point is called the descending node. (See diagram on right.)

Mahābhārata—an epic of some 100,000 verses, said to be an encyclopedia of traditional Indian lore.

Mānasottara Mountain—circular mountain in the center of Puṣkaradvīpa which is traversed by the wheel of the sun's chariot.

Meridian—any great circle of the earth passing through the poles.

Meru, Mount—the central mountain of Jambūdvīpa. It is shaped like an inverted cone, with the city of demigods, Brahmapurī on top, and it represents the cosmic axis. Also called Sumeru.

Nakṣatras—27 or 28 star constellations, situated roughly along the ecliptic, which play a role in Indian astronomy similar to that of the 12 constellations of the zodiac in the west. They are particularly connected with the motion of the moon, which completes one sidereal orbit in about 27.3 days.

The *nakṣatra* constellations are irregular in shape, but the *nakṣatras* are also defined to be angular subdivisions of the ecliptic.

See Appendix 1 (pp. 247–50) for more information.

Planisphere—a plane map of features on a sphere, produced by stereographic projection.

Polestar—a star located near the celestial north pole—the center of daily rotation of the heavens, as seen from the northern hemisphere of the earth. Precession of the equinoxes causes such a star to be displaced. At present, there is a polestar, called Polaris or Alpha Ursa Minoris. In about 2,500 B.C., Thuban or Alpha Draconis was the polestar. But during most of the intervening period, there was no readily visible star at the north pole.

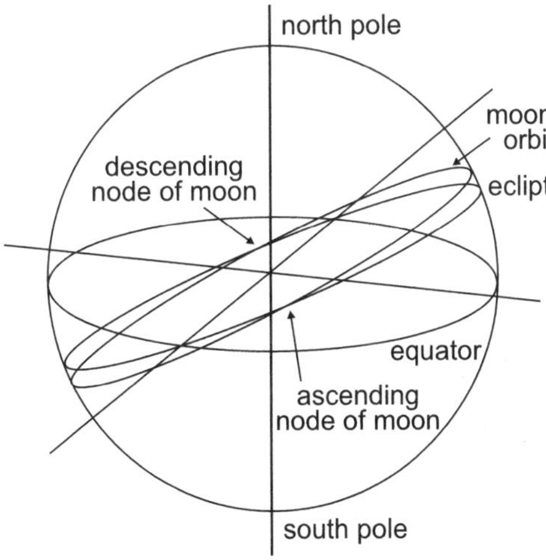

Precession of the equinoxes—the slow shift of the equinoxes relative to the fixed stars. Astronomers attribute this motion to the gradual rotation of the earth's spin axis like a spinning top. This slow rotation takes a "great year" of about 25,700 years to complete one revolution, or about 71.4 years per degree.

Ptolemy, Claudius—second-century Alexandrian astronomer known for his geocentric (earth-centered) epicyclic models for the motion of the planets. These were widely accepted until the heliocentric (sun-centered) theory was introduced by Copernicus in the sixteenth-century.

Purāṇas—Sanskrit texts from India dealing with ten topics, including the creation and annihilation of the universe, the history of humans and demigods, cosmology, and the relation between the soul and God. The word "*purāṇa*" designates ancient lore.

Sapta-dvīpa—the central region of Bhū-maṇḍala consisting of seven (*sapta*) alternating ring-shaped oceans and islands (*dvīpas*).

Sapta-ṛṣi—the Big Dipper constellation, literally the "seven sages."

Sidereal month—the time for the moon to make one orbit relative to the stars (27.32166 days).

Sidereal zodiac—The zodiac is defined to be a division of the ecliptic into 12 equal "signs," named in ancient times after particular constellations. If the starting point of these signs is fixed relative to a star, the zodiac is said to be sidereal. The *Sūrya-siddhānta* uses a sidereal zodiac in which the beginning of the first sign (Meṣa or Aries) is 10' beyond the ecliptic longitude of the star Revatī (Zeta Piscium). See tropical zodiac.

Siddhānta-siromaṇi—a *Jyotiṣa Śāstra,* written by the medieval Indian astronomer Bhāskarācārya, which maps the seven oceans and *dvīpas* into bands of equal latitude around the earth globe.

Śiva, Lord—the destroyer in the Hindu trinity of Brahmā, Viṣṇu, and Śiva, often pictured in meditation on Lord Viṣṇu.

Solstice—As the sun travels around the ecliptic in its yearly course, it reaches its northernmost point 90° after the vernal equinox. This is called the summer solstice, and it is the time of the longest day in the northern hemisphere. The sun reaches its southernmost point 90° after the autumnal equinox. This is the winter solstice, the time of the shortest day in the northern hemisphere. See *ecliptic* for diagram.

Śrīmad-Bhāgavatam—same as *Bhāgavata Purāṇa.*

Stereographic projection—a method of mapping the surface of a globe onto a plane. One form of stereographic projection is defined as follows (see Figure 3.2, p. 48): Assume that we have a sphere and a plane tangent to the north pole of the sphere. Given a point on the surface of a sphere, extend a straight line from the south pole of the sphere through this point, until it intersects the plane. The point on the sphere is mapped to this point.

One advantage of stereographic projection is that any great circle on the sphere is mapped onto a circle in the plane.

Sūrya-siddhānta—a Sanskrit astronomical text (*Jyotiṣa Śāstra*) presenting an epicyclic theory of planetary motion. It also discusses the Indian system of world chronology known as the *yuga* system, the periodic motions of the sun, moon, and planets, distances from the earth to the sun, the moon, and the planets, rules for calculating the times of solar and lunar eclipses, and cosmology and geography.

Synodic month—the time for the faster-moving moon to lap the sun in its orbit around the celestial sphere (assuming mean motions for the sun and moon). This is the time from one new moon, when the moon and sun are conjoined, to the next new moon, and it is 29.53059 days.

Tropical zodiac—The zodiac is defined to be a division of the ecliptic into 12 equal "signs", named in ancient times after particular constellations. If the starting point of these signs in the beginning of Aries is fixed relative to the vernal equinox, the zodiac is said to be tropical. Due to precession of the equinoxes, the tropical zodiac shifts slowly in relation to the sidereal zodiac. In Western countries, the tropical zodiac has been in use since the days of Hellenistic astronomy. The Indian sidereal zodiac (as defined in *Sūrya-siddhānta*) agreed with the tropical zodiac in A.D. 564.

Turning point—The four turning points of a planet's geocentric orbit are defined as follows (see Figure 4.9, p. 96): The inner boundary curve (A) of the planet's geocentric orbit has a point of closest approach to the earth (the perigee) and a point of greatest distance from the earth (perigee+). The outer boundary curve (B) has a point of greatest distance from the earth (the apogee) and a point of closest approach (apogee-). At each of these four points, the boundary curve is tangent to a circle centered on the earth.

Varṣa—any one of the nine subdivisions of Jambūdvīpa, separated from one another by mountain ranges.

Vedas—ancient Sanskrit texts of revealed knowledge which are seen as authoritative in Hindu religion.

Viṣṇu, Lord—the transcendental Supreme Lord, described in the *Bhāgavata Purāṇa* as an expansion of Lord Kṛṣṇa. He is also known as the maintainer in the Hindu trinity of Brahmā, Viṣṇu, and Śiva.

Viṣṇu Purāṇa—one of the eighteen major *Purāṇas.* It contains an extensive section on cosmology which complements the cosmological section of the *Bhāgavatam.*

Yojana—an Indian unit of length, which is used to express distances in the *Bhāgavatam.* Different standard *yojana* lengths have been used, including one of about eight miles.

Index

AGMV Marquis
MEMBER OF THE SCABRINI GROUP
Quebec, Canada
2000